Instrumental Analysis

THE MACMILLAN COMPANY
NEW YORK · CHICAGO
DALLAS · ATLANTA · SAN FRANCISCO
LONDON · MANILA
IN CANADA
BRETT-MACMILLAN LTD.
GALT, ONTARIO

PAUL DELAHAY

Boyd Professor of Chemistry
Louisiana State University

Instrumental Analysis

New York
THE MACMILLAN COMPANY

Library of Congress catalog card number, 57-5212

Preface

This text covers the most important methods of instrumental analysis which are generally not discussed in courses in physics and physical chemistry. The book is intended for undergraduate and graduate students. The material can be covered in about forty to sixty lectures, but a much shorter course is also possible. In this respect, Chapters 2, 3, 4, 8, and 9—which deal with potentiometry, polarography, emission spectroscopy, and absorption spectrometry—are essential even in an abridged course.

Theoretical discussions are quite elementary, but, I hope, rational. Simple diagrams which can be readily drawn on the blackboard are used throughout the book. Basic electrical and optical diagrams are given, but block diagrams are utilized in the representation of electronic circuits. The functions that amplifiers and other electronic components must fulfill in a given instrument are discussed, but I see no point in bewildering students with involved diagrams which are often available in the literature supplied by manufacturers. The reader is referred to Section 1 for further comments on the mode of approach adopted in this text.

Most chapters contain problems dealing with the extension and application of theory and with literature surveys of limited scope. The first group of problems is primarily intended for advanced students, while the two other groups are for general use. The short literature surveys may help undergraduate students to acquire some experience in library work.

Special attention is given to laboratory work to achieve proper balance between experiment and theory. More than fifty experiments are described in twenty-three sections, and suggestions for about twenty additional experiments are given. Experiments deal with the verification of the essential features of the various methods, rather than the application to the analysis of industrial materials. The reasons for this approach are given in Section 15–1.

It is a pleasure to express my sincere thanks to Dean A. R. Choppin of the College of Chemistry and Physics, Louisiana State University, and to Professor H. B. Williams, Head of the Chemistry Department. They helped greatly in creating the proper conditions and atmosphere for the writing of this book.

I am much indebted to Professors H. A. Laitinen and H. V. Malmstadt of the University of Illinois, who read the complete manuscript and made numerous suggestions for the correction of errors and the improvement of the text. Their friendly cooperation proved most helpful and valuable. Comments on Chapter 4 by Professor R. V. Nauman of the Louisiana State University and the review of Chapter 14 by Professor P. E. Yankwich of the University of Illinois were also most valuable. Many thanks are due to Mr. L. Hulett for his help in the verification of some points in the chapter on laboratory work.

Finally, I should like to express my appreciation to Mr. C. J. Malre who had the arduous task of preparing the preliminary version of the text from my hand-written notes. He also typed the final text and collaborated in the verification of references.

April 3, 1956
Baton Rouge, Louisiana   PAUL DELAHAY

Contents

Instrumental Analysis

1

Scope of Instrumental Analysis

1-1. INTRODUCTION

Instrumental analysis deals with the application of methods of physics and physical chemistry to chemical analysis. These methods find an ever increasing number of applications for two reasons: (1) they greatly reduce the duration of many analyses which are quite tedious by noninstrumental methods; (2) they can be applied to the determination of substances under conditions in which classical methods fail.

There is no fundamental difference between instrumental and noninstrumental methods. Even such a classical method as gravimetry involves the use of an instrument, the balance, and the discussion of noninstrumental methods involves physical chemistry. It is true that equipment in instrumental analysis is often more complicated than the balance, but this is only a matter of degree, not a fundamental difference. "Instrumental analysis" is merely a convenient expression for grouping a variety of methods.

The opinion is sometimes advanced that instrumental analysis should be reserved for graduate studies. Yet, it should be recognized that many students find it most helpful to have some knowledge of instrumental analysis, and therefore an undergraduate course in this field fulfills a useful function. Some background in physics and physical chemistry is required, but this background can be acquired with little repetition of the material presented in other courses. A rather deep insight of most instrumental methods can be gained by a relatively simple and yet rational presentation.

Instruments are often composed of rather complicated electronic, optical, and mechanical parts, and a thorough knowledge of instrumentation engineering is essential in instrument design. This is not the case in the discussion of fundamentals of instrumental analysis. Instrumentation, which is encountered in all physical sciences, is a subject different from instrumental analysis.[1] We shall discuss the functions which instruments must fulfill often without going into the detail of instrumentation. For example, block diagrams will be used systematically in the representation of electronic components of instruments. However, fundamental electrical circuits (not electronic ones) and basic optical diagrams will be discussed because they are essential to the understanding of instrumental methods. Commercial instruments will be mentioned, but these will not be discussed in detail since they embody the ideas developed in the text. The student has opportunities to use commercial instruments in the laboratory, and he may find it fruitful to study the literature provided by manufacturers.[2]

Instrumental methods can be classified in various ways according to the criterion which is adopted: quantity being measured, type of methods, etc. We shall divide instrumental methods into the following three broad groups: (1) methods derived from electrochemistry; (2) methods based on the emission or absorption of radiation by matter; (3) miscellaneous methods which do not belong to the first two groups.

1-2. CLASSIFICATION OF ELECTROCHEMICAL METHODS

Instrumental methods derived from electrochemistry, i.e., methods of *electroanalytical chemistry*, will be discussed first because they involve simpler elements of instrumentation than most other methods.

A classification of electrochemical methods can be made by considering the operation of an electrochemical cell. Such a cell is composed of two metallic electrodes immersed in an electrolyte and connected to some device exchanging energy with the cell. A storage battery is an example of an electrochemical cell which supplies energy during discharge and consumes energy during the charging process. The electrochemical behavior of such a cell can be characterized by measuring different electrical quantities: quantity of electricity, voltage, current, resistance, and dielectric constant. The corresponding methods of analysis can be classified accordingly.

Analytical methods based on the measurement of a quantity of electricity are designated by the generic term of *coulometry*. The term is derived from "coulomb," which is one of the units for a quantity of electricity.

---

[1] I. M. Kolthoff, *Chem. Eng. News*, **28**, 2882 (1950).

[2] It is suggested that a file of material on the most important commercial instruments—even those which are not used in the course—be kept in the laboratory and made available to students.

Coulometric methods are based on the proportionality relationship that exists between the quantity of electricity and the quantity of substance transformed during electrolysis.

Potentiometry groups a variety of electrochemical methods in which the result of the analysis is deduced from the voltage across an electrochemical cell. The term *potentiometry* is derived from the word "potential," which is used to designate the voltage across an electrochemical cell under conditions discussed in Chapter 2. The result of the analysis can be computed directly from the voltage across the cell, or the equivalence point of a titration can be determined from the variations of this voltage during titration (*potentiometric titrations*).

Amperometry designates methods involving current measurements. Amperometric methods are generally applied to the detection of the equivalence point of titrations (*amperometric titrations*).

The interpretation of current-voltage characteristics of electrochemical cells leads to several useful methods which are grouped under the general term of *voltammetry*. Various types of electrodes can be utilized in voltammetry, but one of them, the dropping mercury electrode, is particularly useful, and the corresponding voltammetric method is referred to as *polarography*.

The measurement of the resistance of an electrochemical cell can sometimes be useful in chemical analysis. The resistance is the ratio of the voltage applied to the cell to the current through the cell (Ohm's law). As we shall see in Chapter 7, the conductance, which is the reciprocal of the resistance, is generally used in electrochemistry. Methods based on conductance measurements are grouped under the term of *conductometry*. The result of an analysis can sometimes be computed directly from conductance measurements, but conductometry is more frequently applied to the determination of the equivalence point of titrations (*conductometric titrations*).

For reasons discussed in Chapter 7, conductances are generally measured by using alternating current at relatively low frequencies, for example, 1000 cycles per second. The possibility and usefulness of using much higher frequencies (several megacycles per second) were recognized rather recently, and several *high-frequency methods* have been devised. These methods can sometimes be applied to the measurement of dielectric constants.

Separations can be made by electrochemical methods. For example, copper can be removed from a solution of one of its salts by electrodeposition on a platinum electrode. This method, which is called *electrogravimetry*, is somewhat similar to conventional gravimetry inasmuch as electricity can be regarded as the reagent used in the precipitation of the element to be analyzed. A similar procedure can also be applied to the separation of an undesired constituent from a mixture (*electrolytic separation*).

The following order will be adopted in the study of the above methods:

Potentiometry
Voltammetry and Polarography
Amperometric Titrations
Electrogravimetry and Electrolytic Separations
Coulometry
Conductometry and High-Frequency Methods

The understanding of electrode potentials is essential in electroanalytical chemistry, and potentiometry therefore will be treated first. Amperometry is discussed after voltammetry and polarography because the latter two methods have a more general scope than the former one. Electrogravimetry is the simplest and the oldest of electrochemical methods, but it will be discussed after potentiometry and voltammetry because some of the ideas introduced in the treatment of these two methods are essential to the rational understanding of electrogravimetry. The same reason holds for coulometry. Conductometry and high-frequency methods will be treated lastly because they are very different from the other electroanalytical methods.

1-3. CLASSIFICATION OF METHODS INVOLVING EMISSION OR ABSORPTION OF RADIATION

Methods based on the study of absorption and emission of radiation are among the most useful and versatile of chemical analysis. Colorimetry is a familiar example of a simple method based on absorption of light. Methods involving visible and ultraviolet light were first applied to analytical chemistry, but the newer methods cover a much wider range of wave lengths. The following order will be adopted:

Emission Spectroscopy
Absorption Spectrometry in the Visible, Ultraviolet, and Infrared Ranges
Fluorometry
Turbidimetry and Nephelometry
Raman Spectroscopy
X-ray Methods

The characteristic spectrum produced by excitation of elements is applied to qualitative and quantitative analysis in *emission spectroscopy*. Several methods of excitation are employed: arc, spark, and flame. The latter method is used in an emission spectroscopy method referred to as *flame photometry*.

Absorption spectrometry is based on the measurement of the absorption of electromagnetic radiation by matter. The absorption varies with the wave length of the incident radiation, and measurements can be made at a single wave length or over a wide range of wave lengths. Filters are often utilized to obtain a narrow bandwidth radiation, and the corresponding analytical method is known as *filter photometry*. Absorption measurements are also made with a source of monochromatic radiation of variable wave length (*spectrophotometry* or *absorption spectrometry*).

The absorption of light by certain substances is accompanied by re-emission of light in the familiar phenomenon of fluorescence. The measurement of the intensity of fluorescence serves useful analytical purposes, especially in the determination of traces (*fluorometry*).

Analytical determinations can sometimes be made by measuring the opacity of a suspension of small particles (*turbidimetry*), but the application of this method often leads to uncertain results. *Nephelometry*, which involves the measurement of the intensity of light scattered by a suspension of small particles, is somewhat more useful than turbidimetry. Light is scattered mainly without change of wave length (Rayleigh effect), but also with change of wave length (*Raman effect*). Application of the Raman effect to analytical chemistry has proved valuable.

Two other optical methods, namely, *refractometry* and *polarimetry*, find applications in the analytical laboratory. Refractometry, which deals with the measurement of indexes of refraction, is often used in the identification of organic compounds. Quantitative applications are also possible. Polarimetry is applied to the determination of optically active substances, such as dextrose. Refractometry and polarimetry will not be discussed here because these methods are generally covered in courses in organic and physical chemistry.

The optical methods mentioned so far involve measurements over a wide range of wave lengths, which in practice vary from 40 μ (1 micron = 10^{-4} cm) in the infrared to 2000 A (1 angstrom = 10^{-8} cm) in the ultra-violet. Measurements below 2000 A are difficult until the wave length is lowered in the X-ray range (1 A). The applications of X-rays to analysis include *absorption*, *diffraction*, and *emission* (*X-ray fluorescence*) methods.

1-4. MISCELLANEOUS METHODS WHICH DO NOT BELONG TO THE PREVIOUS TWO GROUPS

We shall reserve for the end of our discussion the following methods: (1) *mass spectroscopy* and various methods of gas analysis, and (2) *nuclear radiation methods*.

This does not conclude the list of possible applications of physics and physical chemistry to chemical analysis. For instance, useful analytical determinations can be based on the measurement of the following quantities: melting and boiling points, vapor pressure, density, viscosity, surface tension, etc. However, these methods are discussed in physical chemistry courses and their study in this text would be a duplication of material. Other methods such as electrophoresis, microscopy, and electron microscopy are not covered here for the same reason.

1–5. SELECTION OF THE MOST ADVANTAGEOUS METHOD IN THE ANALYTICAL LABORATORY

A substance can often be determined by a variety of methods, and the analytical chemist generally can save much time and improve the accuracy of results by a critical comparison of the various methods which might possibly be applied. Some methods, such as emission spectroscopy, are particularly suited to routine work, but they are not practical in isolated cases because of a tedious calibration procedure. No simple rule can be prescribed, and only the study and understanding of instrumental analysis can provide the analytical chemist with the necessary background for a proper selection of the most appropriate method in a given situation.

Three essential characteristics of a method, namely, *accuracy, sensitivity,* and *selectivity,* must always be considered, but other criteria such as *cost* of equipment and *duration* of analysis are also of great practical significance. The accuracy is characterized by the absolute and relative errors[3,4] which may affect the results of the analysis. The accuracy should not be confused with the *precision,* which depends on the reproducibility of experimental results. Thus, a method may yield precise but not accurate results if a large systematic error is made. The sensitivity can be expressed in two ways, depending on whether the minimum amount of analyzed substance or the minimum concentration of this substance is quoted. The simultaneous use of both methods for defining the sensitivity is advisable. The selectivity of a method is adequately described by the enumeration of interfering substances.

1–6. BIBLIOGRAPHY

The following books and treatises contain a general treatment of instrumental methods of analysis. References to monographs and reviews articles dealing specifically with a method or a group of methods are listed in each chapter of this text.

W. G. Berl, editor, *Physical Methods in Chemical Analysis,* 2 vols., Academic Press, New York, 1950–1951.

[3] One often hears that the accuracy of a method is x per cent, while it is meant that the *relative error* is x per cent.

[4] For details, see a text on statistical analysis of data. For references, see G. Wernimont, *Anal. Chem.,* **21,** 115 (1949), and R. J. Hader and W. J. Youden, *ibid.,* **24,** 120 (1952).

D. F. Boltz, *Selected Topics in Modern Instrumental Analysis*, Prentice-Hall, New York, 1952.

W. Böttger, editor, *Physikalische Methoden der Analytischen Chemie*, 3 vols., Akademische Verlagsgesellschaft, Leipzig, 1933–1939. Reprinted by Edwards Brothers, Ann Arbor, Michigan, 1943.

G. W. Ewing, *Instrumental Methods of Chemical Analysis*, McGraw-Hill, New York, 1954.

J. H. Harley and S. E. Wiberley, *Instrumental Analysis*, Wiley, New York, 1954.

J. Reilly and W. N. Rae, *Physico-chemical Methods*, 5th ed., 3 vols., Van Nostrand, New York, 1954.

W. Wagner, C. J. Hull, and G. E. Markle, *Advanced Analytical Chemistry*, Reinhold, New York, 1956. Covers some of the instrumental methods.

A. Weissberger, editor, *Physical Methods of Organic Chemistry*, 2 ed., 3 parts, Interscience, New York, 1949–1954.

H. H. Willard, L. L. Merritt, and J. A. Dean, *Instrumental Methods of Analysis*, 2nd ed., Van Nostrand, New York, 1951.

J. H. Yoe and H. J. Koch, Jr., Eds., *Symposium on Trace Analysis*, Wiley, New York, (in press). Covers instrumental and noninstrumental methods.

Most of the journals dealing with analytical chemistry publish papers dealing with instrumental methods. The following list will be useful for orientation purposes:

Analyst
Analytica Chimica Acta
Analytical Chemistry (see especially the periodic reviews and the monthly column on instrumentation by R. H. Müller)
Chimie Analytique
Microchimica Acta
Zavodskaya Laboratoriya (available in English translation from Consultants Bureau, 152 West 42nd Street, New York 18)
Zeitschrift für Analytische Chemie

The following journals deal specifically with instrumentation:

Instrument and Apparatus News
Instrumento
Journal of Scientific Instruments
Review of Scientific Instruments

Many of the articles published in the above journals are of applied nature, and much information about the fundamentals of instrumental analysis can be found in other journals dealing with physics and chemistry.

Abstracts are available in *British Abstracts*, *series A* (discontinued at the end of 1953), *Chemical Abstracts*, and the *Chemisches Zentralblatt*. Abstracts of analytical papers are published by the Society for Analytical Chemistry (England) in *Analytical Abstracts*. *Current Chemical Papers* is a selected list of papers published monthly by the Chemical Society (England). Many papers are listed there several months before they appear in abstracts journals.

A knowledge of electronics is not required in the discussion of the fundamentals of instrumental analysis, but the reader who would like to acquire some background in the field may consult the books listed below. These books also contain references to the numerous works dealing with electronics.

W. C. Elmore and M. Sands, *Electronics—Experimental Techniques*, McGraw-Hill, New York, 1949. Contains much information of practical value.

R. H. Müller, R. L. Garman, and M. E. Droz, *Experimental Electronics*, Prentice-Hall, New York, 1942. Particularly recommended.

L. N. Ridenour and G. B. Collins, Eds., *M.I.T. Radiation Laboratory* Series, 28 vols., McGraw-Hill, New York, 1946–1948.

F. E. Terman, *Radio Engineers' Handbook*, McGraw-Hill, New York, 1943.

2

Electrode Potentials

2-1. ELECTROCHEMICAL CELLS

In electrochemical cells two electrodes of the same metal or of different metals 1 and 2 are immersed in the same or in different electrolytes (Fig. 1). Each compartment is a *half-cell*. Mixing of solutions 1 and 2 when these solutions have not the same composition is prevented by a diaphragm of porous material such as unglazed porcelain or fritted glass. There is contact between solutions 1 and 2, but transfer of solution through the diaphragm is slow and mixing is virtually avoided. Electrodes 1 and 2 are connected to an electrical instrument P, which can exchange electrical energy with the cell. Instrument P in this chapter, dealing with the voltage of electrochemical cells, is a voltmeter or a more accurate device for voltage measurements. The electrical circuit of instrument P may be of a metal different from metals 1 and 2 of the cell, and the following discussion is still valid in that case. It will be assumed for the sake of simplicity that the electrical circuit of P is made of metal 1.

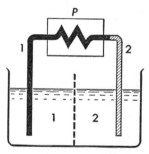

Fig. 1. Schematic diagram of electrochemical cell.

The electrical energy exchanged between the cell and instrument P is liberated or consumed by reactions involving transfer of charge at the electrodes. *Electrons are consumed at the cathode, where reduction occurs, and are supplied by the anode, where oxidation occurs.* The terms *cathode* and *anode* are constantly used in electroanalytical chemistry, and their definition is important. It will become apparent below that the cathode is not necessarily the negative terminal of the cell nor that the anode is the positive terminal.

Free electrons generally do not exist in electrolytes, and electricity is transported through the cell by *migration* of ions. Positive ions migrate toward the negative electrode, and negative ions toward the positive electrode. Migration is not prevented by the plate separating the two compartments of the cell in Fig. 1 because the average diameter of the pores of this plate is much larger than ionic dimensions.

2-2. *DIFFERENCES OF POTENTIAL IN ELECTROCHEMICAL CELLS*

The voltage read on instrument P of Fig. 1 is the algebraic sum of the differences of potential along the electrical circuit. Differences of potential are set up at the various junctions in the electrical circuit, i.e., at the metal-metal contact, the two metal-liquid interfaces, and the liquid-liquid junction. Differences of potential, which are ohmic drops, are observed also in the electrodes and solution when a current flows through the cell. Ohmic drops can be neglected when the current is sufficiently low, as is the case, in general, in the voltage measurements considered in this chapter.

The discussion of differences of potential at the junctions of electrochemical cells requires a clear understanding of the concept of electrical potential, and the reader may find it profitable to review this material in a physics text. The electrical potential at a given point is defined as the work required to bring a unit positive charge from infinity to the point where the potential is defined. This work is generally not the same on each side of an interface, and consequently a difference of electrical potential exists at the junction.[1]

Differences of potential at metal-metal junctions result from differences in the work required to extract an electron from each metal. Values of the *work function*, that is the work of extraction of an electron, cover a range of several electronvolts; for instance, 1.60 and 5.3 electronvolts for potassium and platinum, respectively. Differences of potential between metals can be of the order of a few volts. These are not affected by the electrode reactions in the electrochemical cell, and no further comment is needed here.[2]

We shall discuss differences of potential at liquid-liquid junctions by considering the junction between solutions of potassium chloride and sodium nitrate. We assume that these solutions are separated initially by

---

[1]The definition of the difference of potential at a junction involves difficulties which will be omitted for the sake of simplicity. The advanced student may find a very clear discussion of these difficulties in N. K. Adam's monograph, *The Physics and Chemistry of Surfaces*, 3rd ed., Oxford University Press, London, 1941, pp. 300–362.

[2]For a detailed discussion see Adam, *loc. cit.*

an infinitely thin plate, which can be removed without causing any stirring. As soon as the plate is removed, ions diffuse[3] toward regions of lower concentration. The average velocity of diffusion varies with the nature of the ions, since this velocity depends, among other things, on the size of the ions. As a result of diffusion, the transfer of positive ions is not exactly compensated by the movement of negative ions, and there is a net transfer of charge. A rather small difference of potential (perhaps a few hundredths of a volt or even less) is established.

It is advantageous in precise potentiometric measurements to avoid liquid-liquid junctions by immersion of the two electrodes of a cell in the same solution. If two solutions of different compositions must be used, as is often the case, the liquid-liquid difference of potential is greatly minimized when the following conditions are fulfilled: (1) cations and anions of the electrolyte on one side of the junction diffuse with practically the same velocity; (2) the concentration of these two ions is much higher— perhaps 10 to 50 times higher—than the concentration of electrolyte on the other side of the junction. Potassium and chloride ions diffuse virtually with the same velocity, and this is why potassium chloride is often selected for liquid-liquid junctions (see Section 2–9). The liquid-liquid difference of potential is then as low as a few millivolts.

Theoretical treatments of liquid-liquid differences of potential can be found in physical chemistry and electrochemistry texts (Bibliography, Section 2–11).

Differences of potential at metal-liquid interfaces may result from several causes, but only the most important case in which this cause is an oxidation or reduction will be considered. This discussion requires the introduction of the concept of electrode potential.

2–3. ELECTRODE POTENTIALS

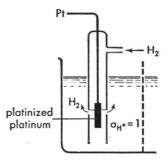

Fig. 2.   Schematic diagram of normal hydrogen electrode.

Since the voltage of an electrochemical cell depends on the characteristics of both electrodes, comparative measurements can be made when only one electrode is changed, the other electrode serving as reference. Any reliable electrode could, in principle, be selected as reference, but the *normal hydrogen electrode*, as was suggested by Nernst, is universally adopted to fulfill this function. The electrode (Fig. 2) is made of a platinum wire, which is covered with a spongy deposit of finely divided platinum (platinized platinum) to increase the area exposed

[3]For a discussion of diffusion see a text of general or physical chemistry; see also Chapter 4.

to the electrolyte.[4] The platinum wire is sealed in a tube immersed in a solution of hydrochloric acid, and hydrogen is bubbled over platinum and allowed to escape through lateral holes under a pressure of one atmosphere (actually, the fugacity is equal to unity; see Section 2–6). Because of the periodic formation of bubbles, the level of liquid inside the tube fluctuates, and a fraction of the wire is alternatively exposed to the solution and hydrogen. The end of the wire is continuously immersed in solution to avoid interruption of the electrical circuit. The concentration of hydrochloric acid is adjusted in such a manner that the activity of hydrogen ion is equal to unity (1.18 M hydrochloric acid at 25°). The reader without background in physical chemistry may not have encountered the expression "activity" before, but this should not deter him from further discussion of the hydrogen electrode. It suffices to know that the concentration of hydrogen ion is adjusted at some determined value. We shall return to the concept of activity in Section 2–5.

Since hydrogen ions and hydrogen are present at the interface electrode-solution, the reaction $2H^+ + 2e = H_2$ may occur in either direction. Note that hydrogen ion is represented by H^+, and not by H_3O^+, to simplify the writing. The same practice will be followed in the writing of the formulas of other hydrated ions.

The normal hydrogen electrode is coupled with some other electrode being studied, and the *potential* of the latter electrode is defined as the voltage of the resulting cell, the experimental conditions being such that the liquid-liquid difference of potential is negligible. Thus, an electrode potentional is a voltage, and the word "potential" in the expression "electrode potential" has not the same meaning as in the definition of an electrical potential in physics. *By convention* one considers that the contribution of the normal hydrogen electrode to the voltage of an electrochemical cell is equal to zero at all temperatures. This means that *the potential of the normal hydrogen electrode is, by convention, equal to zero at all temperatures.*

The selection of the normal hydrogen electrode as reference may seem peculiar, since the choice of an electrode of simpler design (for instance, copper in copper sulfate) might have been more advantageous. The hydrogen electrode was selected for several reasons: (1) the reagents can be easily purified; (2) the hydrogen electrode is very sensitive to some impurities whose effect can readily be detected; (3) the potential of the hydrogen electrode is not affected by mechanical stress of the electrode, while this is not so, for example, for the copper-copper sulfate electrode. Summarizing, the normal hydrogen electrode was selected as reference because its characteristics can be reliably reproduced. However, secondary reference electrodes are generally preferred in actual electrochemical meas-

[4]The reason for increasing the area of the electrode is given in Section 2–10b.

urements (Section 2–9). Potentials are referred to the normal hydrogen electrode, but they are actually measured with respect to a secondary reference electrode. The necessary correction can be readily made when the potential of the secondary reference electrode against the normal hydrogen electrode is known. Unless otherwise indicated, all potentials will be referred to the normal hydrogen electrode (abridged as N.H.E.).

2-4. CONVENTION OF SIGNS

The difference of potential at an electrode-solution interface can be expressed as the difference of potential (1) from electrode to solution, or (2) from solution to electrode. If ψ_e is the potential of the electrode and ψ_s the potential of the solution, the difference of potential is either $\psi_e - \psi_s$ or $\psi_s - \psi_e$, depending on whether the first or second method is adopted. The first method (i.e., $\psi_e - \psi_s$) corresponds to the *European convention* of signs, and the second method ($\psi_s - \psi_e$) to the *American convention*. Either method can be used, but the sign preceding the electrode potential is reversed, as follows, from $\psi_e - \psi_s = -(\psi_s - \psi_e)$.

The American convention is generally followed in this country in physical chemistry texts, but the European convention is adopted elsewhere. Analytical chemists largely use the European convention, and we shall follow this practice.

When an electrode is made increasingly negative with respect to solution, the electrode potential expressed in the European convention becomes more negative. The electrode potential, under the same conditions, becomes more positive in the American convention. The European convention is therefore preferable for convenience of language. Confusion is avoided when the convention being adopted is clearly stated.

The manner in which oxidation and reduction reactions should be written depends on the convention being adopted. Reactions are written as reductions in the European convention and as oxidations in the American convention. Thus one has $Ag^+ + e = Ag$ in the European convention. This point may appear trivial, but it has its importance when electrode potentials are calculated from thermodynamic data. It can be shown that the potential of a half-cell is related to the change in free energy for the electrode reaction. The sign of this free energy change depends on the manner in which the reaction is written, and consistency requires that reactions be properly written.

2-5. THE NERNST EQUATION: METAL AND ITS CATION

a. Half-cells $M^{+n} + ne = M$. The following three types of electrode reactions will be considered: (1) reactions between a metal and cations of this metal, (2) electron transfers between two soluble species, and (3) more involved oxidation-reduction reactions. The first type of reaction, symbolized by

$$M^{+n} + n\,e = M\,, \tag{2-1}$$

will first be considered. The electrode of metal M is immersed in a solution of cations M^{+n} and is coupled with a normal hydrogen electrode as indicated by the schematic diagram

$$M \;\bigg|\; M^{+n} \;\bigg\|\; H^+(a_{H^+} = 1) \;\bigg|\; H_2(1 \text{ atm}) \;\bigg|\; Pt.$$

A single vertical bar indicates a metal-solution interface, and two vertical parallel bars indicate a liquid-liquid junction. The notation, $a_{H^+} = 1$, signifies that the activity of hydrogen ions is equal to unity (Section 2–3). The voltage across this cell is measured by connecting a voltmeter, or some instrument fulfilling the same function, to the terminals M and Pt. It will be assumed for the sake of simplicity that the difference of potential at the liquid-liquid junction can be neglected.

The potential of electrode M depends on the nature of metal M and on the concentration—or rather activity—of cation M^{+n} according to the *Nernst equation*. This equation can be established by thermodynamic reasoning, and the reader with a sufficient background may review the derivation in a physical chemistry or thermodynamics text.[5] So-called simplified derivations can also be found in the literature, but we shall not attempt to derive this equation in a rather inadequate manner for the sake of having a derivation at any cost. The reader without the necessary background for studying the derivation of the Nernst equation can nevertheless understand the significance of this equation and apply it with fruitful results. It is to be noted that the voltage of complete cells is generally computed in thermodynamic treatments whereas electrode potentials are calculated in this text. The latter method is more convenient in the discussion of applications and amounts, in fact, to the calculation of the voltage of a cell of which one half-cell is a normal hydrogen electrode.

The Nernst equation for reaction (2–1) is

$$E = E^0 + \frac{1.983 \times 10^{-4}T}{n} \log a_{M^{+n}}, \tag{2-2}$$

where E is the potential of electrode M, E^0 the *standard potential* for reaction (2–1), n the number of electrons involved in (2–1), T the absolute temperature at which the electrode potential is expressed, and $a_{M^{+n}}$ the activity of cation M^{+n}. The activity $a_{M^{+n}}$ and the term E^0 deserve some comments.

[5]For a derivation in very precise thermodynamic language, see for instance E. A. Guggenheim, *Thermodynamics*, 2nd ed., Interscience, New York, 1950, pp. 331-354.

The term in $\log a_{M^{+n}}$ accounts for the influence of the concentration of ion M^{+n} on potential E. Properties of solutions depend on activities rather than concentrations on account of interaction between species in solution. Such interactions are corrected for by the introduction of the *activity coefficient* f defined by

$$a = fC , \tag{2-3}$$

where a is the activity of an ionic species and C its concentration. At low concentrations of solute, perhaps 0.001 molar, interactions are quite negligible and f is close to unity ($f > 0.9$). The coefficient f becomes appreciably smaller than unity when the concentration increases. In some cases, however, f is larger than unity at sufficiently high concentrations.

The theoretical interpretation and the experimental determination of activities are of great importance in physical chemistry, but this material is not within the scope of this discussion. For the sake of simplicity we shall assume that the numerical value of the concentration, expressed in moles per liter, can be substituted for the activity.

TABLE I
Standard Potentials for Reaction $M^{+n} + ne = M$
(European convention, aqueous solution)[a]

ELECTRODE REACTION	E^0, VOLTS
$Li^+ + e = Li$	-3.045
$K^+ + e = K$	-2.925
$Ba^{++} + 2e = Ba$	-2.90
$Ca^{++} + 2e = Ca$	-2.87
$Na^+ + e = Na$	-2.714
$Mg^{++} + 2e = Mg$	-2.37
$Al^{+++} + 3e = Al$	-1.66
$Mn^{++} + 2e = Mn$	-1.18
$Zn^{++} + 2e = Zn$	-0.763
$Fe^{++} + 2e = Fe$	-0.440
$Cd^{++} + 2c = Cd$	-0.403
$Tl^+ + e = Tl$	-0.3363
$Co^{++} + 2e = Co$	-0.277
$Ni^{++} + 2e = Ni$	-0.250
$Sn^{++} + 2e = Sn$	-0.136
$Pb^{++} + 2e = Pb$	-0.126
$2H^+ + 2e = H_2$	0
$Cu^{++} + 2e = Cu$	0.337
$Hg_2^{++} + 2e = 2Hg$	0.780
$Ag^+ + e = Ag$	0.7991
$Pt^{++} + 2e = Pt$	1.2
$Au^{+++} + 3e = Au$	1.5

[a]Values from Latimer's monograph; see reference in Section 2-11.

When the activity of ion M^{+n} is equal to unity (approximately for a 1 molar solution), the electrode potential E is equal to the standard potential E^0 (Table I). Detailed compilations of standard potentials can be found in the monographs of Latimer and Conway listed in Section 2–11. Standard potentials can also be calculated from thermodynamic data (see physical chemistry or electrochemistry texts). Standard potentials are known with four significant figures for certain metals, while there is much uncertainty in some cases, and only one or two significant figures can be quoted. In consulting tables of standard potentials, one should always ascertain which convention of signs is adopted.

It was suggested by Swift[6] that the Nernst equation be written in terms of concentration rather than activity, and that a *formal potential* be substituted for the standard potential E^0. This method has the advantage of yielding potentials which are directly obtained by experiment without computation of activity coefficients. However, formal potentials depend on the concentration of ion M^{+n} [in the case of reaction (2–1)], since the activity coefficient of this ion varies with concentration. In analytical applications of electrode potentials it is often convenient to substitute concentrations for activities; formal potentials then have a real practical value.

We discussed above the dependence of electrode potentials on the concentration of ion M^{+n} (term in $a_{M^{+n}}$) and on the nature of the electrode (term E^0). Electrode potentials also depend on temperature because the absolute temperature T appears in equation (2–2) and the activity $a_{M^{+n}}$ varies with temperature. Variations of potentials with temperature at room temperature are not very rapid but nevertheless significant. The coefficient $1.983 \times 10^{-4} T$ of equation (2–2) is equal to 0.0591 at 25° and 0.0601 at 30°. By introduction of the former value in equation (2–2), there results

$$E = E^0 + \frac{0.0591}{n} \log a_{M^{+n}}, \qquad (2\text{–}4)$$

which is a form of the Nernst equation often found in textbooks. Equation (2–4) will be applied in subsequent discussions, but it should be remembered that the factor 0.0591 only holds for 25°.

Equations (2–2) and (2–4) are written in the European convention, and the term in $\log a_{M^{+n}}$ is preceded by a plus sign. When the American convention is adopted the signs of electrode potentials are reversed, and the term in $\log a_{M^{+n}}$ is preceded by a minus sign.

b. *Cells of the Type M_1—M_2.* Consider the cell of the general type

$$M_1 \;\bigg|\; M_1^{+n_1}(a_1) \;\bigg\|\; M_2^{+n_2}(a_2) \;\bigg|\; M_2 \,,$$

where M_1 and M_2 are two different metals; for example, copper and zinc.

[6] E. H. Swift, *A System of Chemical Analysis*, Prentice-Hall, New York, 1939.

The voltage across this cell is the absolute value of the difference between the potentials of electrodes M_1 and M_2, provided that the difference of potential at the liquid-liquid junction can be neglected. The positive terminal is the metal whose potential is the more positive or the less negative.

EXAMPLE. Calculate the voltage across the cell (25⁰)

$$\text{Cu} \,\bigg|\, \text{Cu}^{++}(a_{\text{Cu}^{++}} = 2 \times 10^{-2}) \,\bigg\|\, \text{Zn}(a_{\text{Zn}^{++}} = 5 \times 10^{-3}) \,\bigg|\, \text{Zn}.$$

The electrode potentials are

$$E_{\text{Cu}} = 0.337 + \frac{0.0591}{2} \log 2 \times 10^{-2}$$
$$= 0.287 \text{ Volt}$$
$$E_{\text{Zn}} = -0.763 + \frac{0.0591}{2} \log 5 \times 10^{-3}$$
$$= -0.831 \text{ Volt}.$$

These potentials are plotted in Fig. 3, which shows that the voltage of the cell is 1.118 volts. This result can of course be obtained by simply calculating the difference $E_{\text{Cu}} - E_{\text{Zn}}$, but the use of a diagram is perhaps less conducive to errors than the direct calculation. Since E_{Cu} is more positive than E_{Zn}, copper is the positive terminal and zinc the negative terminal.

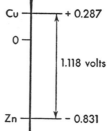

Fig. 3. Calculation of the voltage of an electrochemical cell.

c. Concentration Cells. Consider the cell

$$\text{M} \,\bigg|\, \text{M}^{+n}(a_1) \,\bigg\|\, \text{M}^{+n}(a_2) \,\bigg|\, \text{M,}$$

where the electrodes are of the same metal, and the activities a_1 and a_2 are different. Equation (2-4) holds for both half-cells, and the voltage of the cell is, at 25°,

$$E_1 - E_2 = \frac{0.0591}{n} \log a_1 - \frac{0.059}{n} \log a_2$$
$$= \frac{0.0591}{n} \log \frac{a_1}{a_2}, \tag{2-5}$$

if the difference of potential at the liquid-liquid junction is neglected.

Since the logarithmic term in the Nernst equation is preceded by a positive sign, the electrode potential E becomes more positive or less negative when the activity of ion M^{+n} increases. The positive terminal is the electrode in the compartment having the larger activity of ion M^{+n}.

The voltage of concentration cells does not exceed 0.1 volt unless the ratio a_1/a_2 is very small or very large.

2-6. THE NERNST EQUATION: REACTIONS INVOLVING TWO SOLUBLE SPECIES

We consider reactions involving two soluble species as, for example, the reaction $Fe^{+++} + e = Fe^{++}$. We write such reactions in a general manner

$$xO + n\,e = yR, \tag{2-6}$$

where O symbolizes the species being reduced and R the reduction product, n is the number of electrons involved in the reaction, and x and y are stoichiometric coefficients. Species O and R are soluble in solution and are not gaseous. An electrode made of some inert metal such as platinum or gold is immersed in the solution containing substances O and R, and the resulting half-cell is coupled with a normal hydrogen electrode according to the schematic diagram

$$\text{Inert electrode} \left| O + R \right\| H^+(a_{H^+} = 1) \left| H_2(1 \text{ atm}) \right| Pt.$$

The voltage of this cell, as measured by the method of Fig. 1, is the

TABLE II
Standard Potentials for Reaction $xO + ne = yR$
(European convention, aqueous solution)[a]

REACTION	E^0, VOLTS
$Cr^{+++} + e = Cr^{++}$	−0.41
$2H^+ + 2e = H_2$	0
$S_4O_6^{--} + 2e = 2S_2O_3^{--}$	0.08
$Sn^{+4} + 2e = Sn^{++}$	0.15
$Cu^{++} + e = Cu^+$	0.153
$Fe(CN)_6^{-3} + e = Fe(CN)_6^{-4}$	0.36
$I_2 + e = 2I^-$	0.5355
$Fe^{+3} + e = Fe^{++}$	0.771
$2Hg^{++} + 2e = Hg_2^{++}$	0.920
$Br_2(\text{liquid}) + 2e = 2Br^-$	1.0652
$Tl^{+++} + 2e = Tl^+$	1.25
$Cl_2 + 2e = 2Cl^-$	1.3595
$Ce^{+4} + e = Ce^{+3}$	1.61
$Co^{+3} + e = Co^{++}$	1.82
$Ag^{++} + e = Ag$	1.98
$S_2O_8^{--} + 2e = 2SO_4^{--}$	2.01
$F_2 + 2e = 2F^-$	2.65

[a]Values from Latimer's monograph; see reference in Section 2-11.

potential of the inert electrode, provided that the difference of potential at the liquid-liquid junction can be neglected. Thus, at 25°,

$$E = E^0 + \frac{0.0591}{n} \log \frac{a_O{}^x}{a_R{}^y},\qquad(2\text{--}7)$$

where E^0 is the standard potential, and the a's are the activities. Standard potentials for a few important systems are listed in Table II, and detailed tables can be found in the monographs of Latimer and Conway (see Section 2–11).

Variations of E with the composition of the mixture of O and R are shown in Fig. 4, which was prepared on the assumption that the ratio of

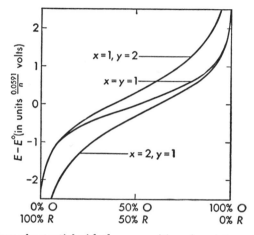

Fig. 4. Variations of potential with the composition of a mixture of species O and R. See equation (2–7).

activities in equation (2–7) is equal to the ratio of the corresponding concentrations. Potential E, according to equation (2–7), should be infinite when one of the activities a_O or a_R is made equal to zero. This conclusion has no physical significance, and it will be shown in Section 2–8b that reduction or oxidation of the solvent occurs when the potential is sufficiently cathodic or anodic. This results in the production of either the oxidized species O in the case of the reduction of the solvent or the reduced species R when the solvent is oxidized.

The potential is equal to the standard potential when the argument of the logarithmic term in equation (2–7) is equal to unit, i.e., for

$$a_O{}^x = a_R{}^y.\qquad(2\text{--}8)$$

If the stoichiometric coefficient x and y are equal to unity, which is often the case, the condition in equation (2–8) is satisfied when the activities of substances O and R are equal. However, it is only when $x = y$ that the standard potential is observed for $a_O/a_R = 1$. If x and y are different, the ratio a_O/a_R at which $E = E^0$ must be determined from equation (2–8). If $x = y/2$, one has[7] $E = E^0$ for $a_O/a_R = 0.618$. Conversely, for $x = 2y$, $E = E^0$ for $a_O/a_R = 1.617$.

The foregoing considerations can be applied to electrode reactions involving a gas; as, for example, the hydrogen electrode. Equation (2–7) can be applied, but the *fugacity* of the gas must be substituted for the activity of the species O or R which is gaseous. The fugacity is to pressure what activity is to concentration. The fugacity of a gas is somewhat different from the pressure because of interaction between molecules, i.e., because of departure from ideality. As a first approximation one may identify fugacity with the numerical value of the pressure in atmospheres.

EXAMPLE.   Calculate the potential of a hydrogen electrode functioning at 25° under a pressure of 0.01 atm, the activity a_{H^+} being unity. Assume that the fugacity is equal to the pressure.
The reaction is

$$2H^+ + 2\,e = H_2$$

and the potential is ($E^0 = 0$ volt)

$$E = \frac{0.0591}{2} \log \frac{a_{H^+}{}^2}{p_{H_2}}$$
$$= \frac{0.0591}{2} \log \frac{1^2}{0.01}$$
$$= 0.0591 \text{ Volt.}$$

At a pressure of 1 atm, the potential is 0 volt, and it can be seen by comparing this value with the potential (0.059) in this example that the effect of the pressure of gas on the potential of a hydrogen electrode is rather small.

Incidentally, it is now obvious why the fugacity of hydrogen and the activity of hydrogen ions are made equal to unity in the case of the normal hydrogen electrode: the logarithmic term in the Nernst equation vanishes.

Equation (2–7) is written with a plus sign before the logarithmic term (European convention). This sign should be minus when the American convention is adopted.

2–7. THE NERNST EQUATION: GENERAL FORM

a. General Form.   The Nernst equation can be applied to reactions represented schematically by the equation

$$xO + mW + ne = yR + zZ, \qquad (2\text{–}9)$$

where O symbolizes the substance being reduced, R the main reduction

[7]This result is obtained by setting $a_O + a_R = 1$ and $a_O = a_R{}^2$, and by solving for a_R.

product, and W and Z some other species. A familiar reaction of this type is the reduction of dichromate ion to chromic ion according to the equation

$$Cr_2O_7^{--} + 14H^+ + 6e = 2Cr^{+++} + 7H_2O.$$

The Nernst equation for electrode reaction (2–9) and for 25⁰ is

$$E = E^0 + \frac{0.0591}{n} \log \frac{a_O{}^x a_W{}^m}{a_R{}^y a_Z{}^z} \qquad (2\text{--}10)$$

This general equation yields the particular forms of the Nernst equation discussed in the preceding sections. Thus, equation (2–4) for the reaction $M^{+n} + ne = M$ is obtained by setting $x = y = 1$, $m = z = 0$, and $a_R = 1$ in equation (2–10). In that case the latter condition $a_R = 1$ states that the activity of the metal is equal to unity—a conclusion which is apparent to readers with a background in physical chemistry. Another special form of the general equation (2–10) is equation (2–7).

An important class of electrode reactions symbolized by equation (2–9) are those for which species W represents hydrogen ion, and Z is water. The potential is at 25°

$$E = E^0 + \frac{0.0591}{n} \log \frac{a_O{}^x a_{H^+}{}^m}{a_R{}^y a_{H_2O}{}^z} . \qquad (2\text{--}11)$$

Values of E^0 for a few reactions involving hydrogen ions are listed in Table III. For solutions which are not very concentrated, say, less than

TABLE III
Standard Potentials for Reaction $xO + mW + ne = yR + zZ$
(European convention, aqueous solution)[a]

REACTION	E^0, VOLTS
$2H^+ + 2e = H_2$	0
$TiO^{++} + 2H^+ + 2e = Ti^{+++} + H_2O$	0.1
$S + 2H^+ + 2e = H_2S$	0.141
$Sb_2O_3 + 6H^+ + 6e = 2Sb + 3H_2O$	0.152
$BiO^+ + 2H^+ + 3e = Bi + H_2O$	0.32
$H_3AsO_4 + 2H^+ + 2e = HAsO_2 + 2H_2O$	0.559
$O_2 + 2H^+ + 2e = H_2O_2$	0.682
$NO_3^- + 3H^+ + 2e^- = HNO_2 + H_2O$	0.94
$NO_3^- + 4H^+ + 4e = NO + 2H_2O$	0.96
$O_2 + 4H^+ + 4e = 2H_2O$	1.229
$MnO_2 + 4H^+ + 2e = Mn^{++} + 2H_2O$	1.23
$Cr_2O_7^{--} + 14H^+ + 6e = 2Cr^{+++} + 7H_2O$	1.33
$PbO_2 + 4H^+ + 2e = Pb^{++} + 2H_2O$	1.455
$ClO_3^- + 6H^+ + 5e = Cl_2 + 3H_2O$	1.47
$MnO_4^- + 8H^+ + 5e = Mn^{++} + 4H_2O$	1.51
$BrO_3^- + 6H^+ + 5e = Br_2 + 3H_2O$	1.52
$F_2 + 2H^+ + 2e = 2HF(aq)$	3.06

[a]Values from Latimer's monograph; see reference in Section 2–11.

1 molar, the activity of water is essentially equal to unity.[8] Equation (2–11) may then be written after introduction of the pH notation ($pH = -\log a_{H^+}$)

$$E = E^0 - 0.0591 \frac{m}{n} pH + \frac{0.0591}{n} \log \frac{a_O{}^x}{a_R{}^y}. \qquad (2\text{--}12)$$

Equation (2–12) is important because it correlates electrode potentials with the pH of the medium. The dependence of potential on pH can be very pronounced, as is readily seen from the following example.

EXAMPLE.   A platinum electrode is immersed in a solution which is 10^{-1} molar in potassium permanganate and 5×10^{-4} molar in manganous sulfate. Calculate the electrode potential at 25° for pH 0 and pH 2 on the assumption that activities can be identified with concentrations.

One has

$$MnO_4^- + 8H^+ + 5e = Mn^{++} + 4H_2O$$

and, in view of equation (2–12),

$$E = 1.51 - 0.0591 \frac{8}{5} pH + \frac{0.0591}{5} \log \frac{a_{MnO_4^-}}{a_{Mn^{++}}}.$$

Hence, $E = 1.54$ volts at $pH = 0$, and $E = 1.35$ volts at $pH = 2$.

Equation (2–12) should not be applied without discrimination over the whole pH range because the nature of the species involved in the electrode reaction may vary with the pH. For example, the reduction of permanganate in alkaline medium does not proceed to the manganous state, but rather to manganese dioxide, i.e., to manganese in the $+4$ state.

b. *Application to Amalgam Electrodes.*   Amalgam electrodes involve the reaction

$$M^{+n} + Hg + n\,e = M(Hg), \qquad (2\text{--}13)$$

where M(Hg) symbolizes the amalgam of metal M. The general form [equation (2–10)] of the Nernst equation is applicable, and the potential at 25° is

$$E = E_a{}^0 + \frac{0.0591}{n} \log \frac{a_{M^{+n}} a_{Hg}}{a_{M(Hg)}}, \qquad (2\text{--}14)$$

where $E_a{}^0$ is the standard potential for the amalgam electrode; i.e., the potential measured when all the a's in equation (2–14) are equal to unity. Potential $E_a{}^0$ is *not* the standard potential for the reaction $M^{+n} + ne = M$, as can be seen from Table IV.

[8]The activity is defined here in a somewhat different manner than by equation (2–3). (See a physical chemistry text.)

Since rather dilute amalgams—say, with less than 1 per cent of metal M by weight—are often used, the activity of mercury is practically equal

TABLE IV

Standard Potentials for Amalgam Electrodes

(European convention, aqueous solution)[a]

METAL	E^0 FOR AMALGAM ELECTRODE, VOLTS	E^0 FOR $M^{+n} + ne = M(Hg)$, VOLTS
Na	−1.89	−2.714
K	−1.86	−2.925
Zn	−0.75	−0.763
Cd	−0.32	−0.403
Tl	−0.19	−0.3363
Pb	−0.13	−0.126

[a]Values of E_a^0 are only approximate and actually are calculated from polarographic half-wave potentials; see J. J. Lingane, *J. Am. Chem. Soc.*, **61**, 2099 (1939).

to unity and equation (2–14) becomes

$$E = E_a^0 + \frac{0.0591}{n} \log \frac{a_{M^{+n}}}{a_{M(Hg)}}. \qquad (2\text{–}15)$$

2-8. SCALE OF ELECTRODE POTENTIALS AND OXIDATION-REDUCTION REACTIONS

a. Direction of Oxidation-Reduction Reactions. An electric current is, by definition, a flow of positive charges from the positive terminal to the negative terminal of the circuit connected to some power supply. This rather old definition of current was introduced before the electron had been discovered. Electrons which are negative charges flow in the opposite direction of the current, i.e., from the negative terminal to the positive one. As an example, consider the cell discussed in Section 2–5b

$$\text{Cu} \mid \text{Cu}^{++}(a_{\text{Cu}^{++}} = 2 \times 10^{-2}) \parallel \text{Zn}^{++}(a_{\text{Zn}^{++}} = 5 \times 10^{-3}) \mid \text{Zn}.$$

The copper electrode is the positive terminal of this cell, and electrons flow in the circuit outside the cell from zinc to copper. Electrons are supplied at the copper electrode, and reduction occurs at this electrode. Thus the reaction $\text{Cu}^{++} + 2e \rightarrow \text{Cu}$ occurs in the direction of the arrow. Conversely, electrons are supplied by the zinc electrode, and zinc is oxidized to zinc ion, i.e., $\text{Zn}^{++} + 2e \leftarrow \text{Zn}$.

It follows that the electrode reaction which has the more positive potential occurs in the direction of reduction. Conversely, the electrode reaction with the more negative potential occurs in the direction of oxidation. These conclusions, which are general (Fig.5), are very important because they enable us to predict from potentials the direction in which oxidation-reduction reactions occur. Students of thermodynamics will readily recognize that the

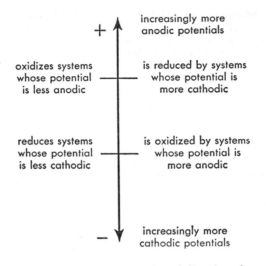

Fig. 5.   Electrode potentials and direction of oxidation-reduction reactions.

above method is derived from the correlation between the change in free energy for a reaction and the direction in which this reaction occurs.

In the comparison of potentials it is essential to consider actual conditions under which the reactions may occur. Variations of pH may profoundly affect potentials, as shown in the example in Section 2–7, and the direction in which a reaction occurs may even be reversed as the pH is changed.

EXAMPLE.   Consider the reaction between the systems ferri-ferrocyanide and Cr(VI)–Cr(III). In acid solution, ferrocyanide ion is oxidized by Cr(VI) (dichromate ion), while in strongly basic medium, ferricyanide ion oxidizes Cr(III) (chromite ion CrO_2^-). This is apparent from the potentials listed below.

In acid medium one has

$$Cr_2O_7^{--} + 14H^+ + 6e = 2Cr^{+++} + 7H_2O$$

and

$$E = 1.33 - 0.0591 \frac{14}{6} pH + \frac{0.0591}{6} \log \frac{a_{Cr_2O_7^{--}}}{a_{Cr^{+++}}^2}$$

at 25°. Conversely, in strongly alkaline solution Cr(VI) exists as chromate ion CrO_4^{--}, and $Cr(III)$ as CrO_2^- [the soluble form of the amphoteric hydroxide $Cr(OH)_3$]. Thus,

and
$$CrO_4^{--} + 4H^+ + 3e = CrO_2^- + 2H_2O$$

$$E = 0.94 - 0.0591 \frac{4}{3} v\text{H} + \frac{0.0591}{3} \log \frac{a_{CrO_4^{--}}}{a_{CrO_2^-}}$$

at 25° C.

For ferro-ferricyanide, one has[9]

and
$$Fe(CN)_6^{-3} + e = Fe(CN)_6^{-4}$$

$$E = 0.36 + 0.0591 \log \frac{a_{Fe(CN)_6^{-3}}}{a_{Fe(CN)_6^{-4}}}$$

Potentials for the above systems can be plotted against pH for a given value of the ratios of activities; for example, for ratios equal to unity (Fig. 6). The change in direction of reaction, as the pH is sufficiently varied, can be readily explained from this diagram. In acid solution

$$E_{Cr(VI)/Cr(III)} > E_{\text{ferri-ferrocyanide}},$$

and ferrocyanide is oxidized by $Cr(VI)$. The order of potentials is reversed in alkaline solution, and ferricyanide oxidizes $Cr(III)$.

b. Stability of Aqueous Solutions of Oxidants or Reductants. The foregoing considerations can be extended to the study of the stability of aqueous

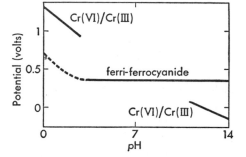

Fig. 6. Potentials of the ferri-ferrocyanide and $Cr(VI) - Cr(III)$ couples as functions of pH.

solutions of oxidants or reductants. Water can be either reduced with evolution of hydrogen or oxidized with evolution of oxygen according to the reactions

$$2H^+ + 2e \rightarrow H_2$$
$$O_2 + 4H^+ + 4e \leftarrow 2H_2O.$$

The potentials for these reactions are at 25° and for a pressure of 1 atm (more precisely for a fugacity of gas equal to unity)

$$E = -0.0591 \, p\text{H}$$

for the evolution of hydrogen,

and
$$E = 1.229 - 0.0591 \, p\text{H}$$

[9]In acid solutions (pH < 4) one should take into account the nonionized or partially ionized forms of the acids, but this is not done for the sake of simplicity. The potential at pH $= 0$ is about 0.7 volt.

for the evolution of oxygen. These potentials are plotted against pH in Fig. 7. Hydrogen or oxygen is evolved when the electrode potential is in the lower or upper shaded area, respectively.

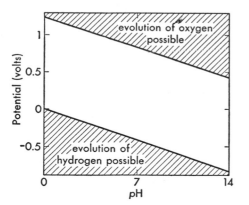

Fig. 7. Potential — pH diagram for water at 25° and for a pressure of 1 atm.

The potential can be adjusted by forming a complete electrolytic cell as in the electrolysis of water, or in the absence of any electrode it may be determined by an oxidation-reduction *couple;* for example, a mixture of Cr(III) and Cr(II). If the potential of the couple, calculated by the Nernst equation, is in one of the shaded areas of Fig. 7, the solution is, in principle, unstable. For example, an aqueous solution of chromous sulfate slowly evolves hydrogen because the potential of the Cr(III)/Cr(II) couple ($E^0 = -0.41$ volt, Table II) is in the lower shaded area[10] of Fig. 7. The evolution of oxygen by an aqueous solution of cobaltic sulfate can be explained in a similar fashion [$E^0 = 1.82$ volts for Co(III)/Co(II), Table II].

The impossibility of preparing a solution containing only one of the components of an oxidation-reduction couple can readily be ascertained from Fig. 7. The potential of such a couple would be in one of the shaded areas of this diagram (see Section 2–6), and water would be oxidized or reduced with the concomitant appearance of the component of the oxidation-reduction couple initially not present.

Rates of oxidation or reduction of water have not been considered in the above treatment, and in certain cases the evolution of hydrogen or oxygen is so slow that the solution is stable for all practical purposes. For instance, ceric sulfate is used as standard reagent in titrimetry although the potential of a solution of ceric sulfate containing only traces of Ce(III) is definitely in the upper shaded area of Fig. 7[$E^0 = 1.61$ volts for the Ce(IV)/Ce(III) couple, Table II]. In this case, oxygen evolution is so slow that the solution can be kept for rather long periods (perhaps several months) without any appreciable decrease in the concentration of ceric ions.

This concludes our study of the fundamentals of electrode potentials, and we must now turn our attention to experimental methods for the measurement of electrode potentials. Applications of this material to analytical chemistry are discussed in the next chapter.

---

[10]Except when there is a tremendous excess of Cr(III).

2-9. EXPERIMENTAL METHODS: REFERENCE ELECTRODES

There are two fundamental problems in the measurement of electrode potentials: (1) How to couple with a reference electrode the electrode whose behavior is being studied; and (2) how to measure or record the voltage of an electrochemical cell. The former problem is discussed in this section, and the latter is reserved for the next section.

The normal hydrogen electrode is adopted as reference of the scale of electrode potentials (Section 2-3), but other electrodes of simpler design and whose potential is well known with respect to the normal hydrogen electrode are generally preferred. These reference electrodes are of the type $M^{+n} + ne = M$. The concentration of ion M^{+n} is conveniently adjusted by saturating the solution with a sparingly soluble salt of metal M; for example, silver chloride for a silver electrode. The solution is saturated if solid silver chloride is present in excess, but the activity of silver ions is markedly affected by traces of chloride unwittingly added to the solution, and the potential is unreliable. This difficulty is avoided when a large excess of chloride ion (potassium chloride) is present. The contribution in chloride ions resulting from dissolution of silver chloride can be neglected, and the activity of chloride ions is determined by the concentration of potassium chloride. Thus,

$$a_{Ag^+} = \frac{S}{a_{Cl^-}}, \qquad (2\text{-}16)$$

where S is the solubility product of silver chloride written in terms of activities rather than concentrations.

The potential of the silver-silver chloride electrode is at 25°

$$E = E_{Ag}^0 + 0.0591 \log \frac{S}{a_{Cl^-}} \qquad (2\text{-}17)$$

where $E_{Ag}^0 = 0.799$ volt and[11] $S = 1.77 \times 10^{-10}$ (25°). The potential for an electrode prepared with a 1 M solution of potassium chloride is ($f_{Cl^-} = 0.61$) 0.236 volt while the experimental value is 0.222 volt. The difference results from errors in the solubility product and activity coefficient[12] and from the neglecting of the formation of complex ions in presence of a large excess of chloride ions. The potential of the silver-silver chloride electrode, as for any other electrode (Section 2-5), depends on temperature (Table V).

An electrode with a deposit of silver chloride is easily formed by oxidizing anodically a silver wire in a solution of hydrochloric acid.[13] The silver-silver chloride electrode is coupled with an agar-agar bridge (Fig. 8, left) to the electrode whose potential is being measured. This bridge is a U-tube

---

[11] E. A. Guggenheim and J. E. Prue, *Trans. Faraday Soc.*, **50**, 231 (1954).
[12] The value of $f_{Cl^-} = 0.61$ is for a 1 *molal* solution and not for 1 molar solution.
[13] For a detailed study, see G. L. Janz and H. Taniguchi, *Chem. Revs.*, **53**, 397 (1953).

TABLE V

Influence of Temperature on Potential of Reference Electrodes[a]

ELECTRODE	POTENTIAL, VOLTS		
Temperature	20°	25°	30°
Silver-silver chloride with 1 M KCl	0.225	0.222	0.219
Calomel electrode with 0.1 M KCl	0.334	0.334	0.333
Calomel electrode with 1 M KCl	0.282	0.281	0.280
Calomel electrode with saturated KCl	0.246	0.242	0.238

[a]See Conway, Section 2–11.

filled with a saturated solution of potassium chloride (about 3.5 M at 25°) containing 4 per cent of agar-agar. A concentrated solution of potassium chloride is used because the differences of potential at the liquid-liquid junctions are minimized (Section 2–2). The potassium chloride solution,

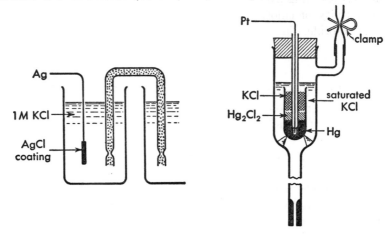

Fig. 8. Silver-silver chloride electrode with agar-agar bridge (left) and saturated calomel electrode (right).

saturated at room temperature, is heated to the boiling point; the agar-agar is added, and the solution is stirred until complete dissolution. The U-tube is filled with the hot solution, which solidifies upon cooling. Instead of an agar-agar bridge one can also utilize a U-tube whose ends are closed by fritted glass disks and which is filled with a saturated solution of potassium chloride.

The *calomel electrode* is another frequently used reference electrode. Calomel, i.e., mercurous chloride, is a sparingly soluble salt ($S = 1.1 \times$

10^{-18}). The activity of mercurous ions in a calomel electrode is controlled by a large excess of potassium chloride, and electrodes prepared with 0.1 or 1 M potassium chloride solution or with a saturated solution of this salt (about 3.5 M) are generally used. The latter electrode—the saturated calomel electrode (S.C.E.)—is often preferred because of the simplicity of its preparation.

The potential of the calomel electrode can be calculated in the same manner as for the silver-silver chloride electrode. Thus,

$$a_{\text{Hg}_2^{++}} a_{\text{Cl}^-}{}^2 = S \tag{2-18}$$

and for 25 ,

$$E = E_{\text{Hg}}{}^0 + \frac{0.0591}{2} \log \frac{S}{a_{\text{Cl}^-}{}^2}, \tag{2-19}$$

where $E^0 = 0.789$ volt and $S = 1.1 \times 10^{-18}$. For example, one calculates ($f = 0.77$, actually for 0.1 molal solution rather than 0.1 molar solution) $E = 0.325$ volt for the electrode prepared with 0.1 M potassium chloride, while the experimental potential is 0.334 volt (see Table V).

An example of saturated calomel electrode is shown schematically in Fig. 8 (right), but many other designs have been proposed. No agar-agar bridge is necessary with the electrode of Fig. 8, since the junction is simply made by a fine capillary at the tip of the electrode. The electrode is contained in the inner small test tube, and the sleeve is filled with a saturated solution of potassium chloride by aspiration through the lateral tube. The solution in the electrode can be easily renewed. Calomel electrodes utilized with commercial pH meters are somewhat similar to that of Fig. 8, but the junction with the other electrode is made through a crack in the end of the electrode. This crack is made by sealing an asbestos filament in the wall of the tube.

Besides the silver-silver chloride and calomel electrodes, many other reference electrodes have been proposed. Some of them are useful, for instance, when the presence of chloride ion is to be avoided. A detailed description is given in Böttger's treatise on physicochemical methods of analysis.[14]

2-10. EXPERIMENTAL METHODS: VOLTAGE MEASUREMENT AND RECORDING

a. Direct Method. The voltage of an electrochemical cell can in principle be measured by connecting a voltmeter to the cell. This method has two disadvantages: (1) it is not very precise, and (2) a relatively large current (perhaps 10^{-3} ampere) is drawn from the cell. Whenever a current flows through an electrochemical cell, reactions occur at the electrodes, and

[14]W. Böttger in *Physikalische Methoden der Analytischen Chemie*, W. Böttger, Ed., Vol. III, Akademische Verlagsgesellschaft, Leipzig, 1938, pp. 478–760. Available from Edwards Brothers, Inc., Ann Arbor, Michigan, 1943.

the composition of the solution is altered. Furthermore, because of the ohmic drop in the cell, the voltage read on the meter is smaller than the value measured with virtually no current through the cell. It is therefore essential to keep the current through the cell at a value which is as low as possible. This result can be achieved by using as voltmeter a galvanometer connected in series with a large resistance, 10^6 ohms, for example. Full-scale deflection can be observed under these conditions for voltages of the order of 1 volt, and the current is rather low, i.e., about 10^{-6} ampere. Such a simple method is useful in potentiometric titrations (Chapter 3).

Another solution to maintain the current through the cell at a very low value is to use a vacuum-tube voltmeter. The voltage to be measured is applied between the grid and cathode of a vacuum tube, and the resulting change in plate current is measured.[15] Several stages of amplifications are often necessary, and the output meter is directly calibrated in voltage units. The current drawn from the cell, i.e., the grid current of the input tube of the amplifier, is of the order of 10^{-8} ampere with ordinary radio tubes. In some applications (measurements with the glass electrode, Chapter 3) such a current is much too large, and a special tube (*electrometer tube*) must be utilized as input tube. The grid current of electrometer tubes is as low as 10^{-14} to 10^{-15} ampere. Commercial vacuum-tube voltmeters for electroanalytical applications are available (Beckman, Macbeth, and Precision Scientific Co. in the United States).

The precision of direct reading instruments is relatively poor because the scale on which readings are made is in general rather short, say, 10 cm. The reading is also affected by errors resulting from the moving of mechanical parts (friction, change in tension of spring, etc.). Voltmeters with an error of 0.5 per cent at full-scale deflection are relatively expensive instruments. Yet, this corresponds to a poor accuracy in the measurement of potentials, in which an error of 0.001 volt of a reading of 1 volt is sometimes significant. Very accurate measurements can be made by the potentiometric method.

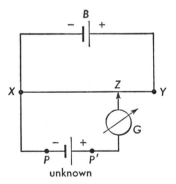

Fig. 9. Principle of the potentiometric method.

b. Potentiometric Method. A thin wire XY of uniform section along which a sliding contact Z can be moved is connected to a battery B (Fig. 9). The cell whose voltage is to be measured is connected to PP', terminals having the same polarity being connected together. Contact Z is adjusted until balance is

---

[15]For a simple discussion and examples of actual circuits, see R. H. Müller, R. L. Garman, and M. E. Droz, *Experimental Electronics*, Prentice-Hall, New York, 1942.

observed, i.e., until the galvanometer indicates a current equal to zero. The unknown voltage across PP', which is then equal to the voltage between XZ, can be read directly on the scale along the wire, provided that the total voltage between XY is known. This can be shown as follows:

There is no current through the galvanometer when balance is obtained and the same current i flows through XZ and XY. The ohmic drops across XZ and XY are

$$V_{XZ} = i \times R_{XZ} \qquad (2\text{-}20)$$

$$V_{XY} = i \times R_{XY}. \qquad (2\text{-}21)$$

Hence,

$$\frac{V_{XZ}}{V_{XY}} = \frac{R_{XZ}}{R_{XY}}, \qquad (2\text{-}22)$$

and the ratio R_{XZ}/R_{XY} is equal to the ratio of the distances XZ/XY along the wire, since the resistance of a wire of uniform section is proportional to its length.

The method can be applied provided that the voltage V_{XY} or any fraction of this voltage is accurately known. The voltage of storage batteries or dry cells varies during discharge, and some reliable *reference cell* is necessary for calibrating the potentiometer. The *Weston cell* generally serves this purpose. The positive terminal is a mercury electrode, and the negative terminal a cadmium amalgam with an excess of cadmium to maintain saturation at all temperatures. The electrodes are prepared in the arms of an H-tube, which is filled with a solution saturated with cadmium sulfate and mercurous sulfate. The reactions at the electrode are

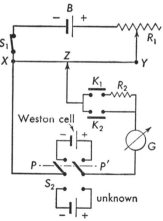

$$Cd^{++} + Hg + 2e = Cd(Hg),$$
$$Hg_2^{++} + 2e = 2\,Hg.$$

The voltage of this cell is known with accuracy and is

$$1.018300 - 4.06 \times 10^{-5}(t - 20)$$
$$- 9.5 \times 10^{-7}(t - 20),$$

where t is the temperature in degrees centigrade.

The calibration of the potentiometer involves the following operations (Fig. 10):

Fig. 10. Layout for potentiometric measurements.

Contact Z is set at the reading equal to the voltage of the Weston cell, switch S_1 being closed. The Weston cell is placed in the circuit by setting switch S_2 in the proper position. The key K_1 is closed, and resistance R_1 is adjusted to obtain balance. A key with spring action is utilized so that the circuit is left open when the key is released. The key K_1 is then released, and key K_2 is closed. The adjustment of R_1 is improved until balance is again obtained. The potentionmeter is now standardized, and resistance R_1 should not be changed during measurement of the unknown voltage. The cell of unknown voltage is inserted in the circuit by reversing switch S_2. Key K_1 is closed and contact Z is moved along XY until balance is observed. Key K_2 is then closed, and the adjustment of Z is refined. The voltage of the cell is read directly on the graduation along the wire XY.

Coarse and fine adjustments are made in the calibration and actual measurement to avoid any excessive current through the standard cell and the cell of unknown voltage. This result is obtained by making the coarse adjustment (key K_1) with a large resistance R_2 in series with the galvanometer. If R_2 is of the order of 10^5 ohms the current through the cell is low, perhaps a few microamperes or less, even if the potentiometer is completely unbalanced. Wild deflections of the galvanometer needle or beam are also avoided by this method. Once balance is obtained with key K_1, key K_2 can be closed and the galvanometer is introduced directly in the circuit without any additional resistance in series.

Calibrated wires are rather cumbersome, and potentiometers of the type shown schematically in Fig. 11 (*student potentiometer*) are often used now-

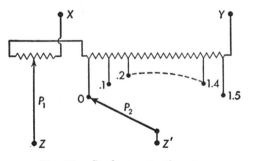

Fig. 11.   Student potentiometer.

adays. The terminals X and Y correspond to the same terminals of Fig. 9 and 10, and the voltage to be compensated is applied to Z and Z'. Potentiometer P_2 provides discrete changes of voltage in steps of 0.1 volt; fine adjustment in the range 0 to 0.1 volt is made with P_1. The coil of P_1 has several hundred windings, and the discontinuity in voltage observed as contact Z is moved from one winding to the next is much less than one millivolt. Student potentiometers offer in a compact unit rather accurate instruments. Commercial instruments are available (Fisher, Leeds and Northrup, and Sargent in the United States).

A balance indicator (G in Fig. 10) of suitable sensitivity should be selected. This sensitivity depends on the resistance of the cell, and in some cases, on the electrode reaction being studied. If R is the resistance of the cell and ΔE volts the unbalance between the potentiometer and the cell, the current through the balance indicator is approximately

$$\Delta i_g \approx \frac{\Delta E}{R} \qquad (2\text{–}23)$$

provided that the resistance of the cell is much larger than that of the balance indicator and the circuit of the potentiometer between X and Z (Fig. 9 or Fig. 10). A galvanometer of relatively poor sensitivity can be utilized if R is of the order of a few thousand ohms. For instance, one calculates the value $\Delta i_g = 2.5 \times 10^{-7}$ amp for $\Delta E = 0.5$ mv and R = 2000 ohms. However, when R is very high, as in pH determinations with the glass electrode (Chapter 3), the current Δi_g is much too low to be detected even by a very sensitive galvanometer. For instance, one has $i_g = 5 \times 10^{-14}$ ampere for $R \times 10^{10}$ ohms and $\Delta E = 0.5\, mv$, while the most sensitive galvanometer can detect currents of the order of 10^{-10} ampere. Vacuum-tube voltmeters with an electrometer tube in the input circuit are then utilized.

Balance indicators with very high sensitivity must sometimes be utilized even when the resistance of the cell is low. This is the case when markedly irreversible electrode reactions are studied. Irreversible processes will be discussed in Chapter 4 and the information given in Fig. 12 will suffice for the time being. The diagram shows the variations of current through the balance indicator with the voltage read on the potentiometer.[16] The current-voltage curve is very steep for reversible electrode reactions (curve 1) and a relatively large current is observed when the potentiometer is set at a value differing by a few millivolts from the voltage V_e at balance. This is the case for the silver-silver ion electrode.

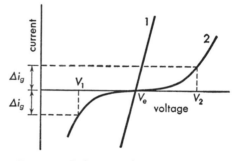

Fig. 12.   Influence of irreversibility in the measurement of electrode potentials.

However, there are many reactions for which the current-voltage curve is very flat in the vicinity of the voltage V_e at balance (curve 2). If Δi_g is the minimum detectable current, balance is *apparently* achieved between V_1 and V_2 over a voltage interval which may be as large as several tenths of a volt even for currents as low as 10^{-10} ampere. A very sensitive balance indicator (vacuum-tube voltmeter with electrometer tube) must be utilized, but even so, measurements may be very difficult on account of interference by impurities.

[16] It is assumed that a steady state is reached.

The current for a given reaction and given conditions of electrolysis increases with the area of the electrode (Chapter 4), and consequently it is advantageous to increase the electrode area in the study of irreversible electrode reactions. This is why the platinum electrode of the normal hydrogen electrode is coated with a spongy deposit of platinum: the area of the electrode is greatly increased, and the interval $V_1 V_2$ of Fig. 12 becomes negligibly small.

c. Pen-and-Ink Recorders. Voltage recording is common in potentiometric methods and instrumental analysis in general, and a brief discussion of recorders is in order. The treatment will be limited to pen-and-ink recorders based on the principle of continuous balance, since these recorders are most frequently used. The voltage to be recorded is applied

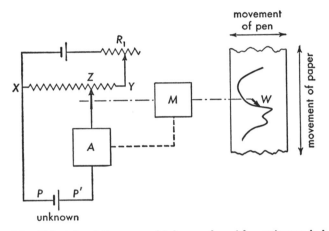

Fig. 13. Principle of the pen-and-ink recorder with continuous balance.

between the terminals X and Z of a potentiometer (Fig. 13) whose sliding contact Z is geared to a reversible motor M operated by the balance indicator A. The latter is an amplifier which detects any unbalance in the potentiometric circuit and causes motor M to rotate in the proper direction until balance is established. As a result, balance is continuously maintained, and the voltage between X and Z is equal to the voltage across P and P'. The recording is made by mechanically linking pen W to contact Z in such a manner that the displacement of the pen depends linearly on the voltage being recorded. The recording is made on a sheet of paper moving at a uniform rate perpendicularly to the direction of the course of the pen.

Since amplifier A corrects unbalance only between the voltages across XZ and PP', no error results from variations in amplifier gain. This is a major advantage of this type of recorder. Commercial recorders are available (Leeds and Northrup, Minneapolis and Honeywell-Brown in the United States).

When the voltage to be recorded varies rather rapidly, the inertia of the mechanical balancing device (motor M and accessories) causes a lag in recording; mechanical and especially cathode-ray oscillographs must then be utilized. Recorders whose pen travels their full scale (10 in.) in approximately 1 sec are available.

2-11. BIBLIOGRAPHY

a. Electrochemistry Texts

J. O.'M. Bockris, Ed., *Modern Aspects of Electrochemistry*, Academic Press, New York, 1954. A monograph for advanced students.

J. A. V. Butler, Ed., *Electrical Phenomena at Interfaces*, Methuen, London, 1951. For advanced students.

M. Dole, *Experimental and Theoretical Electrochemistry*, McGraw-Hill, New York, 1935.

S. Glasstone, *Introduction to Electrochemistry*, Van Nostrand, New York, 1942.

G. Kortüm and J. O'M. Bockris, *Textbook of Electrochemistry*, 2 vols., Elsevier, Houston, Texas, 1951.

D. A. MacInnes, *Principles of Electrochemistry*, Reinhold, New York, 1939.

P. Van Rysselberghe, *Electrochemical Affinity*, Hermann, Paris, 1955. Application of thermodynamics of irreversible processes to electrochemistry.

See also chapters on electrochemistry in physical chemistry texts.

b. Data on Electrode Potentials

B. E. Conway, *Electrochemical Data*, Elsevier, Houston, Texas, 1952. Contains a great variety of electrochemical data.

W. M. Latimer, *Oxidation States of the Elements and Their Potentials in Aqueous Solution*, 2nd ed., Prentice-Hall, New York, 1952. Comprehensive and critical survey of electrode potentials and pertaining data.

c. Potential-pH Diagrams

G. Charlot, *Qualitative Inorganic Analysis—A New Physicochemical Approach*, English translation by R. C. Murray, Wiley, New York, 1954. Systematic application of potential–pH diagrams to the interpretation of inorganic chemistry.

P. Delahay, M. Pourbaix, and P. Van Rysselberghe, *J. Chem. Education*, **27**, 683 (1950). Construction of potential–pH diagrams with examples.

M. Pourbaix, *Thermodynamics of Aqueous Dilute Solutions*, English translation by J. N. Agar, Arnold, London, 1949. Construction of potential–pH diagrams from thermodynamic data.

See also Bibliography in Chapter 3.

2-12. PROBLEMS

1. Calculate the voltage of the following cells at 25°, and indicate which electrode is the positive terminal of the cell. Neglect the difference of potential at the liquid-liquid junction.

a. Cd | Cd^{++}(a = 0.125) ‖ Sn^{++}(a = 0.35) + Sn^{+4}(a = 0.017) | Pt

b. Pb | PbO$_2$ | Pb^{++}(a = 2 × 10^{-4}) buffered at pH 1.5 | Pb

c. Pt | H$_2$(1 atm) | H$^+$(a = 10^{-3}) | H$^+$(a = 10^{-3}) | H$_2$(0.95 atm) | Pt

d. Pt | H$_2$(1 atm) | H$^+$(a = 10^{-14}) ‖ $\begin{array}{l} \text{0.1 Molar KCl} \\ \text{saturated with Hg}_2\text{Cl}_2 \end{array}$ | Hg

(*Note:* Use activity coefficient of a 0.1 molal KCl solution, f = 0.77.)

e. Pt | $\begin{array}{c} \text{Cr}_2\text{O}_7{}^{--}(a = 0.1) + \text{Cr}^{+3}(a = 0.1) \\ \text{buffered at pH 0.5} \end{array}$ ‖ I$^-$(0.1) + I$_2$(0.1) | Pt

f. Pt | Cl$_2$(p = 1 atm) | a_{Cl^-} = 0.1 ‖ buffer, pH = 1 | O$_2$(p = 1 atm) | Pt

g. Pt | $\begin{array}{c} \text{MnO}_4{}^-(a = 0.1) + \text{Mn}^{++}(a = 0.1) \\ \text{buffered at pH 1.3} \end{array}$ ‖ $\begin{array}{c} \text{Mn}^{++}(a = 0.1) \\ \text{buffered at pH 3} \end{array}$ | MnO$_2$ | Pt

h. Na(Hg)(a_{Na} = 0.001) | Na$^+$(a = 0.15) ‖ H$^+$(a = 1) | H$_2$(1 atm) | Pt

2. Calculate the potential of an iron electrode coated with ferric hydroxide and immersed in a ferrous sulfate ($a_{\text{Fe}^{++}}$ = 0.1) solution of pH 2. E^0 for [Fe(OH)$_3$]/Fe^{++} is 1.044 volts.

3. Write the potential for the electrode reaction

$$\text{M}X_m{}^{+(p-m)} + ne = \text{M}X_m{}^{+(p-m-n)}$$

where X is some complexing ion. Correlate the standard potential for this reaction to the standard potential for the reaction $\text{M}^{+p} + ne = \text{M}^{+(p-n)}$ and the instability constants of the two complex ions.

4. Write the potential for the electrode reaction

$$\text{M}X_p{}^{+(n-p)} + ne = \text{M} + p X^-$$

in terms of the instability constant of the complex ion and the standard potential for the reaction $\text{M}^{+n} + ne = \text{M}$.

5. Write the potential for the electrode reaction

$$\text{M(OH)}_n + n\text{H}^+ + ne = \text{M} + n\text{H}_2\text{O}$$

in terms of the solubility product of M(OH)$_n$ and the standard potential for the reaction $\text{M}^{+n} + ne = \text{M}$.

6. The error on the voltage of an electrochemical cell, measured by the potentiometric method, should not exceed 5 × 10^{-4} volt. Calculate the minimum required sensitivity of the balance indicator from the following data: resistance of the cell 5400 ohms, resistance of the galvanometer 350 ohms. The resistance of the potentiometer can be neglected.

3

Potentiometry

3-1. POTENTIOMETRIC METHODS OF ANALYSIS

According to the Nernst equation the potential for an electrode process depends on the activities of the species involved in the reaction. For instance, the potential of a silver electrode in a silver nitrate solution varies with the activity of silver ion. Since activities can be correlated to concentrations by equation (2-3) the determination of electrode potentials can, in principle, serve analytical purposes. However, direct application of potentiometry involves serious difficulties because the conversion of activity to concentration is complicated by the dependence of activity coefficients on the salt content of the solution. This difficulty can be partially overcome by measuring potentials in the presence of a large excess of an electrolyte which does not interfere with the electrode reaction. A large excess of potassium nitrate, for example, could be added to the solution in the determination of silver ion. The concentration of potassium and nitrate ions under such conditions is much higher than for silver ions, and the activity coefficient of silver ion is essentially independent of its concentration. Even so, the conversion of activity to concentration may be quite uncertain. Furthermore, relatively large changes in the activity of the species being analyzed result only in small variations of potential: a tenfold change in silver ion activity is reflected by a variation of potential of only 0.0591 volt at 25° in the case of the silver-silver ion electrode. Measurements of potential must be accurate, and special care should be taken to avoid errors resulting from variations of the difference of potential at the liquid-liquid junction when passing from one determination to the other.

Summarizing, the direct application of potentiometry in chemical analysis is not advantageous, but one application—the potentiometric determination of pH—is very common. Potentiometry is the best available method in that case.

Potentiometric measurements can also be applied to the detection of the end point of titrations. For example, the activity of silver ion varies during the titration of this ion with chloride ion, and the potential of a silver electrode immersed in the solution being titrated varies accordingly. The equivalence point can be determined from a plot of potential against volume of titrant. Potentiometric measurements are applied only in the determination of the equivalence point, and the accuracy is primarily determined by errors in the titrimetric procedure. Results are therefore far more accurate than in direct potentiometry.

The first *potentiometric titration* was described in 1893 by Behrend[1] four years after the publication of Nernst's paper on electrode potentials[2]; it was the titration of chloride, bromide, and iodide with mercurous nitrate. The equivalence point of many titrations for which no suitable indicator is available can be determined by potentiometry, and many applications have been made, thanks to the efforts of Böttger, Erich Müller, Kolthoff, Furman, Willard, and many others.

3-2. DETERMINATION OF pH WITH THE HYDROGEN ELECTRODE

Any electrode reaction which involves hydrogen ions and whose behavior follows the Nernst equation can, in principle, be applied to the potentiometric determination of hydrogen ion activity. The simplest of these reactions is the reduction of hydrogen ion to hydrogen,

$$2H^+ + 2e = H_2.$$

The potential of the hydrogen electrode at the absolute temperature T is (see Section 2–6).

$$E = \frac{1.983 \times 10^{-4}T}{2} \log \frac{a_{H^+}^2}{p_{H_2}}, \qquad (3-1)$$

or after introduction of the pH notation[3] ($pH = -\log a_{H^+}$),

$$E = -1.983 \times 10^{-4}TpH - \frac{1.983 \times 10^{-4}T}{2} \log p_{H_2}. \qquad (3-2)$$

The potential for a given pressure of hydrogen is a linear function of pH. The hydrogen electrode is coupled with some reference electrode—very

---

[1] R. Behrend, *Z. physik. Chem.*, **11**, 466 (1893).

[2] W. Nernst, *ibid.*, **4**, 129 (1889).

[3] The fugacity rather than the pressure of hydrogen should be written in all rigor in equation (3–1). For a detailed discussion of the definition of pH, see Bates' monograph (Section 3–12).

often a calomel electrode—and the pH is calculated from the voltage of the cell.

EXAMPLE. A hydrogen electrode immersed in a solution of unknown pH is coupled with a saturated calomel electrode. The voltage of the cell is 0.674 volt, the calomel electrode being the positive terminal of the cell. The pressure of hydrogen in the cell is 737 mm of mercury, and the temperature is 30°. Calculate the unknown pH.

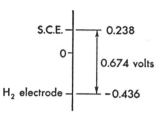

Fig. 14. Calculation of the hydrogen electrode potential.

The potential of the saturated calomel electrode at 30° is 0.238 volt (Table V). Since the voltage of the cell is 0.647 volt and the calomel electrode is the positive terminal, the potential of the hydrogen electrode is -0.436 volt (Fig. 14). In view of equation (3–2), one has ($T = 273.1 + 30 = 303.1$, $p = 737/760$ atm)

$$-0.436 = -1.983 \times 10^{-4} \times 303.1 \times pH - \frac{1.983 \times 10^{-4} \times 303.1}{2} \log \frac{737}{760},$$

e.g.,

$$pH = 7.25.$$

The hydrogen electrode is the most reliable and precise electrode for pH determinations. It is no longer used in most routine determinations since the glass electrode described in Section 3–4 is far more convenient to utilize. However, it should be emphasized that the glass electrode must be calibrated with a standard buffer whose pH has been determined once and for all by the hydrogen electrode. The hydrogen electrode is still used in pH determinations when the glass electrode fails (very acid and very alkaline solutions and nonaqueous media).

The potential of the hydrogen electrode is determined by the reaction $2H^+ + 2e = H_2$, and no other oxidation-reduction reaction should occur on the electrode. The solution whose pH is to be measured should not contain substances which are reduced or oxidized at an appreciable rate at the potential of the hydrogen electrode. For instance, it is not possible to determine with a hydrogen electrode the pH of a solution of copper sulfate, because copper is deposited on the hydrogen electrode. The potential would then depend on two reactions, namely $2H^+ + 2e = H_2$ and $Cu^{++} + 2e = Cu$. This very restrictive condition does not hold for the glass electrode.

3–3. OTHER ELECTRODES FOR pH DETERMINATIONS

The necessity of having a supply of hydrogen renders the use of the hydrogen electrode rather cumbersome. Electrode reactions which do not require hydrogen, but which involve hydrogen ions, have been applied to pH determinations; for instance, the reduction of quinone to hydroquinone

$$C_6H_4O_2 + 2H^+ + 2e = C_6H_4(OH)_2,$$

and the reduction of antimony oxide to the metal

$$Sb_2O_3 + 6H^+ + 6e \rightleftharpoons 2Sb + 3H_2O.$$

The potential for the first reaction is a linear function of pH when the ratio of the activities of quinone to hydroquinone is kept constant. This condition is satisfied when a few crystals of quinhydrone are added to the solution whose pH is to be determined. Quinhydrone is an addition compound in which quinone and hydroquinone are in the ratio of 1 to 1. The resulting *quinhydrone electrode* cannot be used above pH 8 because of the decomposition of quinone. The presence of oxidants or reductants should be avoided for the same reason as for the hydrogen electrode.

The potential of the *antimony-antimony oxide electrode* is also a linear function of pH. Since the solid substances Sb_2O_3 and Sb have an activity equal to unity, adjustment of the activity of the reagents is automatic. The electrode cannot be used in very acid or very alkaline solutions because of the solubility of antimony oxide in these media. Complexing substances in which antimony oxide is soluble should also be avoided. Finally, oxidants or reductants which might react at the antimony electrode should not be present in solution.

The quinhydrone and antimony electrodes have been extensively utilized in the past, but the glass electrode is preferred nowadays.

3–4. THE GLASS ELECTRODE

a. Principle. The potential use of the glass electrode for pH measurements was realized many years ago,[4] but practical applications had to await (about 1935) the development of electronic voltmeters with sufficient high input resistance. The electrode is composed of a glass bulb (diameter 0.5 to 1 cm, a few tenths of a millimeter thick) immersed in the solution of unknown pH. A reference electrode is placed inside the bulb, and the cell is completed by another reference electrode connected to the solution of unknown pH by a salt bridge. The reference electrode in the bulb is generally a silver-silver chloride electrode prepared with a hydrochloric acid solution, and the other reference electrode is often a saturated calomel electrode. The schematic diagram of the cell is

$$\text{Ag} \mid \text{AgCl} \mid \text{HCl} \mid \text{Solution of unknown } pH \parallel \text{KCl} \mid \text{Hg}_2\text{Cl}_2 \mid \text{Hg},$$

where the dashed line indicates the wall of the glass bulb.

[4] F. Haber and Z. Klemenciewicz, *Z. physik. Chem.*, **67**, 385 (1909). For a historical review of the development of the glass electrode, see Dole's monograph (pp. 25–30) listed in Section 3–12.

Hydrogen ions can move through the glass wall, and the above cell can be regarded as a concentration cell. This is a very simplified description of the behavior of the cell, and a more detailed discussion can be found in Dole's monograph (see Section 3–12). The potential of the silver-silver chloride electrode is constant, and the voltage varies linearly with pH. Thus,

$$V = b + 1.983 \times 10^{-4} T\, pH, \qquad (3\text{--}3)$$

where $1.983 \times 10^{-4}\, T$ is the coefficient of the Nernst equation, T the absolute temperature, and b a constant depending on the potentials of the silver-silver chloride and calomel electrodes and on the difference of potential across the glass wall for $pH = 0$. The term b also includes the *asymmetry potential*, which is the difference of potential of a glass electrode for which the electrodes and solutions on each side of the glass wall are the same. One would expect that the voltage of such a symmetrical cell would be equal to zero, but this is generally not the case, probably because of a difference of treatment of each side of the glass wall. Since the term b of equation (3–3) cannot be computed because of the uncertainty about the asymmetry potential, the glass electrode must be calibrated with a buffer of known pH. Standard buffers are available from pH meter manufacturers or they can be prepared by dissolving commercially available tablets. It is advantageous to calibrate the glass electrode with a buffer whose pH is not too different (at least less than 5 pH units) from the pH that is to be measured.

Measurements of pH's in nonaqueous media are also possible, but a trace of water is essential to the proper behavior of the electrode. The significance of the results is questionable but end points of titrations in nonaqueous media can nevertheless be detected.[5] Errors on pH values are observed even with relatively high contents of water (10 to 20%).

The behavior of a glass electrode is not affected by the presence of oxidants or reductants in solution, and this is a very valuable feature of the electrode.

b. Errors in Alkaline and Very Acid Media. The glass electrode gives erroneous results above pH 9 and below pH 0 (Fig. 15): the pH reading is too low in alkaline media and too high in acid solutions; the error in alkaline solutions is especially large for sodium salts. The concentration of hydrogen ions in alkaline solutions is, of course, very low, and the glass electrode is very sensitive to transfer of other cations. Anions, which have larger radii than cations,[6] cannot generally be transferred

---

[5] For applications, see Fritz' monograph listed in Section 3–12.

[6] Crystal radii (in angstroms): Li$^+$, 0.60; Na$^+$, 0.95; K$^+$, 1.33; Ca^{++}, 0.99; Ba^{++}, 1.35 (L. Pauling, *The Nature of the Chemical Bond*, 2nd ed., Cornell University Press, Ithaca, New York, 1945, p. 346). For anions: Cl$^-$, 1.81 A; Br$^-$, 1.95; I$^-$, 2.16; these are anion radii in lithium halides (Pauling, p. 352). Radii of ions in aqueous solution are somewhat different because of hydration.

through the glass membrane but cations in alkaline solutions play essentially the same role as hydrogen ion in more acid solutions, and the electrode responds to the cation concentration. This error can be minimized by changing the composition of the glass to prevent transfer of cations.

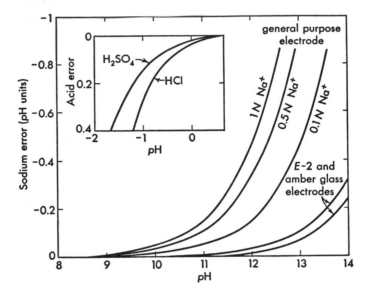

Fig. 15. Errors of glass electrodes. (Data on sodium error supplied by Beckman Instruments, Inc., Fullerton, California; data on acid error from R. G. Bates, *Electrometric pH Determinations*, Wiley, New York, 1954, p. 238).

Electrodes made of Corning glass 015 (72% SiO_2, 22% Na_2O, and 6% CaO) are most frequently used because of their excellent characteristics (relatively low resistance and rapid establishment of potential), but the error in alkaline solution is very large. Electrodes made of glasses with high contents of lithium oxide (25%) and no sodium oxide have very low errors even in very alkaline solution (Fig. 15), but potentials are established more slowly than with the Corning glass 015.[7] The explanation advanced by Dole[8] for errors in very acid solution can be summarized qualitatively as follows: In very acid solution the activity of water is smaller than unity, and since hydrogen ions are transferred through glass as hydrated protons, there is a departure from the behavior expected on the basis of a unit activity of water.

    c. *Measurements.* Voltage measurements can be made with a direct-

[7]For a detailed study of the influence of glass composition, see the monographs of Dole and Kratz listed in Section 3–12. See also the extensive and more recent study of G. A. Perley, *Anal. Chem.*, **21**, 391, 394, 559 (1949).
[8]See Dole's monograph (p. 276) listed in Section 3–12.

reading vacuum-tube voltmeter. Determinations are accurate only to about 0.1 pH unit (about 0.006 volt), but this is adequate in many applications, especially in acid-base potentiometric titrations (see Section 3–6). Very well designed instruments are commercially available (Beckman, Macbeth, Precision Scientific Co. in the United States). More accurate results are obtained by the potentiometric method. Commercial instruments are essentially potentiometers similar to that of Fig. 10, but modifications of circuit are introduced to adapt the instrument to routine determinations. A schematic diagram[9] of a typical instrument is shown in Fig. 16 (compare with Fig. 10).

The current through the potentiometer XYZ is adjusted by balancing the ohmic drop in a calibrated resistance R_c against a Weston cell, key K being in position 1. This adjustment is made with resistance R_1. Potentiometer XZY is directly calibrated in pH units, and consequently the voltage corresponding to one division of the potentiometer should be adjusted according to the temperature of the solution whose pH is being measured [see equation (3–3)]. The temperature adjustment is made by shunting the potentiometer XYZ with re-

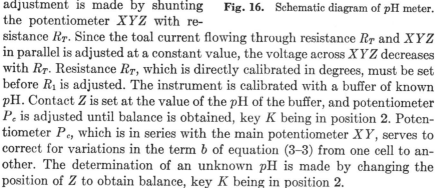

Fig. 16. Schematic diagram of pH meter.

sistance R_T. Since the toal current flowing through resistance R_T and XYZ in parallel is adjusted at a constant value, the voltage across XYZ decreases with R_T. Resistance R_T, which is directly calibrated in degrees, must be set before R_1 is adjusted. The instrument is calibrated with a buffer of known pH. Contact Z is set at the value of the pH of the buffer, and potentiometer P_c is adjusted until balance is obtained, key K being in position 2. Potentiometer P_c, which is in series with the main potentiometer XY, serves to correct for variations in the term b of equation (3–3) from one cell to another. The determination of an unknown pH is made by changing the position of Z to obtain balance, key K being in position 2.

Since the resistance of the cell is very high (10^{10} ohms or more), the balance indicator G is a vacuum-tube voltmeter (Section 2-10b).

Instruments of the type schematically represented in Fig. 16 find many applications, and the reader should make an effort to understand the operations involved in the calibration procedure. Several instruments of

[9]This is a very simplified version of the Beckman pH meter Model G; see A. O. Beckman, *Trans. Electrochem. Soc.*, **80**, 249 (1941).

this type are on the market (Beckman, Coleman, Leeds and Northrup in the United States).

3-5. VARIATIONS OF CONCENTRATIONS DURING TITRATIONS

The remainder of this chapter deals with potentiometric titrations in which the equivalence point is determined by following the potential of an *indicator electrode*, i.e., of an electrode whose potential depends on the activity of one of the substances involved in the titration. A *titration curve* is obtained by plotting this potential against volume of titrant. The interpretation of titration curves requires the calculation of the concentrations of reagents which will now be considered for the ideal case of a quantitative reaction of the type

$$\underset{\text{analyzed substance}}{X} + \underset{\text{titrant}}{T} = Q + U .$$

$$(3\text{--}4)$$

We shall consider first the case in which the dilution of the analyzed solution by the titrant can be neglected. The concentrations are then linear functions of the volume of titrant (Fig. 17). The concentration of

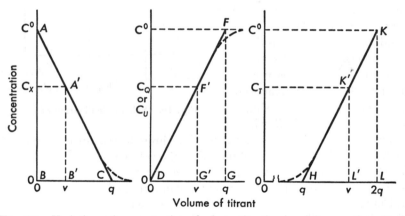

Fig. 17.   Variations of concentrations during a titration involving reactions (3–4).

the substance being analyzed which initially is C^0 drops to zero after the addition of q ml of titrant. After the addition of v ml of titrant, one has (Fig. 17, left)

$$\frac{AB}{A'B'} = \frac{BC}{B'C'},$$

and since $AB = C^0$, $A'B' = C_X$, $BC = q$, $B'C' = q - v$,

$$C_x = C^0 \frac{q - v}{q} \qquad \text{for } v < q.$$

$$(3\text{--}5)$$

For $v > q$, one has $C_X = 0$.

Likewise, one has (Fig. 17, center)

$$C_Q = C_U = C^0 \frac{v}{q} \qquad \text{for } v < q, \qquad (3\text{--}6)$$

and

$$C_Q = C_U = C^0 \qquad \text{for } v > q.$$

Finally, the concentration of titrant after the equivalence point is calculated by recalling that C_T is equal to C^0 when $v = 2q$ (Fig. 17, right). Thus,

$$C_T = 0 \qquad \text{for } v < q,$$

and

$$C_T = C^0 \frac{v - q}{q} \qquad \text{for } v > q. \qquad (3\text{--}7)^i$$

If dilution of the solution by the titrant cannot be neglected, the above concentrations must be multiplied by the dilution factor $v_0/v_0 + v$, v_0 being the initial volume of the solution being analyzed. The influence of dilution on the variations of concentration of substance X is shown in Fig. 18 for

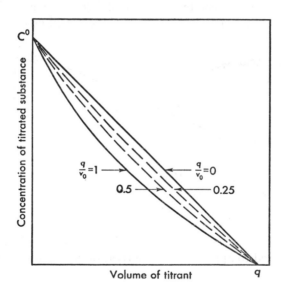

Fig. 18. Influence of dilution on the concentration of titrated substance.

different values of the ratio q/v_0. The effect of dilution will not be taken into account in the following discussion in order to simplify the writing of equations. Moderate dilution ($q/v_0 \leqslant 1$) by the titrant does not hamper the precise determination of the equivalence point in potentiometric titrations.

It was assumed in the above calculations that reaction (3–4) is quantitative, i.e., that the equilibrium constant ($K = a_Q a_U / a_X a_T$), is infinite.

Actually, concentrations vary progressively in the vicinity of the equivalence point (dotted curves in Fig. 17). The departure from the simple behavior predicted by equations (3–5), (3–6), and (3–7) is more pronounced when the equilibrium constant K becomes smaller and v approaches q. Concentrations C_X and C_T at the equivalence point are small in comparison with C^0, but are not equal to zero, and equations (3–5) to (3–7) cannot be applied for $v = q$ and in the immediate vicinity of this point. The equilibrium constant K must then be introduced in the calculations, as we shall see in the following sections. One could of course derive general equations in which the equilibrium constant is introduced in the equations for the complete titration curve, but the algebra is rather heavy.

Four types of reactions will be considered: (1) acid-base neutralizations, (2) precipitations, (3) complex ion formations, and (4) oxidation-reductions.

3–6. ACID-BASE TITRATIONS

The following possible combinations involving monobasic acids and bases will be discussed first. Polybasic acids and bases will be considered after-

wards. The formulas for the pH of buffers and weak acids and bases will not be derived, since this material is available in texts on qualitative and quantitative analysis. Many readers will find it profitable to review the derivation of these equations. Equations will be written in the "classical" manner, but the reader who is familiar with the Brönsted theory of acids and bases is urged to apply it to the derivation of the results given in this section.

a. Strong Acids and Bases. The titration curve for titration of a strong acid by a strong base can be readily deduced from equations (3–5) and (3–7), except in the immediate vicinity of the equivalence point. One has *approximately* $pH = -\log C_{H^+}$ where

$$C_{H^+} = C^0 \frac{q - v}{q} \qquad (3\text{–}8)$$

before the end equivalence point $(v < q)$.

The pH at the equivalence point is obtained directly from the ionic product of water:

$$a_{H^+} a_{OH^-} = K_w \qquad (3\text{--}9)$$

and

$$pH = -\frac{1}{2} \log K_w \ . \qquad (3\text{--}10)$$

At 25°, $K_w \approx 10^{-14}$, and the pH is 7. Note that equation (3–8) holds as long as C_{H^+} is at least 10 times the hydrogen ion concentration at the equivalence point (10^{-7} mol lit^{-1}).

The concentration of hydroxyl ions after the equivalence point is calculated by equation (3–7), and the pH is readily obtained by introducing this value of C_{H^+} in the ionic product of water. Concentrations may be identified with activities in this calculation.

An example of titration curve calculated for $v_0 = 100$ ml, $C^0 = 10^{-2}\ M$, and $q = 10$ ml is shown in Fig. 19, dilution being neglected. It is seen that indicators whose color changes in the pH range 5 to 9 can be utilized in the detection of the end point.

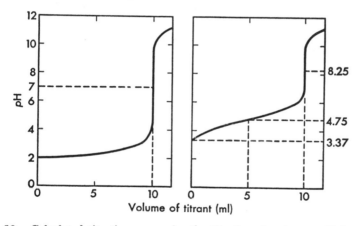

Fig. 19. Calculated titration curves for the titration of a strong acid by a strong base (left) and the titration of a weak acid by a strong base (right).

The foregoing considerations can be readily transposed to the titration of a strong base by a strong acid (see problem 2 in Section 3–13).

b. *Weak Acids and Strong Bases.* Consider the titration of a weak acid HA by a strong base MOH. The initial pH is calculated from the equation

$$a_{H^+} = \sqrt{\frac{K_a^2}{4} + K_a C^0} - \frac{K_a}{2}, \qquad (3\text{--}11)$$

where K_a is the ionization constant of the weak acid. Equation (3–11) is established in qualitative and quantitative analysis courses. If K_a is much smaller than C^0, one has approximately $a_{H^+} = \sqrt{K_a C^0}$.

The pH for $0 < v < q$ is calculated by noting that the solution contains a weak acid, and a salt of this acid and a strong base. Thus (see previous courses in analytical chemistry),

$$pH = pK_a + \log \frac{\text{activity of anion}}{\text{activity of nonionized weak acid}},$$

where $pK_a = -\log K_a$. Since $[X = HA, A = Q$ or U of equation (3–4)], the concentrations are

$$C_{HA} = C^0 \frac{q - v}{q}, \tag{3–12}$$

$$C_{A^-} = C^0 \frac{v}{q}, \tag{3–13}$$

and

$$pH = pK_a + \log \frac{v}{q - v} \qquad \text{for } 0 < v < q. \tag{3–14}$$

Equation (3–14) is not valid for $v = 0$ and $v = q$ because ionization of the electrolyte cannot be neglected at these points and in their immediate vicinity.

The pH at the equivalence point is that of a solution of salt MA at concentration C^0 (see qualitative or quantitative analysis text):

$$pH = \frac{1}{2}(pK_w - pK_a) + \frac{1}{2}\log C^0, \tag{3–15}$$

with $pK_w = -\log K_w$ and $pK_a = -\log K_a$.

The pH after the equivalence point can be calculated from equation (3–7) if hydroxyl ions from the salt produced during titration are neglected:

$$C_{OH^-} = C^0 \frac{v - q}{q} \qquad \text{for } v > q. \tag{3–16}$$

The pH is computed from the ionic product of water as written in terms of concentrations. In all rigor one should take into account the hydroxyl ions produced by hydrolysis of the salt in the calculation of the pH immediately before and after the end point, but the algebra is cumbersome to handle. Details can be found in the monograph of Kolthoff and Furman listed in Section 3–12.

An example of titration curve calculated for $K_a = 1.8 \times 10^{-5}$, $C^0 = 10^{-2} M$, $q = 10$ ml is shown in Fig. 19 (right). This case corresponds approximately to the titration of acetic acid. Indicators can still be used to determine the equivalence point, but the range of pH's in which their color should change is not so wide as for titrations involving strong acids and bases.

The pH at midpoint ($v = q/2$) is pK_a, and consequently the titration curve is shifted toward higher pH's as the acid becomes weaker. Furthermore, the curve is flatter in the vicinity of the equivalence point when K_a decreases. The determination of the equivalence point with an indicator becomes more difficult or even impossible when K_a is very small.

The foregoing analysis can be transposed to the titration of a weak base by a strong acid (problem 3 in Section 3–13).

c. Weak Acids and Bases. Titrations of weak acids by weak bases are of little practical value since one generally can select the titrant to be used. Thus, one selects a strong base—and not a weak one—to titrate a weak acid.

The variations of pH during titration can be studied as in the previous cases. The initial pH is that of a weak acid or weak base, and the pH for $0 < v < q$ is that of a buffer mixture. A salt of a weak acid and weak base is present in solution at the equivalence point, and the pH can be computed readily (see problem 4 in Section 3–13).

d. Polybasic Acids. Acids H_2A are characterized by two ionization constants

$$K_1 = \frac{a_{H^+} a_{HA^-}}{a_{H_2A}}, \tag{3-17}$$

$$K_2 = \frac{a_{H^+} a_{A^{--}}}{a_{HA^-}}. \tag{3-18}$$

Variations of pH during titration can be established, but the writing is rather heavy when K_1 and K_2 are not very different (see Kolthoff and Furman, Section 3–12). We shall limit the discussion to the case in which K_2 is much smaller than $K_1 (K_2 < 10^{-4} K_1)$. The acid HA^- is then much weaker than H_2A, and the titration curve exhibits two steps corresponding to the formation of HA^- and A^-, respectively. The pH of the acid solution is calculated from equation (3–11) if H_2A is a weak acid. In the opposite case, the pH is directly calculated from the initial concentration of acid $(pH \approx -\log C^0)$. For values of v comprised between zero and the first equivalence point, $v = q$, the pH is calculated either as for a strong monovalent acid (see Section 3–6a) or a weak acid (Section 3–6b).

The pH at the first end point is obtained from the equation

$$C_{H^+} = \sqrt{\frac{K_1 K_2 C^0}{K_1 + C^0}}, \tag{3-19}$$

or its simplified form $(C^0 \gg K_1)$

$$C_{H^+} = \sqrt{K_1 K_2}. \tag{3-20}$$

The derivation of equation (3–19) can be found in analytical chemistry texts or in the monograph of Kolthoff and Furman (see Section 3–12).

The pH between the first and second equivalence points $(q < v < 2q)$ is calculated by recalling that the solution is a mixture of a weak acid (HA^-) and its salt (A^{--}). The pH at the second equivalence point is that of a salt of a weak acid (HA⁻) and a strong base. Equation (3–15), where K_a is now K_2, is applied. The pH after the second equivalence point can be approximately calculated from the dilution of the titrant if one neglects hydroxyl ions produced by hydrolysis of the salt M_2A (Section 3–6a).

The principles involved in the study of this case are similar to those discussed in the analysis of a monovalent acid, and the reader is urged to make a detailed calculation of the titration curve as an exercise (see problem 5 in Section 3–13).

Titration curves for polybasic acids can be analyzed in a similar fashion. Orthophosphoric acid is an example of tribasic acid ($K_1 = 7.5 \times 10^{-3}$, $K_2 = 6.2 \times 10^{-8}$, $K_3 = 10^{-12}$), but its third ionization constant K_3 is so small that only the first two steps can be distinguished in the titration curve.

e. Mixtures of Acids or Bases.   This case is very similar to that of a polybasic acid or base. The titration curve exhibits as many steps as there are acids or bases, provided that the ionization constants of the acids or bases are sufficiently different.

f. Titration of Salts of Weak Acids or Bases.   Salts of a weak acid or weak base can be titrated with a strong acid or strong base. For example, ammonium salts can be titrated with sodium hydroxide. The variations of pH in the vicinity of the equivalence point are pronounced when the acid or base of the salt is sufficiently weak. A classical example is the titration of carbonate with a strong acid (problem 6, Section 3–13).

3–7. POTENTIOMETRIC TITRATIONS INVOLVING PRECIPITATION

We consider the titration of the cation M^{+n} of a metal M by anion A^{-n}. The indicator electrode is made of metal M, and the potential of this electrode is followed during titration. If the solubility product of the precipitate MA,

$$a_{M^+}a_{A^-} = S, \tag{3-21}$$

is sufficiently low (S $\leqslant 10^{-10}$) and the concentration C^0 not too low ($C^0 > 5 \times 10^{-3}\,M$), the contribution of the precipitate to the concentration of ion M^{+n} is negligible except in the vicinity of the end point and beyond this point. Equation (3–5) can be applied, and the concentration of ion M^{+n} decreases linearly until the equivalence point is almost reached. Hence

$$C_{M^+} = C^0 \frac{q - v}{q} \qquad \text{for } v < q \tag{3-22}$$

At the equivalence point

$$C_{M^+} \approx a_{M^+} = \sqrt{S}. \tag{3-23}$$

The concentration C_{M^+} after the end point is determined by the solubility of MA. If one neglects the contribution of the precipitate to the concentration of ion A^{-n}, one has [see equations (3–7) and (3–21)] by identifying concentrations and activities

$$C_{A^-} = C^0 \frac{v - q}{q} \qquad \text{for } v > q, \qquad (3\text{–}24)$$

and

$$C_{M^+} = \frac{S}{C^0 \dfrac{v - q}{q}}. \qquad (3\text{–}25)$$

The potential of the indicator electrode of metal M is calculated by introducing the above values of C_{M^+} in the Nernst equation. The two titration curves shown in Fig. 20 on the left were calculated in this manner

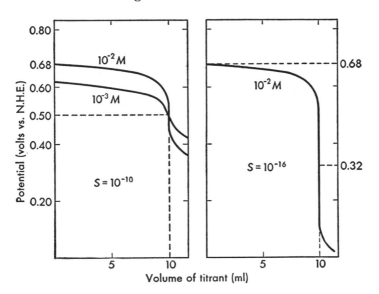

Fig. 20. Calculated titration curves for a precipitation reaction, and influence of initial concentration and solubility product.

for $C^0 = 10^{-2}$ and 10^{-3} M, $S = 10^{-10}$, $q = 10$ ml, $E^0 = 0.799$ volt (titration of an Ag^+ solution with chloride). Figure 20 shows that rapid variations of potential are observed in the vicinity of the equivalence point, which therefore can be determined from an experimental plot of potential against volume of titrant. The titration curve becomes less steep in the vicinity of the equivalence point when the concentration C^0 decreases, and the graphic determination of this point is difficult when the initial concentration is not much larger than $\sqrt{S}$ [see equation (3–23)].

The potential at the equivalence point for different insoluble salts of the same metal M becomes less positive as the solubility product S decreases. This results from the Nernst equation

$$E_{v=q} = E^0 + \frac{0.0591}{n} \log \sqrt{S}. \qquad (3\text{-}26)$$

It follows from equation (3-26) that the variation of potential in the vicinity of the end point becomes greater when the solubility product S is smaller, all other conditions of titration being the same (Fig.20). The curve on the right in Fig. 20 was constructed for the data: $E^0 = 0.799$ volt, $C^0 = 10^{-2}$ molar, $q = 10$ ml, and $s = 10^{-16}$ (approximate value for silver iodide). It is therefore advantageous to select reagents which give precipitates as insoluble as possible. In some cases it may be useful to decrease the solubility of the precipitate by adding an organic solvent miscible with water (ethyl alcohol, dioxane) or by carrying out the titration at 0^0 for precipitates whose solubility decreases with temperature.

The solubility of the precipitate was taken into account only at the equivalence point to simplify calculations, but a more rigorous treatment can be developed. However, the calculations are rather cumbersome and no new idea is involved.

Titrations involving precipitation of a salt M_gA_h can be treated as above, but the writing of equations is somewhat heavier (see the monograph Kolthoff and Furman in Section 3-12). The equivalence point is not the center of symmetry of the titration curve as was the case for a precipitate MA (problem 7 in Section 3-13).

It is sometimes possible to determine two substances in a single titration, provided that the precipitates have rather different solubilities. This is the case in the titration of a mixture of halides with silver ion ($S_{AgCl} \approx 10^{-10}$, $S_{AgBr} \approx 10^{-12}$, $S_{AgI} \approx 10^{-16}$). A detailed analysis will not be made here, and the reader can find this material in some of the monographs listed in Section 3-12 (Kolthoff and Furman, Lingane, etc).

3-8. POTENTIOMETRIC TITRATIONS INVOLVING COMPLEX ION FORMATION

Potentiometric titrations involving complex ion formation are treated by the general method applied in Section 3-7, but the activity of the cation must now be calculated from the instability constant of the complex (see Kolthoff and Furman, Section 3-12). The interpretation may be complicated by the existence of several complexes.[10]

[10]See, for example, J. Bjerrum, *Metal Ammine Formation in Aqueous Solution*, Haase and Son, Copenhagen, 1941.

3-9. *POTENTIOMETRIC TITRATIONS INVOLVING OXIDATION-REDUCTION REACTIONS*

a. Titration of a Single Substance. Consider the titration in which a reductant R_2 is oxidized by the titrant O_1:

$$\underset{\text{titrant}}{O_1} + \underset{\text{analyzed substance}}{R_2} = R_1 + O_2. \tag{3-27}$$

An example of this reaction is the oxidation of ferrous ions by ceric ions, $Ce^{+4} + Fe^{++} = Ce^{+3} + Fe^{+3}$. The potential of the indicator electrode (platinum) is followed during titration, and the equivalence point is determined from the titration curve. The equilibrium constant,

$$\frac{a_{R_1}a_{O_2}}{a_{O_1}a_{R_2}} = K, \tag{3-28}$$

for reaction (3-27) must be larger than unity by several orders of magnitude to have a virtually quantitative reaction, and the concentrations of the various species can then be calculated from equations (3-5) to (3-7), except in the immediate vicinity of the equivalence point. One has for $0 < v < q$

$$C_{O_2} = C^0 \frac{v}{q}, \tag{3-29}$$

$$C_{R_2} = C^0 \frac{q-v}{q}. \tag{3-30}$$

If one identifies concentrations with activities, one obtains (25^0) from the Nernst equation

$$E = E_2^0 + \frac{0.0591}{n} \log \frac{v}{q-v} \qquad \text{for } 0 < v < q, \tag{3-31}$$

where E_2^0 is the standard potential for couple 2, and n the number of electrons involved in the reduction of O_1 and in the oxidation of R_2. At the midpoint of the titration, i.e., for $v = q/2$, $E = E_2^0$, and the potential is the standard potential for the couple being titrated.

The potential for systems 1 and 2 should be the same for any point along the titration curve, and one could also calculate the potential of the indicator electrode from the concentrations of O_1 and R_1. This calculation is more complicated than the above one because the concentration for couple 1 depends on the equilibrium constant K of equation (3-28). In deriving equations (3-29) and (3-30) we do not have to take into account equilibrium considerations, and this simplifies matters. At the equivalence point, however, it is necessary to introduce the equilibrium constant K. Thus,

$$C_{O_1} = C_{R_2}, \tag{3-32}$$

$$C_{R_1} = C_{O_2} \tag{3-33}$$

at the equivalence point. If one identifies activities with concentrations in equation (3–28), one has in view of equations (3–32) and (3–33)

$$\left(\frac{a_{R_1}}{a_{O_1}}\right)^2 = \left(\frac{a_{O_2}}{a_{R_2}}\right)^2 = K. \tag{3-34}$$

The potential at $v = q$ is

$$E = E_1^0 - \frac{0.0591}{2n}\log K, \tag{3-35}$$

or

$$E = E_2^0 + \frac{0.0591}{2n}\log K, \tag{3-36}$$

where the E^0's are the standard potentials for couples 1 and 2. Since the two values of potential E in equation (3–35) and (3–36) must be the same, one has

$$E_1^0 - \frac{0.059}{2n}\log K = E_2^0 + \frac{0.0591}{2n}\log K.$$

or

$$E_1^0 - E_2^0 = \frac{0.0591}{n}\log K. \tag{3-37}$$

Hence, the potential at $v = q$ is, from equations (3–37) and (3–35) or (3–36),

$$E = \frac{E_1^0 + E_2^0}{2}. \tag{3-38}$$

The potential at the equivalence point is independent of the initial concentration of the substance being analyzed and is the average of the standard potentials of couples 1 and 2.

The potential of the indicator electrode beyond the equivalence point is calculated from the activities for couple 1. Thus,

$$C_{O_1} = C^0\frac{v - q}{q} \tag{3-39}$$

$$C_{R_1} = C^0 \tag{3-40}$$

for $v > q$. Hence,

$$E = E_1^0 + \frac{0.0591}{n}\log\frac{v - q}{q}. \tag{3-41}$$

Potential E is equal to the standard potential E_1^0 for the titrant when $v = 2q$.

An example of calculated titration curve is shown in Fig. 21 for the following data: $E_1^0 = 1.6$ volts, $E_2^0 = 0.77$ volt, $C^0 = 10^{-2}$ molar, $q = 10$ ml. These data correspond to the titration of ferrous ion with ceric ion.

Equations (3–31) and (3–41) are not applicable at $v = q$ and in the immediate vicinity of the equivalence point because equilibrium considerations are not introduced in the calculations. The treatment could be improved, but this will not be done here since the essential ideas can be presented in a simple treatment.

The foregoing discussion dealt with reaction (3–27), in which all the stoichiometric coefficients are equal to unity. Cases in which this is not

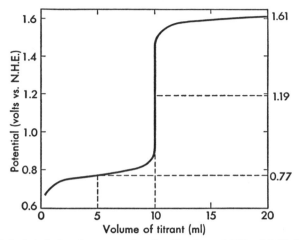

Fig. 21. Calculated titration curve for the titration of 100 ml 0.01 M ferrous ion with 0.1 M ceric ion.

so can be analyzed by following the same method as above. It is found in this manner that the potential at the equivalence point for an asymmetrical reaction is not the average of the standard potentials E_1^0 and E_2^0. For example, one can show (see problem 8, Section 3–13) that the potential at the equivalence point for the reaction

$$2O_1 + R_2 = 2R_1 + O_2 \tag{3-42}$$

is

$$E = \frac{2E_1^0 + E_2^0}{3}. \tag{3-43}$$

b. Stepwise Titration Curves. Titration of two substances by the same titrant is possible provided that the standard potentials of the substances being titrated, and their oxidation or reduction products, differ at least by a few tenths of a volt. Stepwise titration curves are obtained in the titration of substances having several oxidation states or in the titration of mixtures. An example of the former type of titration is the stepwise reduction of cupric ion to the monovalent state and the metal by chromous ion in 6 M hydrochloric acid. The titration of a mixture of Cr(VI), Fe(III) and V(V) by titanous chloride is an example of titration of a mixture. Cr(VI) and V(V) are reduced together to Cr(III) and V(IV) in the first step; Fe(III) is reduced to Fe(II) in the second step, and finally V(IV) is reduced to V(III) in the third step. Chromium is obtained by difference of the volumes of titrant used in the first and third steps.

3–10. EXPERIMENTAL METHODS IN POTENTIOMETRIC TITRATIONS

   a. Titration Cells. The apparatus for potentiometric titrations is quite simple and is essentially composed of a titration cell and a device for determining the voltage of the cell. The cell comprises an indicator electrode and a reference electrode. It is particularly convenient to utilize as reference electrode a commercial calomel electrode (industrial type) available from pH meter manufacturers. Continuous stirring of solution is advantageous, and the design of the cell is simplified when a magnetic stirrer is utilized. Oxygen generally does not interfere in precipitation and neutralization reactions, but many oxidation-reduction titrations must be carried out in an air-free medium. Nitrogen is then bubbled through the solution before and during titration. An example of a titration cell is shown in Fig. 22.

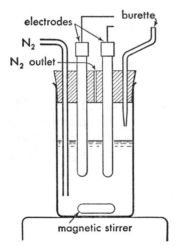

Fig. 22. Cell for potentiometric titrations in air-free medium.

   In titrations involving oxidation-reduction reactions it is sometimes necessary to heat the solution to increase the reaction rate and shorten the duration of the titration.

   b. "Manual" Methods. A rather large variation of electrode potential is observed in many titrations, and the potential of the indicator electrode need not be known with high precision. Direct-reading *titrimeters* and pH meters often are used in practical applications. A galvanometer with large resistance in series (see Section 2–10a) is a simple and inexpensive voltmeter suitable for many titrations, except those involving the use of a glass electrode.

   A student potentiometer can be utilized, but the determination of many points of a titration curve is quite tedious because of the necessity of balancing the potentiometer for each point. The procedure can be simplified (Erich Müller) when the potential of the indicator electrode at the equivalence point is reproducible. The potentiometer is set at the voltage of the cell at the equivalence point; the balance indicator indicates off-balance except at the equivalence point, and the titrant is added until balance is established. The titrant must be added slowly in the vicinity of the equivalence point to achieve equibilibrium conditions. If the titrant is added too rapidly, a rather serious error by excess may be made.

c. Automatic Methods. Potentiometric titrations often are applied in routine control analysis, and methods which eliminate manipulations by the operator during titration are advantageous for reducing the cost of each titration. Two types of such "automatic" methods can be conceived, namely, (1) methods in which the titration curve is automatically recorded, and (2) methods in which the addition of titrant is automatically stopped at the equivalence point. These two methods will be discussed briefly.

The automatic recording of titration curves is simple in principle, but truly practical instruments were designed only about 1948 by Lingane and G. Robinson.[11] The titrant is added at a controlled rate by a syringe

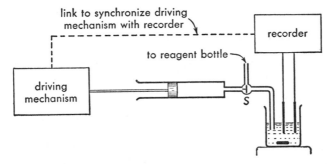

Fig. 23. Automatic recording of titration curves.

(Fig. 23) whose tip is immersed in the solution being titrated to achieve continuous addition of reagent and prevent the formation of drops. The driving mechanism of the syringe is synchronized with a pen-and-ink recorder (see Section 2–10c) to which the voltage of the titration cell is applied. The coordinates in the recording are proportional to the volume of titrant and the cell voltage, and a titration curve is recorded. The syringe is refilled by reversing the driving mechanism, the three-way stopcock *S* being turned in the proper position to connect the syringe to the titrant supply bottle. Since the titrant cannot be added continuously because of sluggishness of reaction near the equivalence point, the apparatus is designed in such a manner that a small increment of titrant is added and so that a new addition of titrant is not made until the potential of the indicator electrode has reached its equilibrium value. A commercial instrument is available in the United States (Precision Scientific Co.).

In the other type of automatic instrument the addition of titrant is stopped at the end point. This result is achieved by connecting the titration cell (Fig. 24) to a potentiometer which is set at the voltage of the cell at the equivalence point. A relay detects the moment at which balance is

[11]For details see the monographs of Lingane and the writer listed in Section 3–12.

obtained and closes the magnetic clamp of the buret delivering the titrant. The titrant is added by increments which automatically become smaller as the equivalence point is approached; errors resulting from sluggishness

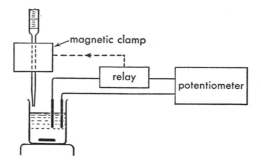

Fig. 24. Automatic determination of equivalence point.

of reaction are thus avoided. This type of automatic instrument is particularly advantageous when the titration curve is very steep in the immediate vicinity of the equivalence point, but it is essential that the potential of the indicator electrode be reproducible. Commercial instruments are available (Beckman, Coleman in the United States).

The addition of titrant also can be stopped automatically by applying the property of the second derivative of the function representing the titration curve to be equal to zero at the inflection point of the titration curve. The inflection occurs at the equivalence point when the titration reaction is symmetrical (same stoichiometric coefficients), and even when this condition is not satisfied, inflection and equivalence points can be identified without any serious error. The first derivative dE/dv exhibits a maximum at the point of inflection, and the second derivative d^2E/dv^2 passes through zero and changes sign at this point. This triggers a relay which stops the addition of titrant[12,13] (Malmstadt method). The titrant must be added continuously in this method, and an error by excess is observed with sluggish titration reactions particularly for dilute solutions (below $10^{-1}\ M$). However, there are many titrations for which this restriction does not hold, and furthermore, the titration error often can be kept constant in routine work; a correction then can be made. A commercial unit based on the second derivative method is available in the United States (Sargent).

It should be emphasized that automatic instruments are interesting only when a large number of titrations must be performed. The accuracy is not better than in the manual method.

[12]H. V. Malmstadt, *Anal. Chem.*, **26**, 1348 (1954); H. V. Malmstadt and E. R. Fett, *ibid.*, **27**, 1757 (1955).
[13]See also P. Delahay, *Anal. Chem.*, **20**, 1212 (1948).

3–11. APPLICATIONS

Numerous applications of potentiometric titrations have been reported, but only a few general comments will be made. Discussion of typical applications is reserved as an exercise (see Section 3–13).

The potentiometric method is particularly valuable in acid-base titrations involving very weak acids or bases and/or colored or nonaqueous media; e.g., whenever indicators are not satisfactory. Titrations involving precipitation are of a rather limited scope, although some useful titrations have been developed (for example, the titration of chloride in water by a silver salt). Numerous titrations involving oxidation-reduction reactions have been studied. It is sometimes possible to combine an oxidation-reduction electrode reaction involving two soluble species with a precipitation reaction. For example, a solution of iodide can be titrated by silver ion in presence of a small amount of iodine. The potential of the indicator electrode (platinum) is determined by the ratio of activities $a_{I_2}/a^2_{I^-}$, i.e., by the activity of iodide if a_{I_2} is constant. The method can be extended to cases in which the indicator electrode does not obey the Nernst equation since it suffices that the potential vary with the concentration of one of the reagents involved in the titration. Such cases are frequently encountered.

Applications have been made mainly in inorganic chemistry but a number of titrations of organic substances have also been developed. A very incomplete list of titrants with a few possible determinations is given below.

Ag^+ (precipitation): halides
MnO_4^-: Fe(II), H_2O_2, Mn(II), Sn(II), U(IV)
$Cr_2O_7^{--}$: As(III), Fe(II), $Fe(CN)_6^{-4}$, Sb(III)
BrO_3^-: I^-, N_2H_4 (hydrazine), Tl(I)
Ti^{+++}: Au(III), Bi(III), Cu(II), Fe(III), H_2O_2, Mo(VI), U(VI), V(VI)
Cr^{++}: Cu(I), Cu(II), Sb(V), Sn(IV)

Potentiometric titrations—as well as any analytical method—can be evaluated by considering three important criteria: *accuracy*, *sensitivity*, and *selectivity*.

The accuracy in potentiometric titrations is primarily determined by the titrimetric procedure, and results with errors not exceeding 0.1 to 0.3 per cent are not especially difficult to obtain at least in the 1 to 0.1 M concentration range.

The sensitivity of the method is primarily limited by the difficulty inherent to the preparation and storage of dilute solutions of titrant (below 10^{-2} to 10^{-3} M). This difficulty can be overcome by electrolytic generation of titrant (coulometric titration) as we shall see in Chapter 6. Microtechniques have been developed for the titration of small volumes (less than 1 ml).

The selectivity is relatively good since stepwise titration curves can be obtained in favorable cases as was shown in Sections 3–6f, 3–7, and 3–9b. Preliminary separations are often necessary in the analysis of mixtures.

The cost of apparatus is low for manual instruments (a few hundred dollars), and even for automatic titrimeters (from 600 to 3000 dollars). Application to routine analysis is easy.

3–12. BIBLIOGRAPHY

R. G. Bates, *Electrometric pH Determinations, Theory and Practice*, Wiley, New York, 1954. Most recent detailed monograph on pH measurements.

W. Böttger (article) in *Physikalische Methoden der Analytischen Chemie*. W. Böttger, Ed., Vol. III, Akademische Verlagsgesellschaft, Leipzig, 1939. Contains a comprehensive survey of literature from 1900 to about 1938.

H. T. S. Britton, *Hydrogen Ions*, 2 vols., Van Nostrand, New York, 1943.

G. Charlot and R. Gauguin, *Les Méthodes d'Analyse des Réactions en Solution*, Masson, Paris, 1951. Chapters on detailed analysis of titration curves and applications to the determination of equilibrium constants; this book contains much valuable information.

W. M. Clark, *The Determination of Hydrogen Ions*, 3rd ed., Williams and Wilkins, Baltimore, 1928. A classical work.

P. Delahay, *New Instrumental Methods in Electrochemistry*, Interscience, New York, 1954. Chapters on voltage measurements and on automatic and differential potentiometric titrations.

M. Dole, *The Glass Electrode*, Wiley, New York, 1941. The monograph on the glass electrode.

J. S. Fritz, *Acid-Base Titrations in Non-aqueous Solvents*, G. F. Smith Chemical Co., Columbus, Ohio, 1952. Gives applications of the potentiometric method.

I. M. Kolthoff and N. H. Furman, *Potentiometric Titrations*, Wiley, New York, 1931. A classic in the field with detailed treatment of titration curves.

I. M. Kolthoff and H. A. Laitinen, *pH and Electro Titrations*, Wiley, New York, 1941. A text giving a good introduction to the field.

I. M. Kolthoff and V. A. Stenger, *Volumetric Analysis*, 2nd ed., Vol. I, Interscience, New York, 1942. This is not a book on potentiometric titrations, but it contains much material on titration curves.

L. Kratz, *Die Glaselektrode und ihre Anwendungen*, Steinkopff, Frankfort, 1950. Valuable information on recent applications.

H. A. Laitinen (article) in *Physical Methods in Chemical Analysis*, W. G. Berl, Ed., Vol. II, Academic Press, New York, 1951. Discussion of fundamentals.

J. J. Lingane, *Electroanalytical Chemistry*, Interscience, New York, 1953. Discussion of fundamentals and a chapter on automatic potentiometric titrations.

L. Michaelis, *Oxidation-reduction Potentials*, Lippincott, Philadelphia, 1930. A classical work.

L. Michaelis (article) in *Physical Methods of Organic Chemistry*, A. Weissberger, ed., 2nd ed., Vol. I, Part 2, Interscience, New York, 1949. The emphasis is on organic chemistry, but fundamentals are also discussed.

E. Müller, *Die Elektrometrische Massanalyse*, 6th ed., Steinkopff, Dresden, 1942.

Another classic on potentiometric titrations, especially valuable for the systematic discussion of applications.

J. E. Ricci, *Hydrogen Ion Concentration—New Concepts in a Systematic Treatment,* Princeton University Press, Princeton, 1952. A detailed mathematical analysis of titration curves.

Reviews: N. H. Furman, *Ind. Eng. Chem. Anal. Ed.,* **2,** 213 (1930); **14,** 367 (1942); *Anal. Chem.,* **22,** 33 (1950); **23,** 21 (1951); **26,** 84 (1954). C. N. Reilley, *ibid.,* **28,** 671 (1956). Fundamentals and applications are critically reviewed.

3-13. PROBLEMS

a. Extension of Theory

1. Derive equations similar to (3–5), (3–6), and (3–7) for a titration involving the reaction $aX + bT = dQ + gU$.

2. Discuss the titration of a solution of strong base by a strong acid, and plot the titration curve for the following case: initial concentration of base $5 \times 10^{-2} M$; initial volume of base 50 ml; concentration of titrant $10^{-1} M$. Make the calculations first by neglecting dilution and then by taking dilution into account. Compare the titration curves.

3. Discuss the titration of a weak base by a strong acid and apply your analysis to the titration of 50 ml $10^{-2} M$ ammonium hydroxide ($K_b = 1.8 \times 10^{-5}$) with $2 \times 10^{-1} M$ hydrochloric acid. What is the value of the pH at the midpoint of the titration. Neglect dilution in the calculations. Which indicator—phenolphthalein (pH 8.0 to 9.8) or methyl red (pH 4.2 to 6.2)—would you select for determining the end point?

4. Discuss the titration of a weak acid by a weak base and apply your analysis to the titration of 100 ml $10^{-2} M$ acetic acid ($K_a = 1.8 \times 10^{-5}$) with 1 M ammonium hydroxide ($K_b = 1.8 \times 10^{-5}$). Plot the titration curve and compare it with the curve in Fig. 19 (right). Neglect dilution in the calculations.

5. Plot the titration curve for the titration of 100 ml of $10^{-2} M$ sulfurous acid with 1 M sodium hydroxide. Ionization constants: $K_1 = 1.25 \times 10^{-2}$, $K_2 = 5.6 \times 10^{-8}$. What is the pH for $v = 0.5$ and 1.5 ml? Note that in this case the condition $K_1 \ll C°$ is not satisfied; see equation (3–11). Neglect dilution in the calculations.

6. Discuss the titration of a salt M_2A with a strong acid for the case in which H_2A and HA^- are weak acids. The difference between the ionization constants K_1 K_2 is so large that the titration curve exhibits two steps. Apply this analysis to the titration of 100 ml of 0.01 M sodium carbonate with 1 M hydrochloric acid. Assume that no carbon dioxide escapes from the titration vessel during titration, and neglect dilution in the calculations. Which indicator would you utilize for determining the two equivalence points? Deduce from these considerations a method for the analysis of mixtures of sodium carbonate and bicarbonate. Ionization constants for carbonic acid: $K_1 = 4.16 \times 10^{-7}$ and $K_2 = 4.84 \times 10^{-11}$.

7. Discuss the titration curve for a titration involving the formation of a precipitate M_2A. Apply this analysis to the titration of 50 ml of 0.01 M silver nitrate with 0.1 M potassium chromate ($S = 1.9 \times 10^{-12}$). Neglect dilution in the calculations.

8. Discuss the titration curve for the reaction $2O_1 + R_2 = 2R_1 + O_2$ and derive equation (3–43). Apply this analysis to the titration of 50 ml of 0.01 M stannic chloride by 0.2 M chromous sulfate. Plot the titration curve and indicate remarkable points on the curve. Neglect dilution.

b. Application to Theory

9. Calculate the relative error on the activity of hydrogen ion for an absolute error of 0.2 pH unit.

10. A hydrogen electrode functioning under a pressure of 683-mm mercury is coupled with a saturated calomel electrode. The voltage of the cell is 0.287 volt at 23°, the saturated calomel electrode being the positive terminal. Calculate the pH of the solution in which the hydrogen electrode is immersed.

11. The voltage of a cell composed of a glass electrode coupled with a saturated calomel electrode is 0.343 volt with a buffer of pH 3.57 at 27.5°, the calomel electrode being the positive terminal. The unknown pH of a solution is determined with this electrode, and a voltage of 0.291 volt is measured at the same temperature as the calibration. Calculate the unknown pH.

12. Calculate the pH of a mixture of 0.05 M sodium bicarbonate and 0.1 M sodium carbonate which is to be measured with a glass electrode made of 015 Corning glass. Ionization constants for carbonic acid: $K_1 = 4.16 \times 10^{-7}$ and $K_2 = 4.84 \times 10^{-11}$. See also Fig. 15.

13. In the titration of 75 ml of a strong acid solution by a strong base the following readings were made:

$$pH = 2.911 \text{ after the addition of 2 ml of titrant}$$
$$pH = 3.093 \text{ after the addition of 3 ml of titrant}$$

Calculate the initial concentration of acid, knowing that the initial volume of solution being titrated is 75 ml. Identify activity with concentration in the calculations.

Note: Take into account the dilution of the acid solution; call x the volume of titrant at the equivalence point, and y the initial concentration.

14. Construct the titration curve for the titration of 50 ml of 0.1 M potassium bromate with 0.2 M titanous chloride. The solution of potassium bromate contains a large excess of potassium bromide and is initially 1 M in hydrochloric acid. Construct the curve first by assuming that the pH does not vary during titration and that there is no dilution of the solution. Then calculate a few points of the curve by taking into account pH variation and dilution. E^0 for BrO_3^-/Br^- couple, 1.44 volts.

Note: Identify activities with concentrations and keep in mind that Ti(IV) is present as TiO^{++}.

c. Survey of Literature

15. Prepare an outline of procedure for the potentiometric titration of the substances listed below. Furman's reviews and possibly Müller's monograph are recommended for orientation purposes. There is a choice of several titrants in some cases,

and a brief comparison of the advantages and disadvantages of each titrant may be made.

Substances: Ag^+, BrO_3^-, CrO_4^{--}, Cu^{++}, $Fe(CN)_6^{-4}$, $HAsO_2$, H_2O_2, I^-, $Mo(V)$, NO_3^-, Tl^+, UO_2^{++}, Zn^{++}.

16. Discuss the potentiometric determination of the functional groups —OH, —NH₂, —CO, —CHO, and —CO₂R in organic compounds by means of lithium aluminum hydride (LiAlH₄).

Note: See T. Higuchi, *Anal. Chem.*, **22**, 955 (1950); T. Higuchi, C. J. Lintner, and R. H. Schleif, *Science*, **111**, 63 (1950); C. J. Lintner, R. H. Schleif, and T. Higuchi, *Anal. Chem.*, **22**, 534 (1950). For a general review, see article by T. Higuchi in *Organic Analysis*, J. Mitchell, Jr., I. M. Kolthoff, E. S. Proskauer, and A. Weissberger, eds., Vol. 2, Interscience, New York, 1954.

17. Discuss the method of D. A. MacInnes and M. Dole [*J. Am. Chem. Soc.*, **51**, 1119 (1929)] for obtaining the first derivative of the titration curve by means of a concentration cell.

4

Polarography and Voltammetry

4–1. MASS TRANSFER PROCESSES

Electrode potentials are measured by drawing virtually no current from the electrochemical cell. It is true that a very small current flows through the cell even when the balance indicator apparently shows zero current, but this can be neglected for all practical purposes.[1] We now turn to methods in which an appreciable current flows through the cell, and we shall discuss relationships between current and electrode potential, and their applications to chemical analysis. These methods are designated by the terms *voltammetry* in general and *polarography* in the particular case in which a dropping mercury electrode is utilized.

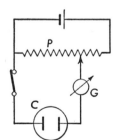

Current-potential characteristics are studied with the apparatus of Fig. 25, in which the voltage applied to the cell C is adjusted by means of potentiometer P and the current through the cell is read on galvanometer G. Since the voltage applied to the cell is the algebraic sum of the two electrode potentials (see Section 2–5b) and the ohmic drop in the solution between the electrodes, the interpretation of experimental current-voltage curves is simplified when the following two conditions are fulfilled: (1) the ohmic drop in the cell is negligible (a few millivolts); (2) the

Fig. 25. Schematic diagram of apparatus for the study of current-potential characteristics.

potential of one electrode is independent of current; this electrode is said to be *unpolarized;* the other electrode, *polarized.* The conditions for which

[1]However, see Section 2–10b.

an electrode is polarized or unpolarized will be discussed at length in this chapter, and the preparation of unpolarized electrodes is described in Section 3–10b. The following relationship holds when the above two conditions are satisfied,

$$\left|\text{Applied voltage}\right| = \left|\text{potential of unpolarized electrode}\right.$$

$$\left. - \text{ potential of polarized electrode }\right|,$$

where the vertical bars indicate that the voltage is taken in absolute value. This relationship is valid regardless of the convention adopted for potentials.[2]

The voltage applied to the cell is equal to the potential of the polarized electrode when the potential of the unpolarized electrode is taken as reference. This method of reporting values of potentials often is adopted in polarography and voltammetry for the sake of convenience, the saturated calomel electrode being the reference. The expression "versus S.C.E." should then follow the value of the potential of the polarized electrode to avoid confusion with potentials referred to the normal hydrogen electrode. The conversion of potentials from one scale to the other is immediate.

The reaction occurring on the polarized electrode—a reduction, for example—may be represented by the equation

$$O + n\text{e} = R \tag{4–1}$$

where O symbolizes the substance being reduced and R its reduction product. Since substance O is consumed in the electrode reaction, its concentration is smaller at the electrode surface than in the bulk of the solution. We shall designate the concentrations of O at the electrode surface by $(C_O)_{x=0}$, where x is the distance from the electrode. The concentration of substance O in the bulk of the solution (say, for $x > 10^{-2}$ cm) will be represented by C^0. When $(C_O)_{x=0}$ is smaller than C^0, there is *concentration polarization* at the electrode.

Concentration $(C_O)_{x=0}$ would decrease immediately after the beginning of electrolysis, if it were not for the *mass transfer* of substance O toward the electrode surface. Such a transfer occurs by *diffusion* of substance O toward the electrode. Furthermore, there is *convection* of substance O toward the electrode when the solution is stirred either by a mechanical device or because of differences in density or temperature from one point

[2] In accurate determinations one should correct for the ohmic drop. This is a simple matter, since the current through the cell is known and the resistance of the cell can easily be measured; see Section 4–10.

of the solution to another. If substance O is a reducible ion, the *migration* of this ion in the electric field in solution is a third possible mode of mass transfer. Thus, positive ions migrate toward the negative electrode, and negative ions toward the positive electrode.

The interpretation of current-potential curves is simplified when only one or two of the above modes of mass transfer have to be considered. Migration of the ions reacting at the electrode is minimized by the addition of a large excess of *supporting electrolyte*, i. e., an electrolyte which does not interfere with the electrode reaction. For instance, the electrolysis of a $10^{-3} M$ solution of silver nitrate would be carried out in presence of potassium nitrate at a concentration of 1 mole per liter. Potassium ion, which is much more difficult to reduce than silver ion (see Table I, Chapter 2), does not interfere with the reduction of the latter ion. For each silver ion in solution there are one thousand potassium and nitrate ions, which almost entirely "carry" the current. In the absence of supporting electrolyte, migration increases or decreases the rate of mass transfer, depending on the sign of the ion and the polarity of the electrode toward which it moves. Thus, migration of a cation toward the cathode of a polarographic cell increases the rate of mass transfer, whereas migration hampers mass transfer of an anion toward the cathode. The difference between the current observed without and with supporting electrolyte is the *migration current*.

4–2. CURRENT CONTROLLED BY DIFFUSION AT A PLANE ELECTRODE

a. Conditions of Electrolysis.   We first consider the simplest possible case in which substance O of reaction (4–1) is reduced on a plane electrode under the following two conditions: (1) there is no convection, and (2) molecules or ions of substance O are reduced as soon as they reach the electrode. The former condition is fulfilled when the electrode does not move (*stationary electrode*), the solution is not stirred, and the duration of electrolysis is relatively short, say, one minute or so. When the electrolysis is prolonged, small vibrations of the bench on which the cell is installed cause enough stirring to interfere seriously with diffusion. The second condition—that O is readily reduced at the electrode—is satisfied when the electrode potential is properly adjusted. If one assumes that the Nernst equation can be applied even when a current flows through the cell, one has at 25°

$$E = E^0 + \frac{0.0591}{n} \log \frac{(a_O)_{x=0}}{(a_R)_{x=0}}, \qquad (4\text{–}2)$$

where E^0 is the standard potential, and the a's the activities. The subscript $x = 0$ indicates that the activities are taken at the electrode surface. The condition, $x = 0$, must be specified because the activities of substances O and R are not the same at the electrode surface as in solution when there is concentration polarization. If potential E is more negative than the standard potential by several tenths of a volt, the logarithmic term in equation (3–2) must be markedly negative, and the condition

$$\frac{(a_O)_{x=0}}{(a_R)_{x=0}} \ll 1 \tag{4-3}$$

must be satisfied. If activities are identified with concentrations, condition (4–3) implies that virtually all molecules or ions of substance O reaching the electrode must be reduced to R. Hence,

$$(C_O)_{x=0} \ll C^0, \tag{4-4}$$

where C^0 is the concentration of substance O in the bulk of the solution.

It can be shown that condition (4–4) is also fulfilled, even when the Nernst equation cannot be applied, provided that the potential is sufficiently negative.

b. Rate of Diffusion and Variations of Current. Since $(C_O)_{x=0}$ is much smaller than the bulk concentration C^0, the concentration C_O varies with the distance from the electrode (Fig. 26, left), and at a sufficient dis-

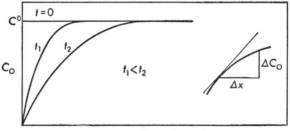

Distance from electrode

Fig. 26. Variations of concentration at 0, t_1, and t_2 sec after the beginning of electrolysis (left); definition of the gradient of concentration (right).

tance from the electrode (say 10^{-2} cm) C_O is practically equal to C^0. Initially the concentration C_O is equal to C^0 everywhere.[3] The effect of depletion extends farther away in solution as the electrolysis proceeds.

Since substance O is readily reduced at the electrode, the current is entirely determined by the rate at which O is transferred to the electrode. This rate is larger at time t_1 than t_2 because the curve showing concentration against distance from electrode is steeper at the origin at time t_1 than at t_2. This is to be expected since the driving force for diffusion is

[3]Adsorption on the electrode is neglected here; this simplification is justified in most cases.

the difference in concentration from one point to another. This can be expressed in a precise manner by considering the *gradient of concentration*, which is the limit of $\Delta C_O/\Delta x$ as Δx approaches zero (Fig. 26, right). The gradient is the slope of the tangent to the curve C_O versus x at the point at which it is expressed. It is observed that the rate of diffusion per unit area at a given point of the solution is proportional to the gradient of concentration of the diffusing substance (Fick's law). The proportionality factor is the *diffusion coefficient*, D_O, and is generally expressed[4] in units cm^2sec^{-1}.

The gradient of concentration at the electrode surface decreases continuously during electrolysis, and the slope of the tangent to the C_O versus x curve at $x = 0$ decreases as t increases (Fig. 26). It can be shown that the rate of diffusion per unit area for the conditions of electrolysis considered here is given by the relationship:

$$\text{Number of moles diffusing to the electrode surface per unit area and per unit of time} = C^0\sqrt{\frac{D_O}{\pi t}}, \qquad (4\text{--}5)$$

where t is the time elapsed since the beginning of electrolysis. This rate is proportional to the bulk concentration, C^0, of the substance diffusing toward the electrode. This is to be expected; if C^0 is doubled, the ordinates in Fig. 26 are doubled, and the slope of the tangent at $x = 0$ is twice as large.

Equation (4–5) will not be derived here, but the reader with some knowledge of calculus will be able to follow the derivation in some of the monographs[5] listed in Section 4–13.

The current through the cell is defined as the quantity of electricity consumed per unit of time. This quantity of electricity is proportional to the quantity of electricity involved in the reduction of 1 mole of O and to the number of moles consumed per second; i.e., to the rate of diffusion of substance O at the electrode. It was shown by Faraday that one faraday ($F = 96{,}494$ coulombs) is consumed per mole in a reaction involving one electron. Since n electrons are involved in the reduction of substance O according to reaction (4–1), nF faradays are needed to reduce one mole of O, and it follows then from equation (4–5) that the current for an electrode of area A is

$$i_d = nFAC^0\sqrt{\frac{D_O}{\pi t}}, \qquad (4\text{--}6)$$

where the subscript d indicates that the current is controlled by the rate of diffusion. The area A appears in equation (4–6) because the rate of dif-

---

[4]Rate of diffusion (in mol sec^{-1}) = D (in $cm^2\ sec^{-1}$) $\times$ gradient (in mol cm^{-4}) $\times$ area (in cm^2).

[5]Particularly Kolthoff and Lingane.

fusion in (4–5) is given for 1 cm². The current decreases continuously and approaches zero, as is apparent from Fig. 27, which corresponds to $n = 1$, $F = 96,494$ coulombs, $A = 0.02$ cm², $C^0 = 10^{-6}$ mol cm⁻³, $D = 10^{-5}$ cm² sec⁻¹. These are conditions similar to those in polarography, as will be seen in the subsequent section.

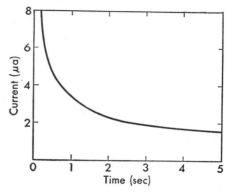

The resistance of the cell and the measuring circuit is not taken into account in the derivation of equations (4–5) and (4–6), and the implication of (4–6), that the current is infinite for $t = 0$, does not correspond to actual experimental conditions; the current immediately after the beginning of electrolysis is partially controlled by the resistance of the cell. Afterwards, the

Fig. 27. Variations of current during electrolysis with control by diffusion toward a plane electrode; see data in text.

effect of the circuit resistance can be neglected and equation (4–6) holds.

The current i_d is proportional to C^0 and may thus be applied to analytical determinations. However, the current continuously decreases and the conventional polarographic method with the dropping mercury electrode is of much greater practical value. The foregoing considerations are nevertheless essential to the understanding of diffusion at the dropping mercury electrode.

4–3. DIFFUSION AT THE DROPPING MERCURY ELECTRODE: THE ILKOVIC EQUATION

a. Diffusion Current. The dropping mercury electrode is essentially composed of a capillary connected to a mercury reservoir. The bore of the capillary (approximately 0.03 mm), the length of the capillary (about 8 cm), and the head of mercury (40 to 80 cm) are adjusted in such a manner that a drop is dislodged every 2 to 5 sec. A platinum[6] wire is immersed in the mercury reservoir, and the dropping mercury electrode is coupled with an unpolarized electrode. The cell is connected to a potentiometer as shown in Fig. 25.

The use of the dropping mercury electrode in chemical analysis was originated at the Charles University in Prague in the early nineteen twenties by Heyrovsky who coined the word "polarography" to designate this new method. The method was progressively developed by this investigator and his co-workers, and the fundamentals were well understood by

[6]Platinum is used to avoid contamination of mercury. Most other metals would dissolve with the formation of an amalgam.

1935. This is about the time at which the method became well known outside Czechoslovakia, thanks to the efforts of many investigators, in particular Kolthoff and his students (Lingane, Laitinen, and others) in the United States, von Stackelberg in Germany, Semerano in Italy, etc.

The work of Heyrovsky is of great significance in electroanalytical chemistry because it paved the way to new modes of approach (polarographic and voltammetric methods, coulometry). Thus, potentiometry, electrogravimetry (Chapter 6), and conductometry (Chapter 7) were the main methods of electroanalytical chemistry during the first quarter of this century, while polarography is now the most important and versatile of all the electrochemical methods.[7] Several thousand papers have been published in the field.

We first consider the simple case in which the conditions stated at the beginning of Section 4–2 are fulfilled: (1) a large excess of supporting electrolyte is present and diffusion is the only mode of mass transfer to be considered; (2) the potential of the dropping mercury electrode is adjusted at a value at which condition (4–4) is satisfied, i.e., molecules or ions of substance O are reduced as soon as they reach the electrode. The analysis of Section 4–2 can be transposed to the dropping mercury electrode, but three new conditions resulting from the use of a growing drop as electrode must be taken into consideration: (1) the electrode is essentially a sphere; (2) the electrode area varies continuously; and (3) the electrode surface moves toward the solution because of the expansion of the drop. This first of these three conditions can be neglected since it can be shown (see problem 1 in Section 4–14) that equation (4–6) is *approximately* applicable to a spherical electrode provided that t is small (a few seconds) and the radius of the sphere is not too small (1 mm). The second condition, namely, the variation of electrode area, is readily taken into consideration. Thus, the area of the mercury drop is $4\pi r^2$ (r radius of the drop) if one assumes—as is essentially correct—that the drop is a sphere. This expression of the drop area can be modified by introduction of the following easily measurable quantities: the *rate of flow of mercury*, m, and the *time*, t, elapsed since the beginning of the drop life. The volume of the drop is mt/d, d being the density of mercury. This volume is also $(4/3)\pi r^3$, and consequently

$$r = \sqrt[3]{\frac{3mt}{4\pi d}}\,,\tag{4-7}$$

and
$$A = 4\pi r^2$$
$$= 4\pi \left(\frac{3}{4\pi d}\right)^{2/3} m^{2/3} t^{2/3}.\tag{4-8}$$

[7]An interesting account of the circumstances surrounding the discovery of polarography has been given by R. Brdicka, *Collection Czechoslov. Chem. Communs.*, **15**, 691 (1950).

The effect of the movement of the electrode surface toward the solution cannot be taken into account as easily as the increase of area, but it can be shown that equation (4–5) for the rate of diffusion still holds provided that its right-hand member is multiplied by $\sqrt{7/3}$. Equation (4–6), which is directly deduced from (4–5), thus can be applied to the dropping mercury electrode provided that the factor $\sqrt{7/3}$ is introduced in the second member. The fall of each drop stirs the solution and destroys the gradient of concentration previously established. Current-time curves for consecutive drops remain the same. It is true that the substance being electrolyzed is progressively removed from solution, but the quantity of substance removed in an ordinary cell (10 ml or more) is negligible even over a period of 1 hr (problem 2 in Section 4–14).

By combination of equations (4–6) and (4–8) there follows after the introduction of the factor $\sqrt{7/3}$

$$ i_d = \sqrt{\frac{7}{3}} \times 4\pi^{1/2} \left(\frac{3}{4\pi d}\right)^{2/3} nFm^{2/3}t^{1/6}D_0^{1/2}C^0. \tag{4-9}$$

It is useful to adapt the units in equation (4–9) to the order of magnitude encountered in practice and to write (4–9) in the form

$$ i_d = 708 n m^{2/3} t^{1/6} D_0^{1/2} C^0, \tag{4-10}$$

where the coefficient 708 holds for 25°, and the units are as follows: i in microamperes, m in mg sec^{-1}, t in sec, D_0 in cm^2 sec^{-1}, and C^0 in millimoles per liter. The conversion from equation (4–9) to (4–10) is made by introducing numerical data for d (13.53 g cm^{-3} at 25°) and F (96,494 coulombs), and by making the suitable correction for the change in units.[8]

Equation (4–10), which was derived by Ilkovic[9] in 1935, is of great importance because some of the essential features of polarographic currents can be deduced from it.

The rate of diffusion of the susbstance being reduced or oxidized at the electrode controls the current given by reaction (4–10), which is therefore called *diffusion current.*

The current during drop life is proportional to $t^{1/6}$ while it is inversely proportional to $t^{1/2}$ for a plane electrode [equation (4–6)]. The increase in the drop area ($t^{2/3}$) more than compensates the effect of depletion in the vicinity of the electrode ($1/t^{1/2}$), and the current is proportional to $t^{2/3}/t^{1/2}$, or $t^{1/6}$. Variations of current during drop life are shown in Fig. 28 for $n = 1$, $m = 0.9$ mg sec^{-1}, $D = 10^{-5}$ cm sec^{-1}, and $C^0 = 1$ millimol lit^{-2}. These values of n, D, and C^0 are the same as for Fig. 27,

[8] The units in equation (4–9) are the same as in (4–10) except that i is in amperes, m in g sec^{-1}, and C^0 in mol cm^{-3}.

[9] D. Ilkovic, *Collection Czechoslov. Chem. Communs.*, **6**, 498 (1934); *J. chim. phys.*, **35**, 129 (1938).

and the area of the drop for $t = 4$ sec is the same as the area (0.02 cm²) of the stationary electrode of Fig. 27 (compare the two diagrams).

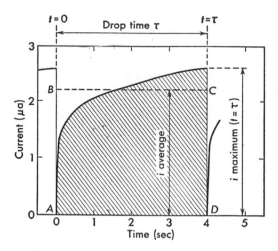

Fig. 28. Variations of current during drop life; see data in text.

The current varies too rapidly during the drop growth to be followed by an ordinary galvanometer, but the average current during the drop life τ can be measured with a well-damped galvanometer. The average current, $\bar{\imath}$, is defined by the condition that the product $\bar{\imath}\tau$ is equal to the area under the current-time curve. Hence, the shaded area in Fig. 28 is equal to the area of rectangle $ABCD$. It can be shown[10] that the average current is equal to 6/7 of the current at the end of the drop life. Hence

$$\bar{\imath}_d = 607nm^{2/3}\tau^{1/6}D_0^{1/2}C^0, \tag{4-11}$$

where $607 = (6/7)708$ and τ is the drop time in seconds, the units being the same as in equation (4-10).

Damping is generally not sufficient to eliminate completely the oscillations of the galvanometer beam, but these oscillations are of the same amplitude on each side of the position corresponding to the average current. It should be emphasized that this is not the case for pen-and-ink recorders which are often preferred nowadays to galvanometers in polarographic measurements. These recorders are sufficiently rapid to follow the current during the second half of the drop life, and the maximum current during drop life can be measured. Equation (4-10), where t is made equal to τ, the drop life, is then applied. The measurement of average currents with pen-and-ink recorders should be discouraged. Average currents will

[10]One has $\bar{\imath}\tau = \int_0^\tau i\,dt$, or $\bar{\imath} = (1/\tau)\int_0^\tau i\,dt$. The integration of $t^{1/6}$ introduces the coefficient 6/7 since $1/\tau \int_0^\tau t^{1/6}dt = 6/7\ \tau^{1/6}$.

be discussed in the following treatment, but conclusions can be readily transposed to maximum currents since $\bar{\imath} = (6/7)i_{t=\tau}$.

b. Influence of the Head of Mercury. The rate of flow of mercury and the drop time depend on the head of mercury; i.e., on the difference in level between the tip of the capillary and the surface of mercury in the reservoir attached to the capillary. This dependence determines how accurately the head of mercury must be adjusted.

The rate of flow of mercury is proportional to the head of mercury (Poiseuille's law, see problem 3, Section 4–14), and

$$m = m_0 H, \tag{4-12}$$

where m_0 is the value of m when H is equal to unity. In all rigor one should correct H for the back pressure resulting from the drop formation, but this correction is minor. The relationship between τ and H is readily obtained on the basis of the following considerations. The drop remains attached to the capillary as long as the force resulting from interfacial tension is larger than the gravity force (see problem 4, Section 4–14). The interfacial force depends on the radius of the capillary bore and the composition of the solution, but is independent of the head of mercury. It follows that the critical weight at which the drop is dislodged for a given capillary in a given medium is independent of the head of mercury. The time, τ, required to reach this critical weight decreases as the rate of flow of mercury increases, and τ is inversely proportional to H. Thus,

$$\tau = \frac{\tau_0}{H}, \tag{4-13}$$

where τ_0 is the value of τ when H is equal to unity.

Since i_d is proportional to $m^{2/3} \tau^{1/6}$ or $(m_0^{2/3} \tau_0^{1/6} H^{2/3})/H^{1/6}$, (i.e. $H^{1/2}$), *the diffusion current is proportional to the square root of the head of mercury.* Since H is of the order of 500 mm, a variation of H of 1 mm causes an error of approximately 0.1 per cent. Because of various experimental errors diffusion currents are obtained with errors generally higher than 0.1 per cent, and the adjustmemt of the head of mercury is not particularly critical. One nevertheless should verify that H is constant within 1 or 2 mm in comparative measurements.

c. Influence of Potential. The diffusion current was calculated on the assumption that the potential of the dropping mercury electrode is such that molecules or ions of the analyzed substance are reduced or oxidized "as soon" as they reach the electrode. This condition is fulfilled when the potential is adjusted at a sufficiently negative or positive value, as was shown in Section 4–2. The potential does not appear in the equation for the diffusion current, but this current depends indirectly on potential because of variations of the interfacial tension mercury-solution with potential. Ions and especially anions are adsorbed on the mercury drop over a wide range of potentials, thus causing a change of interfacial tension with potential. It follows that the force holding the mercury drop, and consequently the drop time and the diffusion current, vary with potential (Fig. 29). The relative variations of current are far less

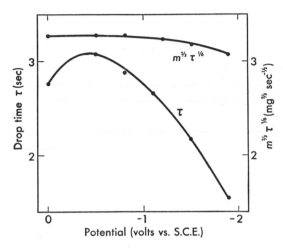

Fig. 29. Variations of τ and $m^{2/3}\tau^{1/6}$ with potential for 0.1 M potassium chloride at 25° [Data of J. J. Lingane and I. M. Kolthoff, *J. Am. Chem. Soc.*, **61**, 825 (1939)].

pronounced than those of the drop time because $\tau^{1/6}$ varies far less rapidly with potential than τ. The rate of flow of mercury is virtually independent of potential.

d. Influence of Temperature. All the terms in equation (4–11), except n, depend on temperature, and it is essential to determine the degree of temperature control required in the application to chemical analysis. The coefficient 607 depends on temperature because it includes the density of mercury [see equation (4–9)] which, of course, varies with temperature. The rate of flow of mercury, m, depends on the viscosity of mercury, and is a function of temperature. The drop time, τ, varies with temperature because the interfacial tension mercury-solution depends on temperature. The diffusion coefficient, D_O, is also a function of temperature, because the energy of the diffusing particles, and consequently the mean free path of these particles in solution, increases with temperature. Finally, the concentration, C^0, depends on temperature because of variations of volume of the solution with temperature. A detailed analysis of the temperature coefficient for the different terms in equation (4–11) was made,[11] and it was shown that the temperature dependence of the diffusion co-

[11]See pp. 90–93 of the monograph of Kolthoff and Lingane listed in Section 4–13.

efficient is determinative. By taking the logarithm of both sides of equation (4–11) and differentiating with respect to temperature, one obtains after retaining only the term in D_O

$$\frac{1}{\bar{\imath}}\frac{d\bar{\imath}}{dT} \approx \frac{1}{2D_O}\frac{dD_O}{dT}, \tag{4-14}$$

where T is the temperature. It is observed that the temperature coefficient $(1/D_O)(dD_O/dT)$ at $25°$ is generally comprised between 0.02 and 0.04, and the temperature coefficient of diffusion currents is between 1 and 2 per cent per degree at room temperature. The temperature of the solution should thus be known or controlled within $0.1°$. Better control of temperature is not necessary because of other experimental errors.

e. Modified Forms of the Ilkovic Equation. It follows from equation (4–11) that the quantity $\bar{\imath}_d/m^{2/3}\,\tau^{1/6}$ should be independent of drop time for otherwise identical conditions of electrolysis. It was found experimentally that $\bar{\imath}_d/m^{2/3}\,\tau^{1/6}$ does vary somewhat (perhaps 5 per cent) with drop time, and this has led several authors to refine Ilkovic's treatment. Modified forms of the Ilkovic equation are in better agreement with experiment, but there is still some discrepancy. The Ilkovic equation can be used for all practical purposes, and reference will be made to the monograph of Kolthoff and Lingane listed in Section 4–13 for details (problem 10, Section 4–14).

4-4. CURRENT-POTENTIAL CURVES: REVERSIBLE PROCESSES

a. General Treatment. The concentration of electrolyzed substance at the electrode surface, $(C_O)_{x=0}$, is negligible in compariosn with the bulk concentration C^0 in the conditions for which the Ilkovic equation is derived. We now consider the more general problem in which $(C_O)_{x=0}$ is not negligible in comparison with C^0, and we shall first discuss the case in which the Nernst equation is applicable. Processes for which this equation can be applied under polarographic conditions are said to be *reversible*.

If the product of electrolysis (substance R) is soluble, the potential of the dropping mercury electrode is at $25°$

$$E = E^0 + \frac{0.0591}{n}\log\left(\frac{f_O C_O}{f_R C_R}\right)_{x=0}, \tag{4-15}$$

where E^0 is the standard potential for the reaction $O + n\,e = R$, the f's are the activity coefficients (see Section 2–5), and the C's the concentrations. The subscript $x = 0$ indicates that the f's and C's are taken at the electrode surface. It follows from equation (4–15) that the ratio $(C_O/C_R)_{x=0}$ is determined by the potential E, and the current-potential

relationship is obtained by expressing this ratio in terms of the current.[12]
The current is [see equation (4–11)]

$$\bar{\imath} = 607 n m^{2/3} \tau^{1/6} D_O^{1/2} [C^0 - (C_O)_{x=0}]$$

$$= \bar{\imath}_d - 607 n m^{2/3} \tau^{1/6} D_O^{1/2} [(C_O)_{x=0}], \tag{4–16}$$

and

$$\bar{\imath} = 607 n m^{2/3} \tau^{1/6} D_R^{1/2} [(C_R)_{x=0}], \tag{4–17}$$

where the D's are the diffusion coefficients of substances O and R. Equations (4–16) and (4–17) can be derived,[13] but we shall rest content to verify that they are valid in three simple cases. When $(C_O)_{x=0} = C^0$ substance O is not consumed at the electrode surface, and the current is equal to zero. When $(C_O)_{x=0} = 0$ the diffusion current is observed, and equation (4–16) is identical to (4–11). When $(C_R)_{x=0} = 0$, substance R is not produced at the electrode and the current according to equation (4–17) is equal to zero, as it should be.

By deducing $(C_O)_{x=0}$ and $(C_R)_{x=0}$ from equations (4–16) and (4–17) and introducing the resulting values in (4–15), one obtains

$$E = E_{1/2} + \frac{0.0591}{n} \log \frac{\bar{\imath}_d - \bar{\imath}}{\bar{\imath}}, \tag{4–18}$$

where $E_{1/2}$ groups several terms as follows:

$$E_{1/2} = E^0 + \frac{0.0591}{n} \log \frac{f_O D_R^{1/2}}{f_R D_O^{1/2}}. \tag{4–19}$$

Current-potential characteristics, calculated from equation (4–18), are

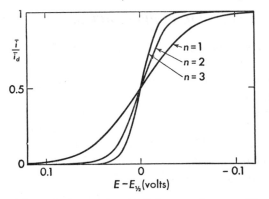

Fig. 30. Theoretical current-potential curves for reversible processes.

shown in Fig. 30 for electrode reactions involving one, two, and three electrons, respectively. Note that the current-potential curves become steeper

[12]J. Heyrovsky and D. Ilkovic, *Collection Czechoslov. Chem. Communs.*, **7**, 198 (1935).

[13]Equations (4–16) and (4–17) were postulated by Heyrovsky and Ilkovic[12], but they can be derived (see the writer's monograph listed in Section 4–13). However, this is a minor point.

as n increases. The shape of current-potential curves can be accounted for qualitatively as follows: In the lower segment of the curve the potential is more positive than the standard potential by at least 0.1 volt. It follows from the Nernst equation that $(C_O/C_R)_{x=0} \gg 1$, i.e., that substance O is virtually not reduced and that there is no current. As the potential becomes more negative, the ratio $(C_O/C_R)_{x=0}$ decreases and the current increases. In the upper plateau $(C_O/C_R)_{x=0} \ll 1$, and molecules or ions of substance O are reduced as soon as they reach the electrode.

The shape of current-potential curves led Heyrovsky to coin the term *wave* to designate polarographic current-potential characteristics. This term has been generally adopted, and the diffusion current is sometimes referred to as *wave height*.

The following properties of waves are immediately deduced from equation (4–18): $i \to 0$ for $E \to +\infty$; $i \to i_d$ for $E \to -\infty$; $E = E_{1/2}$ for $i = i_d/2$. The *half-wave potential* $E_{1/2}$ given by equation (4–19) is simply related to the standard potential E^0 and is characteristic of the couple involved in the electrode reaction. In general, the activity coefficients f_O and f_R are not very different, and the diffusion coefficients have about the same value. The argument of the logarithmic term in equation (4–19) is close to unity, and the half-wave potential is approximately equal to the standard potential. The half-wave potential is also a point of inflection (see problem 5 in Section 4–14).

Prior to the introduction of half-wave potentials, polarographic waves were characterized by their *decomposition potentials* at which the current "begins to increase." This potential depends on the sensitivity of the instrument used in the measurement of the current, and it is no longer utilized. References to decomposition potentials are found in the older literature (before 1935).

It follows from equation (4–18) that a plot of $\log{[(i_d - i)/i]}$ against potential yields a straight line whose reciprocal slope is $0.0591/n$ at 25°. This property is often applied to ascertain that an electrode reaction is reversible, i.e., that the Nernst equation can be applied. The number of electrons n can also be determined from such a plot, but the coulometric method discussed in Chapter 6 is sometimes preferable.

The foregoing considerations are still valid if maximum currents during drop life, instead of average currents, are considered.

b. Reactions Involving Hydrogen Ions. The potential for the reduction of one mole of a substance O, in which m moles of hydrogen ions are consumed, is [see equation (2–12)] at 25°

$$E = E^0 - \frac{0.0591}{n} mpH + \frac{0.0591}{n} \log\left(\frac{f_O C_O}{f_R C_R}\right)_{x=0}. \qquad (4\text{--}20)$$

Equation (4–20) is identical to (4–15) except for the term in pH. Equation (4–18) for the wave is still valid, but the term in pH must now be introduced in equation (4–19), which becomes

$$E_{1/2} = E^0 - \frac{0.0591}{n} mpH + \frac{0.0591}{n} \log \frac{f_O D_R^{1/2}}{f_R D_O^{1/2}}. \qquad (4\text{–}21)$$

A plot of $E_{1/2}$ against pH yields a straight line whose slope is $-0.0591\, m/n$, and the number m can be determined from this slope provided that the reaction is reversible.

c. Reduction with Amalgam Formation. Equation (4–18) is valid for the reduction of a metal with amalgram formation. The reduced species (the metal) diffuses in mercury, and D_R is the diffusion coefficient for this process. The half-wave potential is given by equation (4–19) where the standard potential E_a^0 for the amalgam electrode is now substituted for E^0. It was pointed out in Section 2–7b that E_a^0 may be appreciably different from the standard potential for the metal-metal cation electrode.

d. Reduction of a Complex Ion with Amalgam Formation. Equation (4–18) can also be applied to the reduction of a metal complex ion, but the half-wave potential now depends on the standard potential E_c^0 for the reduction of the complex ion. Potential E_c^0 can be correlated to the standard potential E_a^0 for the reduction of the aquocomplex of the metal, as was shown independently by Lingane[14] and von Stackelberg.[15] Thus,

$$MX_p^{+(n-p)} = M^{+n} + pX^-, \qquad (4\text{–}22)$$

and

$$\frac{a_{M^{+n}} a_{X^-}^p}{a_{MX_p^{+(n-p)}}} = K, \qquad (4\text{–}23)$$

where K is the instability constant of the complex. Furthermore,

$$E = E_a^0 + \frac{0.0591}{n} \log a_{M^{+n}}, \qquad (4\text{–}24)$$

or

$$E = E_c^0 + \frac{0.0591}{n} \log a_{MX_p^{+(n-p)}}. \qquad (4\text{–}25)$$

By introducing the value of $a_{MX_p^{+(n-p)}}$ from equation (4–25) in (4–23), and identifying the resulting value of E with (4–24), one has

$$E_a^0 + \frac{0.0591}{n} \log a_{M^{+n}} = E_c^0 + \frac{0.0591}{n} \log \frac{a_{X^-}^p}{K} + \frac{0.0591}{n} \log a_{M^{+n}}, \qquad (4\text{–}26)$$

or

$$E_c^0 = E_a^0 + \frac{0.0591}{n} \log \frac{K}{a_{X^-}^p}. \qquad (4\text{–}27)$$

[14] J. J. Lingane, *Chem. Revs.*, **29**, 1 (1941).
[15] M. von Stackelberg, *Z. Elektrochem.*, **45**, 466 (1939).

The half-wave potentials are

$$E_{1/2} = E_a^0 + \frac{0.0591}{n} \log \frac{f_{M^{+n}} D_M^{1/2}}{f_M D_{M^{+n}}^{1/2}} \qquad (4\text{--}28)$$

for the reduction of the aquocomplex ion, and

$$(E_{1/2})_c = E_c^0 + \frac{0.0591}{n} \log \frac{f_{MX_p^{+(n-p)}} D_M^{1/2}}{f_M D_{MX_p^{+(n-p)}}^{1/2}} \qquad (4\text{--}29)$$

for the reduction of the complex ion. By introducing the value of E_c^0 from equation (4–27) into (4–29), one deduces

$$(E_{1/2})_c = E_a^0 + \frac{0.0591}{n} \log \frac{K}{a_{X^-}^p} + \frac{0.0591}{n} \log \frac{f_{MX_p^{+(n-p)}} D_M^{1/2}}{f_M D_{MX_p^{+(n-p)}}^{1/2}}, \qquad (4\text{--}30)$$

or in view of equation (4–28),

$$(E_{1/2})_c = E_{1/2} + \frac{0.0591}{n} \log K - p \frac{0.0591}{n} \log C_{X^-}$$
$$+ \frac{0.0591}{n} \log \frac{f_{MX_p^{+(n-p)}}}{f_{M^+} f_{X^-}^p} \frac{D_{M^{+n}}^{1/2}}{D_{MX_p^{+(n-p)}}}, \qquad (4\text{--}31)$$

where C_{X^-} is in moles per liter. The half-wave potential $(E_{1/2})_c$ depends on the instability constant K of the complex and the concentration of complexing agent X^-. A plot of $(E_{1/2})_c$ against the logarithm of the concentration of complexing agent yields a straight line whose slope is $-0.0591\, p/n$. The coordination number p can thus be determined from such a plot provided that the number of electrons n involved in the reduction of the complex ion is known. The instability constant K can be deduced[16] from equation (4–31) when the concentration C_{X^-} and the half-wave potential $E_{1/2}$ for the aquocomplex ion are known. The last term in equation (4–31) can often be neglected since the argument of the logarithm is not very different from unity. One should ascertain before making such calculations that the electrode reaction is reversible.

The difference between the half-wave potentials $E_{1/2}$ and $(E_{1/2})_c$ can be as large as 1 or 2 volts, when K is very small, and the complex ion is very stable. It follows that the position of the wave for the deposition of a metal can be adjusted in the scale of potentials by proper selection of the complexing agent (Table VI and Meites' book listed in Section 4–13). This method of shifting waves is most valuable in applications to analytical chemistry.

e. Stepwise Electrode Reactions and Electrolysis of Mixtures of Several Substances. Stepwise reductions occurring at sufficiently different potentials yield as many consecutive waves as there are steps. For

---

[16]For the case in which several complex ions of comparable stability exist, see D. D. DeFord and D. N. Hume, *J. Am. Chem. Soc.*, **73**, 5321 (1951).

example, the reduction of the ammine complex of cupric ion yields two waves corresponding to the reduction to the $+1$ state and the metal, respectively. The half-wave potentials in this case are -0.24 and -0.50 volt (versus S.C.E.), respectively, in a solution which is $1\,M$ in ammonium hydroxide and ammonium chloride. The electrolysis of a mixture of sub-

TABLE VI

Half-wave Potentials and Diffusion Current Constants for Inorganic Substances[a]

Substance	Supporting Electrolyte	Half-wave Potential Volts versus S.C.E.	Diffusion Current Constant[b]
Ba^{++}	$0.1\,M$ $N(CH_3)_4Cl$	-1.94	3.57
Bi^{+++}	$0.5\,M$ H_2SO_4	-0.04	
BrO_3^-	$0.1\,M$ KOH	-1.85	
Cd^{++}	$1\,M$ HNO_3	-0.59	3.06
	$0.1\,M$ KCl	-0.64	3.51
	$1\,M$ KI	-0.74	
	$1\,M$ KCN	-1.18	
Co^{++}	$0.1\,M$ KCl	-1.20	
Cr^{+++}	$0.1\,M$ KCl	-0.91 (1st wave)	
		-1.47 (2nd wave)	
CrO_4^{--}	$1\,M$ NaOH	-0.85	
Cu^{++}	$0.1\,M$ KCl	0.04	3.23
	$1\,M$ NH_4OH $+$ $1\,M$ NH_4Cl	-0.24 (1st wave)	3.75 (for
		-0.50 (2nd wave)	double wave)
Fe^{++}	$0.1\,M$ KCl	-1.3	
Fe^{+++}	$0.5\,M$ tartrate, pH 9.4	-1.20 (1st wave)	
		-1.73 (2nd wave)	
IO_3^-	$0.1\,M$ $HClO_4$	-0.04	
	$0.1\,M$ KOH	-1.21	
K^+	$0.1\,M$ $N(CH_3)_4OH$	-2.10	1.69
Li^+	$0.1\,M$ $N(CH_3)_4OH$	-2.31	1.16
Mn^{++}	$1\,M$ KCl	-1.51	
Na^+	$0.1\,M$ $N(CH_3)_4Cl$	-2.07	1.40
Ni^{++}	$1\,M$ KCl	-1.1	
	$1\,M$ KCNS	-0.70	
	$1\,M$ KCN	-1.36	
O_2	buffer of any pH	-0.1 (1st wave)	12 (for
		-0.9 (2nd wave)	double wave)
Pb^{++}	$1\,M$ HNO_3	-0.40	3.67
	$1\,M$ NaOH	-0.75	3.39
	$0.5\,M$ tartrate $+$ $0.1\,M$ NaOH	-0.75	2.39
Sb^{+++}	$1\,M$ HCl	-0.15	
Sn^{++}	$1\,M$ HCl	-0.47	4.07
Zn^{++}	$0.1\,M$ KCl	-0.99	3.42
	$1\,M$ NaOH	-1.53	3.14
	$2\,M$ NH_4OH $+$ $1\,M$ NH_4Cl	-1.33	3.82

[a]From I. M. Kolthoff and J. J. Lingane, *Polarography*, 2nd ed., Interscience, New York, 1952.
[b]In units $\mu a.mg^{-2/3}\ sec^{1/2}\ millimol^{-1}\ lit.$

stances also yields consecutive waves provided that each half-wave potential differs by at least 0.2 or 0.3 volt form the others. Diffusion currents in stepwise or consecutive reductions (or oxidations) are additive; i.e., each wave can be studied independently of the others.

f. Anodic Processes. The foregoing treatment can be applied to anodic waves obtained for electrode reactions in which the products of electrolysis are soluble. Anodic waves are also observed with anions whose mercurous salts are insoluble (chloride, sulfide, etc.). The treatment of such waves may be taken up as exercise (see problem 7 in Section 4-14).

4-5. CURRENT-POTENTIAL CURVES: IRREVERSIBLE PROCESSES

It was assumed in the preceding section that the Nernst equation can be applied under the conditions prevailing in polarography although this equation is, in principle, valid only when no current flows through the cell. This extension of the Nernst equation is justified for a large number of electrode reactions; for instance, in the reduction of the cations of thallium, lead, cadmium, etc. However, the Nernst equation cannot be applied in the treatment of numerous polarographic current-potential curves, which are said to be *irreversible*. Irreversible waves are very often obtained in the electrolysis of organic substances, but they are also encountered in inorganic chemistry; for example, in the reduction of divalent nickel and cobalt, hydrogen peroxide, and iodate ion. Little was done about the interpretation of irreversible waves until about 1950, but these waves can now be interpreted just as well as reversible waves. The ideas were developed almost simultaneously by several investigators (Evans, Eyring, Kambara and Tachi, Smutek, Tanaka, and the writer)[17] for diffusion toward a plane electrode, and the calculations for the dropping mercury electrode were made by Koutecky.[18]

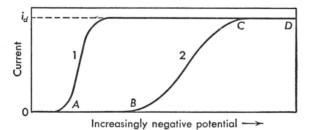

Fig. 31. Reversible (curve 1) versus irreversible (curve 2) waves.

The difference between reversible and irreversible waves is shown qualitatively in Fig. 31. Curve 1 is the wave which would have been obtained

---

[17]For a detailed treatment see reference in Section 4-13.
[18]J. Koutecky, *Chem. Listy,* **47,** 323 (1953); *Collection Czechoslov. Chem. Communs.,* **18,** 597 (1953).

had the Nernst equation been applicable, and curve 2 is the experimental wave. Because of irreversibility, wave 2 is markedly shifted (sometimes by 1 volt or more) toward more negative potentials with respect to curve 1 in the case of a reduction. The shift would have been in the other direction, i.e, toward more positive potentials, for an oxidation. It is also observed that irreversible waves are flatter than reversible ones. The diffusion current, however, obeys the Ilkovic equation.

The degree of irreversibility of the electrode reaction can be characterized by the *overvoltage* defined as follows:

$$\text{Overvoltage} = \left\{ \begin{array}{l} \text{potential at which the re-} \\ \text{action occurs under given} \\ \text{conditions} \end{array} \right\} - \left\{ \begin{array}{l} \text{potential calculated from} \\ \text{the Nernst equation for} \\ \text{the same experimental} \\ \text{conditions} \end{array} \right\}.$$

Since the overvoltage depends on the conditions of electrolysis, and particularly on the current (see below), it is essential to indicate experimental details in reporting overvoltage values. The sign preceding the overvoltage if often dropped, and absolute values are quoted.

The phenomena accounting for differences between reversible and irreversible waves can be explained as follows. The current in the lower segment AB of wave 2 is very small in comparison with the diffusion current because the electrode reaction virtually does not occur. Molecules or ions of substance O reacting at the electrode must overcome an energy barrier, which is so high at potentials corresponding to segment AB that there is practically no reaction at the electrode. The number of moles of a substance O reduced per square centimeter at the electrode and per unit of time is[19] $k(C_O)_{x=0}$ where k is a *rate constant* whose value depends on the height of the energy barrier to be overcome by molecules or ions of substance O. The rate constant k increases when the potential is made more negative (in the case of a reduction) because electrical energy is supplied to the reacting species. It is found experimentally, and it can be shown on theoretical grounds that k is an exponential function of potential. Thus, one has at 25°

$$k = k^0 e^{-2.303\beta E/0.0591}, \qquad (4\text{--}32)$$

where E is the potential in volts referred to the normal hydrogen electrode, k^0 is the value of k when $E = 0$, and β is a parameter which is characteristic of the electrode reaction for given conditions of electrolysis. The value of β is between 0 and 1 for many electrode reactions.[20] Thus, irreversible electrode reactions can be characterized by two parameters k^0 and β,

[19]The backward reaction is neglected here for the sake of simplicity, but it could be taken into account.

[20]The parameter β is the product of the transfer coefficient by the number of electrons involved in the activation step.

while only one parameter (the standard potential) is needed for reversible reactions.

The current for an electrode of A square centimeters is proportional to the rate of reduction of substance O and to the charge involved in the reduction of one mole of O. Thus,

$$i = nFAk(C_O)_{x=0},\qquad(4\text{--}33)$$

where n is the number of electrons involved in the reduction of one molecule or ion of substance O, and F is the faraday. The quantity of electricity nF is consumed per mole of substance O. The current is in view of equation (4–32)

$$i = nFA(C_O)_{x=0}k^0 e^{-2.303\beta E/0.0591}.\qquad(4\text{--}34)$$

When the potential is made more negative, the current increases (segment BC in Fig. 31) and the concentration $(C_O)_{x=0}$ decreases because of consumption of substance O. The quantity $k^0 \exp(-2.303\beta E/0.0591)$ is very large in the upper plateau of the wave (segment CD, Fig. 34), and molecules or ions of O are thus reduced "as soon" as they reached the electrode. These are the conditions we postulated in the treatment leading to the Ilkovic equation. When E tends to $-\infty$, $(C_O)_{x=0}$ approaches zero, and the current given by equation (4–34) becomes of the form $0 \times \infty$. It can be shown that equation (4–34) then reduces to the Ilkovic equation.

The complete calculation of the current involves the derivation of concentration $(C_O)_{x=0}$ for any point along the wave, but we shall not go into this matter. Examples of waves corresponding to the same value of k^0, but to different values of β, are shown in Fig. 32. It is seen that waves be-

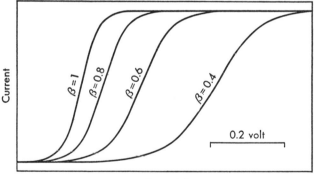

Fig. 32. Examples of calculated irreversible waves for different values of β and the same value of k^0.

come flatter as the parameter β decreases, and that irreversible waves may spread over a rather wide range of potentials (compare with Fig. 30).

The parameters k^0 and β, which characterize the electrode reaction can be deduced from experimental waves as indicated in problem 8 of Section 4–14.

The half-wave potential of irreversible waves is characteristic of the substance being electrolyzed, but is much more negative (perhaps 1 volt or more) for cathodic reactions—and more positive for anodic processes— than the standard potential for the electrode reaction. This contrasts irreversible waves with reversible ones for which half-wave and standard potentials are virtually the same.

We considered only processes whose rate constant can be expressed by equation (4–32). This is the case when only one step in the over-all reaction controls the rate of the electrode process, but more involved processes may be encountered, especially with organic substances.

4–6. KINETIC AND CATALYTIC PROCESSES

The substance reacting at the electrode in the processes considered thus far is available in solution in a reducible or oxidizable form. There are cases, however, in which the substance reacting at the electrode is supplied by a chemical process preceding the electrochemical step. Consider for instance the reduction of formaldehyde which exists in two forms in aqueous solution: the aldehyde $HCHO$ and the hydrated form $CH_2(OH)_2$. The latter is in great excess and is not reducible, while the aldehyde form is reduced according to the reaction

$$HCHO + 2H^+ + 2e = CH_3OH.$$

As the reduction proceeds, the aldehyde form is consumed at the electrode surface, and the hydrated form is transformed into $HCHO$ by the reaction

$$CH_2(OH)_2 \longrightarrow HCHO + H_2O.$$

If the potential of the dropping mercury electrode is adjusted at a value at which molecules of the aldehyde form are reduced as rapidly as they reach the electrode, the current is controlled by diffusion of the species $HCHO$ and $CH_2(OH)_2$ and by the rate of the dehydration reaction. A wave is observed for such a *kinetic process*, but the wave height or limiting current does not obey the Ilkovic equation. Note that one refers to the wave heights as a *limiting current* and not as a diffusion current because there is mixed control by diffusion and a chemical reaction.

When the chemical reaction preceding the electron chemical step is sluggish, the kinetic limiting current is much smaller than the diffusion current which would be observed under the same conditions if the species in solution had not to undergo a chemical transformation prior to reduction or oxidation. Under these conditions, there is virtually no concentration polarization during drop life, and the current is proportional to the area of the drop. This area is proportional to $m^{2/3}\tau^{2/3}$, and since $m = m_0H$ and $\tau = \tau_0/H$, [see equations (4–12) and (4–13)], kinetic limiting currents are independent of the head of mercury. This is in contrast with diffusion currents which are proportional to the square root of the head of mercury (Section 4–3b). An intermediate behavior between these two extreme cases is observed when the chemical step is sufficiently fast, but not rapid enough to have pure diffusion control. The limiting current in the intermediate case is a complex function of the head of mercury.

The treatment of kinetic currents was developed by Brdicka and coworkers in Prague in the late 1940's. This material is beyond the scope of this text, and the reader is referred to some of books in Section 4–13.

Limiting currents depending on the rate of a chemical reaction are also encountered with *catalytic processes*, in which the substance being electrolyzed is partially regenerated by a chemical reaction. Consider for instance the reduction of ferric ion in presence of hydrogen peroxide. This reduction can be carried out at the dropping mercury electrode at potentials at which hydrogen peroxide is virtually not reduced electrolytically on account of marked irreversibility. Ferrous ions resulting from the reduction of ferric ions are reoxidized by hydrogen peroxide:

$$2\,Fe^{+++} + 2e = 2\,Fe^{++}$$

$$2\,Fe^{++} + H_2O_2 + 2H^+ = 2\,Fe^{+++} + 2H_2O.$$

The limiting current for the reduction of ferric ions is thus enhanced because of regeneration of ferric ions by oxidation of ferrous ions by hydrogen peroxide. The Ilkovic equation is not applicable under such conditions. Theoretical interpretation of limiting currents has been reported, and references will be made to the specialized literature (Section 4–13).

Kinetic and catalytic processes are rare in comparison with reversible and irreversible processes without chemical kinetic complications, and the Ilkovic equation can thus be applied to the great majority of electrode reactions.

4–7. RESIDUAL CURRENT—GRAPHIC DETERMINATION OF DIFFUSION CURRENTS

It was assumed so far that the current through the cell is equal to zero when no electrode reaction takes place. This is a simplification, since there is a *residual current* even when no substance is reduced or oxidized at the dropping mercury electrode. The cause of the residual current can be explained as follows:

A *double layer* is built up at the interface electrode-solution as a result of electrostatic interaction and adsorption effects. If the mercury drop is positive with respect to the solution, anions are attracted and cations are repelled, and *vice versa*. The interface can be compared to a capacitor of large capacity (perhaps 20 to 50 mμF per square centimeter of electrode). The capacity of a capacitor with two parallel plates is proportional to the area of the plates, and since the area of the mercury drop increases during its growth, the capacity of the double layer also increases continuously during drop life. This capacity c is, in view of equation (4–8),

$$c = pc_0t^{2/3}, \tag{4-35}$$

where c_0 is the capacity for an electrode of 1 sq cm, and p represents the quantity $4\pi m^{2/3}(3/4\pi d)^{2/3}$.

The capacity c must be kept charged at the difference of potential existing between electrode and solution, and one has by definition of a capacity,

$$q = c(E - E_m), \tag{4-36}$$

where q is the quantity of electricity involved in the charge of the capacitor of capacity c, E_m is the potential at which $q = 0$, and E is the potential at which q is expressed. Potentials E_m and E are measured with respect to some reference electrode; for example, the normal hydrogen electrode. It follows from equation (4–36) that the electrode has a positive charge when $E > E_m$. By differentiation of equation (4–36) with respect to time, there results the *capacity current*

$$i_c = \frac{dq}{dt} = \frac{dc}{dt}(E - E_m) + c\frac{dE}{dt}. \tag{4-37}$$

The potential of the dropping mercury electrode is essentially constant during drop life, and the term in dE/dt in equation (4–37) can be dropped. By combining the resulting simplified equation with (4–35), one obtains

$$i_c = \frac{2pc_0}{3t^{1/3}}(E - E_m) \tag{4-38}$$

for the instantaneous capacity current and

$$\bar{i}_c = \frac{pc_0(E - E_m)}{\tau^{1/3}} \tag{4-39}$$

for the average capacity current during drop life.[21] There, $\bar{i}_c$ is in amperes, c_0 in farads cm^{-2}, τ in seconds, $(E - E_m)$ in volts, and p is calculated by expressing m in units gram sec^{-1} and d in gram cm^{-3}.

Equation (4–39) shows that the current varies linearly with the potential E and the capacity c_0. The capacity c_0 also varies with E, and

$$^{21}\bar{i}_c\tau = \int_0^\tau i_c\,dt = \frac{2pc_0(E - E_m)}{3}\int_0^\tau t^{-1/3}dt = pc_0(E - E_m)\left[t^{2/3}\right]_0^\tau = pc_0(E - E_m)\tau^{2/3}.$$

consequently the dependence of i_c on potential is quite complex. At any rate, the capacity current is equal to zero at $E = E_m$, where there is no charge on the electrode (Fig. 33). Potential E_m is of the order of -0.25 to -0.35 volt (versus N.H. E.) for many electrolytes.[22]

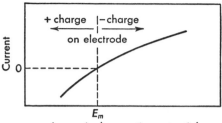

Experimental currents measured with the supporting electrolyte alone are often larger than the value predicted from equation (4–39) because of the presence in solution of reducible (or oxidizable) impurities. The resulting *residual current* is thus equal to the sum of the capacity current and the diffusion currents of the impurities in the supporting electrolyte.

Fig. 33. Variations of average capacity current with potential.

The order of magnitude of the average capacity current can be judged from the following example: for $c_0 = 20$ μF cm^{-2}, $m = 10^{-3}$ gram sec^{-3}, $\tau = 4$ sec, $E - E_m = 1$ volt, one has $\bar{\iota}_c = 0.054$ μA. The average diffusion current calculated from equation (4–11) for the same value of m and τ is $2.40 \times C^0$ μA, C^0 being the bulk concentration of electrolyzed substance in millimoles per liter. If $C^0 = 10^{-2}$ millimol lit^{-1}, i.e., 10^{-5} mol lit^{-1}, the average diffusion current, which is equal to 0.024 μA, is smaller than the above calculated capacity current. The resulting wave is then so distorted that the precise determination of the diffusion current is virtually impossible. *This is why conventional polarography cannot be easily applied to determinations of concentrations below 10^{-5} M.* It is true that the capacity current can be compensated, but serious difficulties are encountered because i_c is not a simple function of the electrode potential [dependence of c_0 on potential; see equation (4–39)].

Residual currents are not negligible in comparison with diffusion currents, even with concentrations of electrolyzed substance of the order of 10^{-3} M; and experimental waves are distorted, as indicated with some exaggeration in Fig. 34. In addition to the residual current, variations of $m^{2/3}\tau^{1/6}$ with potential in the upper plateau of the wave also cause a distortion of the wave (see Section 4-3 c). Rather empirical graphic methods have been devised for the analysis of waves, and, among these the two methods indicated in Fig. 33 are quite satisfactory. The graphic construction on the left is applied when the wave is not markedly distorted. The lines AC and GK are traced perpendicularly to the abscissa axis, and points B and H are determined from the conditions $AB = BC$ and $GH = HK$.

[22]Currents in Fig. 33 are plotted according to the polarographic convention which prescribes that cathodic currents are positive. Note that $i_c < 0$ for $E < E_m$.

Line BH is traced, and the intersection $E_{1/2}$ with the wave is marked. The vertical line through $E_{1/2}$ is traced, and FD is taken as the diffusion current. The construction is based on the property of the half-wave potential

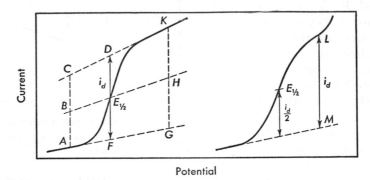

Fig. 34.   Two graphic methods for the determination of diffusion currents.

to be the abscissa at which $\bar{\imath} = \bar{\imath}_d/2$. This method yields diffusion currents which are obviously too low when the wave is very much distorted, as in Fig. 34 right. This case is encountered when two consecutive waves are so close that the upper plateau of the first one is poorly defined. One then determines the point of inflection L in the upper plateau and takes the vertical segment ML as diffusion current. This procedure yields only approximate results, which nevertheless are reproducible if the same potential is selected for point L.

Because of the uncertainty resulting from their graphic determination, half-wave potentials generally cannot be quoted with more than two decimals. However, shifts in the half-wave potential for a given substance with variation of the electrolysis conditions (complex formation, variation of head of mercury, etc.) often can be determined up to the millivolt.

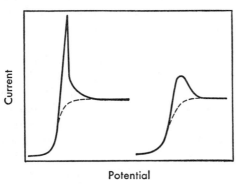

Fig. 35.   Types of maxima.

4-8. MAXIMA

It is observed that many waves exhibit a maximum which may be either a very sharp peak or a rounded hump (Fig. 35). Maxima are observed, whether the wave is reversible or irreversible. It is also found that a trace of an adsorbable substance, such as gelatin or a dye, *generally* removes the maximum. Gelatin at a concentration from 0.001 to 0.01

per cent is very satisfactory as a *maximum suppressor* in many cases. Organic substances, such as dyes, also suppress maxima. An excess of maximum suppressor should be avoided because of the resulting distortion of waves (particularly with gelatin), the increase in viscosity, and the concomitant decrease in diffusion current [term in $D_0^{1/2}$ in equation (4–11)].

The interpretation of maxima is involved and not within the province of this book. A detailed review will be found in the monograph of Kolthoff and Lingane, listed in Section 4–13. See also problem 25 in Section 4–14C.

4-9. VOLTAMMETRY WITH A ROTATED ELECTRODE OR STATIONARY ELECTRODE IN STIRRED SOLUTION

The dropping mercury electrode cannot be utilized at markedly positive potentials because of the oxidation of mercury. One calculates from the Nernst equation that the potential of a mercury electrode in a $10^{-6} M$ solution of mercurous ions is 0.61 volt ($E^0 = 0.789$ volt; see Table I). When mercury is made more positive than 0.61 volt, the concentration of mercurous ions becomes larger than $10^{-6} M$, i.e., mercury is oxidized at an appreciable rate. Mercury therefore cannot be utilized at potentials more positive than 0.5 to 0.6 volt (versus N.H.E.). This limit can be lowered by several tenths of a volt in presence of complexing agents or anions whose mercurous salts are insoluble.

Other metallic electrodes are then utilized; platinum, which is very inert, is generally selected. Stationary electrodes in unstirred solution are not practical because the current varies continuously during electrolysis (Section 4–2), and either the solution is stirred or the electrode is rotated. The substance being electrolyzed is brought at the electrode at a constant rate by convective transfer, and a steady current is obtained.

The theoretical interpretation of current-potential curves is difficult because hydrodynamic considerations are involved, but the simple model proposed by Nernst may be used. It is assumed that the concentration of electrolyzed species does not vary up to a distance δ from the electrode and that diffusion is the only mode of mass transfer in the *diffusion layer* of thickness δ (Fig. 36). The curve concentration-distance from the electrode thus is re-

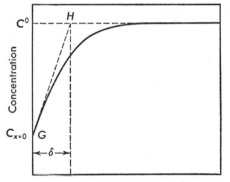

Fig. 36. Definition of diffusion layer thickness.

placed by two segments of straight lines. The gradient of concentration (see definition in Section 4–2) is

$$\frac{C^0 - C_{x=0}}{\delta}$$

where C^0 is the bulk concentration of the substance being electrolyzed and $C_{x=0}$ the concentration of this substance at the electrode surface. The rate of diffusion per unit area is now $D(C^0 - C_{x=0})/\delta$, and the current (see treatment in Section 4–2) is

$$i = \frac{nFAD(C^0 - C_{x=0})}{\delta}. \qquad (4\text{--}40)$$

When the potential is sufficiently negative (reduction) or positive (oxidation), the concentration of the substance being electrolyzed is equal to zero at the electrode surface, and a *limiting current*

$$i_l = \frac{nFADC^0}{\delta}, \qquad (4\text{--}41)$$

proportional to the concentration of electrolyzed substance, is observed. We refer here to a limiting current and not to a diffusion current because diffusion is not the sole mode of mass transfer. It should be emphasized that we have not said anything about the diffusion layer thickness δ which may implicitly contain various parameters characteristic of the conditions of electrolysis (diffusion coefficient D, viscosity, etc.). It follows from equation (4–41) that i_l is proportional to the concentration C^0. This conclusion is verified experimentally.

It is possible to develop a detailed theory of current-potential curves, and it can be shown that the equation

$$E = E_{1/2} + \frac{0.0591}{n} \log \frac{i_l - i}{i}, \qquad (4\text{--}42)$$

with

$$E_{1/2} = E^0 + \frac{0.0591}{n} \log \frac{f_O D_R \delta_O}{f_R D_O \delta_R}, \qquad (4\text{--}43)$$

holds at 25° for reversible processes involving the reaction $O + n\,\mathrm{e} = R$, O and R being soluble. The notations in equation (4–43) are: E^0, standard potential; the f's, activity coefficients; the D's, diffusion coefficients; and the δ's, the diffusion layer thicknesses. Note that equation (4–42) has the same form as the corresponding relationship [equation (4–18)] for a reversible polarographic wave.

The foregoing treatment is valid whether a stationary electrode in a stirred solution or a rotated electrode is utilized. Stationary electrodes have one disadvantage: The efficiency of stirring varies somewhat with the position of the electrode in the electrolysis cell, and the current changes accordingly. Rotated electrodes do not have this disadvantage. The rotated electrode devised by Laitinen and Kolthoff[23] is a platinum wire protruding a few millimeters from the wall of a glass tube, which rotates at constant speed [600 rpm, for example, (Fig. 37)]. Electrical contact is obtained by filling the bottom of the tube with mercury and by immersing a platinum wire in it. The speed of the motor rotating the electrode should be perfectly constant so that the same conditions of mass transfer prevail in comparative experiments. Reproducible current-potential curves are obtained, provided that the electrode is kept clean and the same cleaning procedure is followed in comparative measurements.

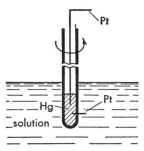

Fig. 37. A rotated platinum electrode.

The overvoltage for hydrogen evolution is much smaller for platinum than for mercury, and the value of the equilibrium potential for the reaction $2H^+ + 2e = H_2$ is practically the most negative potential up to which platinum electrodes can be utilized. The range of positive potentials which can be explored is limited by evolution of oxygen (see Section 2–8b), but fortunately this reaction involves an overvoltage of several tenths of a volt even at very low current densities. Electrode reactions occurring at potentials as positive as 1 volt (*versus* S.C.E.) can be studied with the platinum electrode.

Other types of electrodes with convective transfer (mercury jet, rotated mercury electrode, vibrating electrodes) have been devised; reference is made to the specialized literature (Section 4–13).

4-10. EXPERIMENTAL METHODS

a. Preparation of Solution. The solution being electrolyzed must contain a large excess of supporting electrolyte (see Section 4–1) and, in general, a maximum suppressor. The concentration of supporting electrolyte is very often between 0.1 and 1 M, and the concentration of maximum suppressor comprises between 0.001 and 0.01 per cent. The supporting electrolyte should not interfere with the electrode reaction, and salts which are difficult to reduce or to oxidize are utilized for cathodic (or anodic) processes. Sodium and potassium salts are very often selected because these metals are not deposited on mercury at an appreciable rate until a potential of about -1.8 to -1.9 volts (versus S.C.E.) is reached (Table VI). Slightly more negative potentials, i.e., up to about -2.0 volts (versus S.C.E.), can be explored with lithium salts. Tetraalkylammonium salts—particularly tetramethylammonium bromide $N(CH_3)_4Br$—are used

[23]H. A. Laitinen and I. M. Kolthoff, *J. Phys. Chem.*, **45**, 1079 (1941).

in the electrolysis of difficultly reducible organic substances, and potentials up to about -2.6 volts (*versus* S.C.E.) can be studied. Salts of this type with a rather large alkyl group (tetrabutylammonium iodide, for instance) are often used when the electrolysis is carried out in a mixture of water and an organic solvent.

Whenever the electrode reaction involves hydrogen ions it is generally advisable to buffer the supporting electrolyte. Hydrogen ions are consumed or liberated in the immediate vicinity of the mercury drop, and a local variation of pH of the order of a few pH units at the electrode surface may result in unbuffered electrolytes. The interpretation of waves is unnecessarily complicated by poor buffering capacity.

Hydrogen ions are reduced at the dropping mercury electrode in a very irreversible process: the half-wave potential for 10^{-3} M hydrochloric acid in 0.1 M potassium chloride is -1.58 volts (*versus* S.C.E.) at 25°, while the equilibrium potential for the recation $2H^+ + 2e = H_2$ for $a_{H^+} = 10^{-3}$ and $p_{H_2} = 1$ atm is approximately -0.43 volt against the saturated calomel electrode. Because of reduction of hydrogen ions, the range of potentials which can be explored in acid solution does not extend beyond -1.3 volts (versus S.C.E.) in acid solution. In neutral or alkaline solutions the concentration of hydrogen ion is so low that the discharge of this ion does not interfere.[24]

Organic solvents are utilized in the analysis of organic substances insoluble in water. Dioxane-water mixtures are often used because dioxane is miscible with water in all proportions. Dioxane must be redistilled to remove reducible impurities. A 0.1 M solution of lithium chloride in a 1:1 mixture of benzene and methanol is also very useful. Ethyl ether is not utilized because it is readily oxidized by air with formation of polarographically reducible peroxides.

Dissolved oxygen must be removed from the analyzed solution when the range of electrode potentials being explored extends beyond 0 volt (*versus* S.C.E.) toward negative potentials. Oxygen is reduced at the dropping mercury electrode in two steps involving the formation of hydrogen peroxide and water, respectively. The corresponding half-wave potentials are approximately -0.1 and -1 volt (versus S.C.E.), and consequently the two oxygen waves cover a major fraction of the range of potentials which can be explored. Air saturated solutions contain about 8 ppm of oxygen (approximately 0.25 millimolar) at room temperature. This is precisely the order of magnitude of the concentrations most frequently determined by polarography, and the removal of oxygen is thus essential.

Since the solubility of oxygen is proportional to the partial pressure of this gas above solution (Henry's law), oxygen can be removed from solu-

---

[24]However, water supplies hydrogen ions as this ion is consumed at the electrode, but the rate of ionization of water is too low to cause any serious interference.

tion by bubbling another gas (generally nitrogen) through the solution. The rate of removal of oxygen increases with the area of contact between the gaseous and liquid phases, and the use of a gas disperser (tube closed by a fritted glass plate) speeds up oxygen removal. Bubbling of nitrogen for about 10 min, or even a shorter time with a gas disperser, suffices to eliminate almost completely the dissolved oxygen from aqueous solutions. Organic solvents are more difficult to free from oxygen because this gas is often more soluble in them than in water. Very pure nitrogen is commercially available, and no further purification of the gas is needed in most cases.

Oxygen may be removed also by chemical means; for example, by adding to the solution about a decigram of sodium sulfite per 10 ml of solution. Sulfite ion is rapidly oxidized (10 min or less) to sulfate by oxygen. This method cannot be applied below pH 7 because sulfite yields a wave in acid solution.

b. Cells. Since the potential of the polarized electrode is deduced from the voltage across the cell and the potential of the unpolarized electrode, the latter potential must remain constant, regardless of the current through the cell. This result is achieved by avoiding concentration polarization at the unpolarized electrode. The substances involved in the reaction occurring at this electrode must be present at a sufficiently high concentration, and the electrode area must be much larger (10 to 100 times) than for the polarized electrode. A saturated calomel electrode with a mercury pool having a diameter of 1 to 2 cm is generally satisfactory at the current intensities utilized in polarography and voltammetry. When a saturated calomel electrode is used as anode, mercury is oxidized to mercurous ions, and the activity of Hg_2^{++} is automatically controlled by common ion effect (precipitation of Hg_2Cl_2, large excess of KCl). When the electrode functions as a cathode, mercurous ions are reduced. In general, the use of calomel electrodes available from pH meter manufacturers is not recommended in polarography for two reasons: (1) the electrode area is rather small, and there is danger of concentration polarization; (2) the resistance of these electrodes is too high (see description in Section 2–9), and the ohmic drop is rather high, perhaps 0.1 volt. As a final comment, it should be remembered that an electrode may be virtually unpolarized, but that there is no unpolarizable electrode. Danger of polarization increases with the current through the cell.

Many types of cells have been designed, as one can ascertain by consulting the specialized literature (reference in Section 4–13). Three typical cells are shown in Fig. 38. The unpolarized electrode in cell A is the mercury pool. Mercury is oxidized to Hg(I), and unless an anion is present whose mercurous salt is sparingly soluble, the potential of the mercury pool varies during electrolysis because of the production of mercurous ions. The use of cell *A* is thus restricted to cases in which the supporting electrolyte is a chloride, bromide, etc. Nitrogen can be bubbled through the

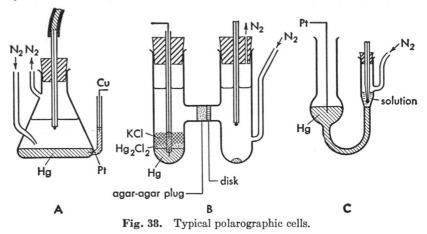

Fig. 38. Typical polarographic cells.

solution prior to electrolysis. *No gas should be passed during determination of a current-potential curve* because stirring of the solution would interfere with diffusion at the dropping mercury electrode. Quite obviously, cell *A* cannot be utilized when the solution to be analyzed oxidizes mercury.

The necessity of utilizing a supporting electrolyte whose anion forms an insoluble mercurous salt is avoided in the H-cell of Fig. 38B. The unpolarized electrode is a saturated calomel electrode. Mixing of the solution being electrolyzed with the potassium chloride solution of the saturated calomel is virtually prevented by a fritted glass disk and an agar-agar plug (see preparation in Section 2–9). This cell is also very useful in electrolysis with rotated electrodes. Limiting currents with the latter type of electrode are much larger than those observed with the dropping mercury electrode, and depletion of the substance being electrolyzed may be pronounced when the volume of solution is too small (less than 10 ml) and the electrolysis is prolonged (more than perhaps 10 to 20 min.).

Cell *C* of Fig. 38 is useful in electrolysis of small volumes of solution, i.e., 1 ml or even less. The unpolarized electrode is either the mercury pool or a calomel electrode with a fine tip immersed in solution. If the electrolysis is prolonged beyond a few minutes, depletion of the substance being electrolyzed is noticeable because of the small volume of solution.

c. Determination of Current-Potential Curves. Current-potential curves may be determined either "manually," by plotting them point by point, or automatically, by using a recording instrument. Manual instruments (Aminco, Fisher, Sargent in the United States) include two essential components: the source of variable voltage and the current measuring device. The voltage applied to the cell is adjusted by means of a potentiometer which is calibrated by measuring the voltage across its terminals with a voltmeter (Fig. 39) or by means of a standard cell, as indicated in Sec-

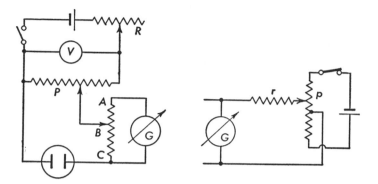

Fig. 39. Schematic diagram of manual polarograph (left) and compensation circuit (right).

tion 2–10b. The latter method is, of course, more precise than the former, but the method involving direct reading on a voltmeter is adequate in many analytical applications in which potentials need not be known with high accuracy. The voltage across the potentiometer is adjusted with resistance R. The current through the cell is read on the scale of galvanometer G, whose sensitivity is adjusted by means of an Ayrton shunt. The function tion of this shunt can be discussed as follows.

The current through the cell i_c is the sum of the current i_{BC} through BC and the current i_g through the galvanometer. Thus

$$i_c = i_{BC} + i_g. \tag{4–44}$$

In view of Ohm's law, one also has

$$i_{BC}R_{BC} = i_g(R_{AB} + R_g), \tag{4–45}$$

where R_g is the resistance of the galvanometer. By combining equations (4–44) and (4 15), one deduces

$$i_g = i_c \frac{R_{BC}}{R_{AB} + R_{BC} + R_g}. \tag{4–46}$$

Since the sum $R_{AB} + R_{BC} + R_g$ has a fixed value for a given shunt and galvanometer, the fraction i_g of the current i_c can be adjusted by changing R_{BC}. Shunts are generally provided with discrete changes in sensitivity, and the ratio i_c/i_g may have the following values: 1, 2, 5, 10, 20, 50, 100, 500, 1000.

Instead of using a galvanometer one can determine currents by measuring the ohmic drop in a calibrated resistance with a potentiometer or a vacuum-tube voltmeter.

Manual polarographs generally have a compensation circuit (Fig. 39, right) for bringing the galvanometer reading to any desired value. The galvanometer in series with a large resistance r (10^5 ohms) is connected to a potentiometer p which enables one to adjust the compensation current. The sensitivity of the galvanometer is virtually not affected by the compensation circuit because resistance r is larger than the galvanometer resistance by several orders of magnitude. Compensation is useful in the analysis of multicomponent systems. Consider a mixture of two substances 1 and 2, in which 1 is predominant, and assume that substance 2 is reduced at more cathodic potentials than 1. Under these conditions the diffusion current for substance 2 cannot be determined accurately without compensation, but the accuracy is improved if the diffusion current for substance 1 is compensated and the galvanometer sensitivity increased. Compensation is not so useful as it might appear, because the compensating current is constant, while the current to be compensated varies continuously on account of the periodic formation of mercury drops. As a result, the galvanometer needle oscillates wildly when its sensitivity is increased. It is often necessary to separate the more easily reducible substance by chemical (precipitation, extraction) or electrochemical (see Chapter 6) methods, or to shift wave 1 to more negative potentials than wave 2 by change in the conditions of electrolysis (complexes, pH change, etc.).

Current-voltage curves obtained by the above method can be identified with current-potential curves, provided that the ohmic drop in the cell and galvanometer does not exceed a few millivolts. Otherwise, a correction must be made. This is a simple matter since the current is known and the resistance of the circuit can easily be measured; for instance, with a bridge (see Chapter 7).

Instead of determining a complete current-potential curve, one can deduce the diffusion current from the current readings $\bar{\imath}_1$ and $\bar{\imath}_2$ at two preselected potentials E_1 and E_2. The diffusion current is approximately equal to the difference $\bar{\imath}_2 - \bar{\imath}_1$, but an error is made because the residual current is not the same at E_1 and E_2. The accuracy of this procedure is sometimes adequate in routine analysis.

Recording instruments are of two types: photographic polarographs and pen-and-ink recorders. Photographic instruments based on the first polarograph devised by Heyrovsky and Shikata have been used for many years, but reliable instruments with pen-and-ink recorder have become available and are preferred nowadays. The principle of the photographic recording polarograph is as follows: The sliding contact of potentiometer P in Fig. 39 is geared to a motor and a drum in such a manner that the radial displacement of the drum is proportional to the voltage applied to the cell. A sheet of photographic paper is rolled around the drum. The position of the galvanometer is such that its beam moves in a plane passing through the axis of the drum, and the distance between the mirror of the galvanometer coil and the photographic paper is large (perhaps 1 meter) in comparison with the length of the drum (about 15 cm). The deflection recorded on the paper is practically proportional to the current, under such conditions. A current-voltage curve is thus recorded. A commercial instrument is available in the United States (Sargent).

In pen-and-ink recording polarographs (Leeds and Northrup, Sargent in the United States), the galvanometer of the manual instrument in Fig. 39 is replaced by a calibrated adjustable resistance, and a recorder with continuous balance (Section 2–10c) is connected across this resistance. The ohmic drop in the calibrated resistance is proportional to the current through the cell, and this current thus is recorded as a function of time. The sliding contact of potentiometer *P* in Fig. 39 is geared to a synchronous motor, and the voltage applied to the cell increases linearly with time. A current-voltage current thus is recorded. Provisions are also made for compensation as in manual instruments. As was pointed out in Section 4–3a, the average of the oscillations of the pen of the recorder is not equal to the average current during drop life, and the maximum of the oscillations should be determined.

The theory of polarography was developed on the assumption that the potential of the dropping mercury electrode is constant. This assumption is practically valid with recording instruments when the potential of the dropping mercury electrode varies by only 0.01 volt so so during drop life. As a result, the recording over a 2-volt span should take at least 5 min. The theory developed in this chapter is no longer applicable if the recording is made at a much faster pace.

Manual and recording polarographs can also be utilized in studies with stationary and rotated electrodes.

d. Methods of Collecting and Analyzing Data. Concentrations can be determined by applying the Ilkovic equation, provided that there is no kinetic or catalytic effect.

The drop time τ can be determined easily by measuring (chronometer or electric timer) the time required for the fall of a certain number of drops; 20 drops, for instance. The rate of flow of mercury *m* is calculated from the weight of mercury flowing in a given time. Mercury is collected in a small cup which can be swung under the capillary, and the resulting mercury globule weighing perhaps 0.4 gram is collected on a watch glass. The globule is washed with distilled water, alcohol, and ether (avoid peroxides which oxidize mercury). The quantities *m* and τ should be determined at the potential at which the diffusion current is measured to avoid any error resulting from variations of m and τ with potential.

The diffusion coefficient D is generally now known, but a polarographic diffusion current can be calculated from experimental diffusion currents for known concentrations of the analyzed substance. The diffusion coefficient of a given substance varies somewhat with the medium.

Lingane[25] has suggested to group the terms $607\, n\, D_0^{1/2}$ in the Ilkovic equation in a diffusion current constant I (see problem 10 in Section 4–14). It is readily seen from the values of I in Table VI that the diffusion coefficient for a given substance depends on the medium. Values of I reported in the literature are calculated for average currents, and they should be multiplied by 7/6 if maximum currents during drop life are measured with a pen-and-ink recorder. The use of diffusion current constants requires control of the temperature of the analyzed solution with a water bath. For detailed lists of diffusion current constants, see the monograph of Kolthoff and Lingane and Meites' book (Section 4–13).

Instead of applying the Ilkovic equation, one can determine concentrations for given conditions of electrolysis by preparing a calibration curve. Temperature control is also necessary if the maximum possible accuracy is required.

A third method involves the addition to the solution being analyzed of a known volume of a standard solution of the substance to be determined. Waves are determined before and after the addition of the standard solution, and the unknown concentration can be computed from the change in wave height (see problem 11 in Section 4–14). The temperature need not be controlled provided that the standard solution and the solution to be analyzed are at the same temperature.

4–11. NEW VOLTAMMETRIC METHODS

Methods have been devised in which the potential of the polarized electrode is a linear or a sinusoidal function of time. The polarized electrode is a stationary electrode in either case; for example, a mercury pool having a diameter of 2 to 3 cm. The method involving linear variations of potential, sometimes called oscillographic polarography, is useful in the determination of low concentrations ($10^{-5}\, M$ or less). Electrolysis with alternating voltage is very valuable in the study of the kinetics of fast electrode reactions.

Instead of controlling the voltage applied to the cell and measuring the current, one can do the opposite. The resulting voltammetric method at constant current is valuable in chemical analysis.

The theory of these various methods is well advanced, and the reader

[25] J. J. Lingane, *Ind. Eng. Chem., Anal. Ed.*, **15**, 583 (1943).

may find the details in the specialized literature (see Section 4–13). See also problems 21 and 22 in Section 4–14.

4–12. APPLICATIONS

A great variety of substances can be analyzed by polarography or voltammetry. Almost all the metallic cations and several anions (iodate, bromate, halides, chromate, sulfurous acid, selenite, etc.) can be determined.

Elements such as oxygen and sulfur are reduced at the dropping mercury electrode. Numerous substances can be analyzed in organic chemistry: aliphatic and aromatic unsaturated hydrocarbons, halogen compounds, aldehydes, ketones, quinones, nitro compounds, azo and diazo compounds, and many other substances.

The sensitivity is very good for an electrochemical method since concentrations as low as $10^{-5}\,M$ can be determined and the upper limit of concentrations is about $10^{-2}\,M$. There are more sensitive electrochemical methods (for example, coulometry), but none of these methods is as versatile as polarography. The quantity of substance needed for analysis is very small, perhaps one μg, since volume even smaller than 1 ml can be used if necessary.

The polarographic method is rather selective, since waves are observed in definite ranges of potentials. Many substances have approximately the same half-wave potentials, and one must have some idea about the composition of the solution before qualitative polarographic identification is possible.

The accuracy of the method is rather good, since relative errors are of the order of 1 to 2 per cent, and in some cases, as low as 0.2 per cent. The uncertainty in the graphic determination of diffusion currents is the main source of error. Some other electrochemical methods, especially titrimetric methods, are more accurate, but errors of 1 to 2 per cent in polarography are tolerable in many cases.

The method can be adapted to routine work, since the duration of each analysis is rather short. The time-consuming operation is the elimination of oxygen (bubbling of nitrogen). The polarographic method is not well suited to continuous analysis, although applications of this nature have been made (oxygen determination in streams).

4–13. BIBLIOGRAPHY

a. Books and Articles

P. Delahay, *New Instrumental Methods in Electrochemistry*, Interscience, New York, 1954. See detailed discussion of irreversible, kinetic, and catalytic currents, electrodes with convective transfer, and treatment of newer methods.

J. Heyrovsky in *Physikalische Methoden der Analytischen Chemie*, W. Böttger, Ed., Vol. II, Akademische Verlagsgellschaft, Leipzig, 1936. The first detailed discussion after the fundamentals had been well established.

J. Heyrovsky, *Polarographie*, Springer, Vienna, 1941. A classical work by the originator of the method.

J. Heyrovsky in *Physical Methods in Chemical Analysis*, W. G. Berl, Ed., Vol. II, Academic Press, New York, 1951. Oriented toward applications in metallurgical analysis.

H. Hohn, *Chemische Analysen mit dem Polarographen*, Springer, Berlin, 1937. An introductory treatment with description of typical experiments.

I. M. Kolthoff in *Recent Advances in Analytical Chemistry* (Frontiers in Chemistry, Vol. VII, R. E. Burk and O. Grummitt, Eds.), Interscience, New York, 1949. An outline of the method.

I. M. Kolthoff and H. A. Laitinen, *pH and Electro Titrations*, John Wiley, New York, 1941. See chapter on polarography and amperometric titrations; an introductory treatment.

I. M. Kolthoff and J. J. Lingane, *Polarography*, 2nd ed., 2 vols., Interscience, New York, 1952. A classic in the field.

L. Meites, *Polarographic Techniques*, Interscience, New York, 1955. Excellent for an introduction to the field; contains much practical information and a very detailed compilation of half-wave potentials for inorganic substances.

O. H. Müller in *Physical Methods of Organic Chemistry* (*Technique of Organic Chemistry*, Vol. I, Part II, A. Weissberger, Ed., 2nd ed., Interscience, New York. 1949. A discussion of fundamentals and applications in organic chemistry.

O. H. Müller, *The Polarographic Method of Analysis*, 2nd ed., Mack Printing Co., Easton, Pennsylvania, 1951. Valuable for an introduction to the method from the theoretical and experimental points of view.

P. J. Elving in *Organic Analysis*, J. Mitchell, Jr., I. M. Kolthoff, E. S. Proskauer, and A. Weissberger, Eds., Vol. 2, Interscience, New York, 1954. Survey written from the practical viewpoint.

M. von Stackelberg, *Polarographische Arbeitsmethoden*, de Gruyter, Berlin, 1950. Discussion of theory and systematic review of applications.

b. Reviews

Numerous reviews have been published: J. J. Lingane, *Anal Chem.*, **21**, 45 (1949); **23**, 86 (1951); S. Wawzonek, *Anal. Chem.*, **21**, 61 (1949); **22**, 30 (1950); **26**, 65 (1954); **28**, 638 (1956); D. N. Hume, *ibid.*, **28**, 625 (1956). See also H. A. Laitinen, *Ann. Rev. Phys. Chem.*, **1**, 309 (1950); C. Tanford and S. Wawzonek, *ibid.*, **3**, 247 (1952); P. Delahay, *ibid.* (1957, in press).

c. Bibliographies

Comprehensive lists of publications are periodically prepared by Heyrovsky and Müller, by Semerano and co-workers, and by manufacturers of polarographic instrumentation (Leeds and Northrup in Philadelphia and Sargent in Chicago). Two journals of abstracts of papers on polarography are published: *The Radiometer Polarographics* and *Leybold Polarographische Berichte*.

J. Heyrovsky and J. Klumpar, *Collection Czechoslov. Chem. Communs.*, **10**, 153 (1938); J. Heyrovsky, *ibid.*, **11**, 98, 677 (1939); **12**, 156 (1947), **19**, supplement (1954); J. Heyrovsky and O. H. Müller, *ibid.*, **12**, 667 (1947); **13**, 481 (1948); **14**, 569 (1949); **16**, 430 (1951). See detailed list in *Sbornik Mezinarod Polarog. Sjezdu Pracze*, 1st congr., 1951, Part II, Bibliography 1922–1950.

G. Semerano, *Bibliographia Polarografica*, Supplement A *Ricerca Sci.*, **19** (1949); E. Gagliardo, *ibid.*, **19** (1949); **21** (1951); M. Menagus-Scarpa and E. Gagliardo, *ibid.*, **23** (1953); M. Menagus-Scarpa, *ibid.*, **24** (1954); M. Menagus-Scarpa and M. Tosini, *ibid.*, **25** (1955); M. Tosini, *ibid.*, **26** (1956).

4-14. PROBLEMS

a. Extension of Theory

1. It can be shown that the rate of diffusion toward a spherical electrode of radius r_0 is

$$\left\{ \begin{matrix} \text{Number of moles diffusing at} \\ \text{electrode surface per unit} \\ \text{area and per unit of time} \end{matrix} \right\} = C^0 \left[\sqrt{\frac{D_O}{\pi t}} + \frac{D_O}{r_0} \right],$$

where the notations are the same as in equation (4–5). Calculate the current and apply the resulting equation to electrolysis under the following conditions: $n = 1$, $C^0 = 10^{-6}$ mol cm^{-3}, $A = 0.02$ cm^2, $D_O = 10^{-5}$ cm^2 sec^{-1}, and $0 < t < 5$ sec. Plot in the same graph the current obtained with a plane electrode under the same conditions (see Fig. 27) and determine the approximation achieved by the application of equation (4-6) for linear diffusion to spherical diffusion.

2. Calculate on the basis of the Ilkovic equation the relative decrease in concentration of reducible substance after 1 hr in an electrolysis with a dropping mercury electrode in the following conditions: $n = 1$, $m = 1.2$ mg sec^{-1}, $\tau_. = 3$ sec, $D = 1.31 \times 10^{-5}$ cm^2 sec^{-1}, initial concentration $C^0 = 2.3$ millimol lit^{-1}, volume of solution 15 ml. Assume that the current is constant during electrolysis (see Section 6–2a for a more rigorous approach.)

Note: Apply Faraday's law; see Section 4–2.

3. According to Poiseuille's law the volume of liquid v flowing per second through a capillary having a length l and an internal radius r is

$$v = \frac{\pi r^4 p}{8 l \eta},$$

where p is the pressure (in dyne cm^{-2}) and π is the viscosity of the liquid. Apply this equation to the calculation of the rate of flow m (in mg sec^{-1}) of mercury through a capillary under the following conditions: head of mercury, 60.7 cm, $r = 0.0031$ cm, $l = 7.2$ cm, $\eta_{Hg} = 0.0152$ dyne sec cm^{-2} (25°).

Note that $p = Hgd$ (H, head of mercury; g, the acceleration of gravity, that is 980.6 cm sec^{-2}; and d, the difference between the densities of mercury and the solution). Neglect the back pressure due to the formation of drops.

4. The interfacial tension force holding a mercury drop at the tip of a capillary is $2\pi r \sigma$, where r is the internal radius of the capillary and σ is the surface tension in dynes cm^{-1}. The gravity force is Mg where M is the mass of the drop and g is the acceleration of gravity. Calculate the drop time of a dropping mercury electrode

functioning under the following conditions: $r = 0.0035$ cm; $\sigma_, = 420$ dynes cm^{-1}. One also has $g = 980.6$ cm sec^{-2}, and d (density of mercury, drop in air) $= 13.53$ gram cm^{-3} at 25°. Assume that the drop is spherical.

5. Show that the half-wave potential of equation (4–19) is a point of inflection of the wave represented by equation (4–18).

Note: calculate dE/di and d^2E/di^2.

6. Derive the equation of the wave obtained with a mixture of reducible (O) and oxidizable (R) substances. Calculate the potential at which $i = 0$.

Follow the same procedure as in Section 4–4a, but write

$$\bar{\imath} = 607\ nm^{2/3}\tau^{1/6}D_R^{1/2}[(C_R)_{x=0} - C_R^0]$$

instead of equation (4–17). Note that there are two diffusion currents $i_{d,c}$ and $i_{d,a}$ for the cathodic and anodic processes, respectively. Plot the waves for values of $i_{d,a}$, equal to $0.1i_{d,c}$, $0.5i_{d,c}$, and $i_{d,c}$, respectively. Assume n $= 2$ and E$_{1/2} = 0$ (for $i_{d,a} = i_{d,c}$).

7. Derive the equation of an anodic wave obtained with an anion whose mercurous salt is sparingly soluble. Plot the wave for chloride ion for the following conditions: $m = 0.86$ mg sec^{-1}, $\tau = 4.27$ sec, $C^0 = 1.25$ millimol lit^{-1}, $f_{Cl^-} = 0.80$, $D_{Cl^-} = 2.0 \times 10^{-5}$ cm sec^{-1}, $S_{Hg_2Cl_2} = 1.1 \times 10^{-18}$.

Note: Assume in the derivation that the solution is initially saturated with the sparingly soluble mercurous salt.

8. It was shown by Koutecky (see footnote 18) that the parameter [$\lambda = (12/7)^{1/2}k\tau^{1/2}/D_O^{1/2}$] varies as follows along an irreversible wave when the maximum current during drop life is considered [k, rate constant of equation (4–32), τ drop time, D_O diffusion coefficient of the substance being electrolyzed]:

λ	$(i/i_d)_{t=\tau}$	λ	$(i/i_d)_{t=\tau}$
0.1	0.0828	1.8	0.662
0.2	0.155	2.0	0.690
0.3	0.219	2.5	0.740
0.4	0.275	3.0	0.777
0.5	0.325	3.5	0.803
0.6	0.369	4.0	0.827
0.7	0.409	4.5	0.844
0.8	0.444	5	0.858
0.9	0.476	6	0.880
1.0	0.505	8	0.909
1.2	0.555	16	0.953
1.4	0.597	20	0.963
1.6	0.632	∞	1

With the help of this table and equation (4–32), determine the parameters k^0 and β for the irreversible wave on which the following measurements were made:

$i_{t=\tau}$ μa	E volts versus S.C.E.
0.31	−0.419
0.62	−0.451
1.24	−0.491
1.86	−0.515
2.48	−0.561
2.79	−0.593

The diffusion current (maximum current during drop life, not the average current) was 3.10 μa for the following conditions: $n = 2, m = 1.26$ mg sec^{-1}, $\tau = 3.53$ sec, $C^0 = 0.88$ millimol lit^{-1}. By applying now equation (4–34) it is possible to calculate the concentration $(C_O)_{x=0}$ for $i_{t=\tau}$ as a function of potential. Make this calculation and plot the results. Plot on the same graph the current values listed above.

Note: Calculate D_O from the Ilkovic equation. Make a plot of log k against E (versus N.H.E.) to obtain k^0 and β.

9. It can be shown that $(k\tau^{1/2})/D_O^{1/2}$ (see preceding problem) is equal to 0.76 at the half-wave potential of an irreversible wave when the maximum current during drop life is measured. Show that the half-wave potential depends on drop time, and derive the relationship between $E_{1/2}$ and τ.

10. According to Lingane and Loveridge [*J. Am. Chem. Soc.*, **72**, 438 (1950)] and Strehlow and von Stackelberg [*Z. Elektrochem.*, **54**, 51 (1950)], the following equation,

$$\bar{i}_d = 607nm^{2/3}\tau^{1/6}D_O^{1/2}C^0 \left(1 + \frac{gD_O^{1/2}\tau^{1/6}}{m^{1/3}}\right),$$

is less approximate than the Ilkovic equation (see Section 4–3e). The constant g is equal to 39, according to Lingane and Loveridge, and to 17, according to Strehlow and von Stackelberg. Calculate the diffusion current constant I on the basis of this new equation, and introduce some typical numerical values to evaluate the difference between values of I calculated from the above equation or from the Ilkovic equation.

Note: $I = 607 \, nD_O^{1/2}$.

11. A wave having a height of h_i mm was obtained in the analysis of a given substance. V_s ml of a standard solution of concentration C_s mol lit^{-1} were added to the cell, which contained V_0 ml of the initial solution. The wave height after the addition of standard solution was h_f. Calculate the initial concentration of the substance being analyzed as a function of h_i, h_f, V_o, V_s, and C_s.

b. Application of Theory

12. An average diffusion current of 6.72 μa was obtained in the electrolysis of a given substance under the following conditions: $n = 1$, $m = 1.37$ mg sec^{-1}, $\tau = 3.93$ sec, $C^0 = 1.21$ millimoles per liter. Calculate the polarographic diffusion coefficient of this substance.

13. An average diffusion current of 1.71 μa was obtained with a head of mercury of 64.7 cm. Calculate the average diffusion current for a head of mercury of 83.1 cm. Neglect the back pressure.

14. The following measurements were made on a reversible polarographic wave at 25°:

E (volts versus S.C.E.)	Average current (μa)
-0.395	0.48
-0.406	0.97
-0.415	1.46
-0.422	1.94
-0.431	2.43
-0.445	2.92

The average diffusion current was 3.24 μa. Calculate the number of electrons involved in the electrode reaction. Calculate the standard potential (versus N.H.E.) of the couple involved in the electrode reaction on the assumption that the activity coefficients and diffusion coefficients of the reducible and reduced species are the same.

15. The following half-wave potentials were obtained at 30° for the reduction of a substance in various buffers (reversible waves):

pH	$E_{1/2}$ (volts versus S.C.E.)
1.37	-0.647
3.02	-0.779
6.41	-1.050
8.36	-1.205

Calculate the number of hydrogen ions involved in the electrode reaction, knowing that $n = 3$. Calculate the standard potential (versus N.H.E.) on the assumption that the activity coefficients and diffusion coefficients of the reducible and reduced species are the same.

16. The following measurements were made at 25° on the reversible wave for the reduction of a metallic complex ion:

Concentration of complex forming salt (moles per liter)	$E_{1/2}$ volts versus S.C.E.
0.1	-0.448
0.5	-0.531
1	-0.566

Calculate the coordination number of the complex knowing that $n = 2$. Calculate the instability constant of the complex from the above data and the value $E_{1/2} = +0.081$ volt observed in the absence of a complex forming salt. Assume that the diffusion coefficients of the aquocomplex and complex ions are the same and that the activity coefficients of the various substances are equal to unity.

17. Calculate the capacity current during drop life for the data given below and for the following values of t: 0.01, 0.1, 0.5, 1, 2, 3, and 4 sec. Characteristics of the electrode: $m = 0.9$ mg sec^{-1}, $c_0 = 27$ μf per cm^2, and $E - E_m = 0.5$ volt. Density of mercury: 13.53 gram cm^{-3}. Plot the results and compare the resulting curve with Fig. 28.

c. Survey of Literature

18. Outline procedures for the polarographic determination of the following elements: aluminum, cadmium, chromium, cobalt, copper, iron, lead, manganese, nickel, oxygen, sodium, sulfur, tin, and zinc.

19. Outline procedures for the polarographic analysis of the following mixtures: (a) thallium and lead; (b) nickel and cobalt; (c) nickel and zinc.

20. Discuss the polarographic determination of the following substances: for-

maldehyde, acetaldehyde, benzaldehyde, acetophenone, benzoin, nitromethane, azobenzene, proteins.

21. Discuss the application of voltammetry with continuously varying potential and stationary electrode (mercury pool polarography) to trace analysis. See C. A. Streuli and W. D. Cooke, *Anal Chem.*, **25,** 1691 (1953); see also Chapter 6 of the writer's monograph (reference in Section 4–13a).

22. Prepare a review of the fundamentals of voltammetry at constant current. See P. Delahay and G. Mamantov, *Anal. Chem.*, **27,** 478 (1955); C. N. Reilley, G. W. Everett, and R. H. Johns, *ibid.*, **27,** 483 (1955).

23. Discuss the application of the rotated silver amalgam electrode to trace analysis. See W. D. Cooke, *Anal. Chem.*, **25,** 215 (1953).

24. Discuss the automatic compensation of the ohmic drop in pen-and-ink recording polarographs. See M. M. Nicholson, *Anal. Chem.*, **27,** 1364 (1955); W. Jackson, Jr., and P. J. Elving, *ibid.*, **28,** 378 (1956).

25. Prepare a seminar on the interpretation of polarographic maxima. Use the excellent review of M. von Stackelberg, *Fortschr. Chem. Forsch.*, **2,** 229 (1951).

5

Amperometric and
Voltammetric Titrations

5-1. CLASSIFICATION OF VOLTAMMETRIC TITRATIONS

Polarography and voltammetry can be applied to the determination of the equivalence point of quite a large number of titrations. Since diffusion (dropping mercury electrode) and limiting (stirred solutions) currents are proportional to the concentration of reducible or oxidizable substance, variations of concentration of the reagents can be followed during titration, and the equivalence point can be determined by graphical extrapolation.

Titrimetric methods based on the application of voltammetry can be classified according to the nature of the electrical quantity being measured. Two broad groups can be distinguished according to whether the voltage (*potentiometric titrations*) across the cell or the current (*amperometric titrations*) through the cell is measured. The current through the cell in potentiometric titrations may be equal to zero[1] or it may be constant but different from zero. Furthermore, the cell may comprise one or two polarized electrodes.

The following classification can be made on the basis of the preceding comments:

Potentiometric titrations at zero current
Potentiometric titrations at constant current
    a) With one polarized electrode,
    b) With two polarized electrodes.

[1]Actually the current is smaller than the minimum current which is detectable by the balance indicator of the potentiometer.

106

Amperometric titrations
  a) With one polarized electrode,
  b) With two polarized electrodes.

Two of these methods are widely used, namely, potentiometric titrations at zero current and amperometric titrations with one polarized electrode. The former method was discussed in detail in Chapter 3 and the latter is reviewed in this chapter. Amperometry with two polarized electrodes is an elegant method of detecting the equivalence point of certain titrations. A brief discussion of this method will also be given in this chapter. Reference is made to the specialized literature (Section 5–5) for the other methods listed above and not discussed in this chapter.

The first amperometric titration with one polarized electrode was devised by Heyrovsky and Berezicky[2], who titrated barium ion with sulfate. Majer[3] called such titrations *polarometric titrations*, but the expression *amperometric titrations* suggested by Kolthoff and Pan[4] is generally preferred. Amperometric titrations are very advantageous in some cases, and a great number of titrations have been developed, especially by Kolthoff and his students. Rather old references[5] to amperometric titrations with two polarized electrodes are in the literature, but this type of titrimetric end point was rediscovered by Foulk and Bawden[6] in the 1920's. These authors coined the expression "dead-stop end point" to designate their method, and this expression is now commonly used. The method was originally applied rather empirically, and an adequate interpretation of titration curves was developed only about 1950.

5–2. AMPEROMETRIC TITRATIONS WITH ONE POLARIZED ELECTRODE

a. Types of Titration Curves. A polarized electrode coupled with an unpolarized electrode (a saturated calomel electrode, for example) is immersed in the solution being titrated. The polarized electrode is a dropping mercury electrode, a rotated electrode, or a stationary electrode. In the latter case the solution must be stirred mechanically. The cell is connected to a manual polarograph (Section 4–10c), and the potential of the polarized electrode is adjusted at a value at which the diffusion current (dropping mercury electrode) or the limiting current (rotated electrode or stationary electrode in stirred solution) is observed. The current through the galvanometer of the polarograph is the sum of the diffusion (i_d) or

[2] J. Heyrovsky and S. Berezicky, *Collection Czechoslov. Chem. Communs.*, **1**, 19 (1929).
[3] V. Majer, *Z. Elektrochem.*, **42**, 120 (1936).
[4] I. M. Kolthoff and Y. D. Pan, *J. Am. Chem. Soc.*, **61**, 3402 (1939).
[5] E. Salomon, *Z. physik. Chem.*, **24**, 55 (1897); **25**, 365 (1898); *Z. Elektrochem.*, **4**, 71 (1897).
[6] C. W. Foulk and A. T. Bawden, *J. Am. Chem. Soc.*, **48**, 2045 (1926).

limiting (i_l) current and the residual current (i_r) at the potential at which measurements are made. Thus (note that average currents are used for the dropping mercury electrode),

$$\bar{\imath} = \bar{\imath}_d + \bar{\imath}_r \qquad (5\text{--}1)$$
$$i = i_l + i_r \qquad (5\text{--}2)$$

or, since i_d or i_l are proportional to the concentration, C, of the substance being reduced or oxidized,

$$\bar{\imath} = KC + \bar{\imath}_r \qquad (5\text{--}3)$$
$$i = K'C + i_r. \qquad (5\text{--}4)$$

The constant K is readily deduced from the Ilkovic equation [see equation (4–11)] and K' can be calculated from equation (4–41). If several substances are reduced simultaneously, $\Sigma K_i C_i$ or $\Sigma K_i' C_i$ should be written in equations (5–3) and (5–4) instead of KC or $K'C$.

The concentration C in equations (5–3) and (5–4) varies during titration, as was shown in Section 3–5. If there is virtually no dilution during titration, the concentrations of analyzed substance and titrant vary linearly during titration except in the vicinity of the equivalence point. Four types of titration curves are observed, depending on whether or not the analyzed substance and the titrant are reducible or oxidizable. Diagrams A, B, and C in Fig. 40 are self-explanatory. Titration curves of the type D are ob-

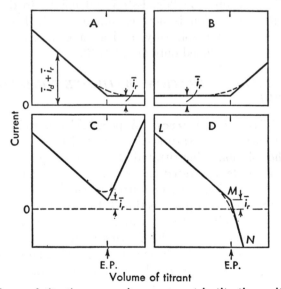

Fig. 40. Types of titration curves in amperometric titrations with one polarized electrode (the residual current is exaggerated). (A) The substance being analyzed is reducible (or oxidizable) and the titrant is not. (B) The substance being analyzed is not reducible (or oxidizable) and the titrant is. (C) Both the substance being analyzed and the titrant are reducible (or oxidizable). (D) The substance being analyzed is reducible and the titrant is oxidizable or vice versa.

tained when the substance being analyzed is reducible and the titrant is oxidizable, or vice versa, at the potential at which the polarized electrode is adjusted. Reduction (or oxidation) occurs at the polarized electrode before the equivalence point, and oxidation (or reduction) occurs after this point. The current would be reversed at the equivalence point, if the residual current were equal to zero. Actually, the current is positive or negative at the equivalence point, depending on the sign of the residual current. The slopes of the lines *LM* and *MN* in Fig. 40D are different because the coefficient K or K' in equations (5–3) and (5–4) is not the same before and after the equivalence point because of differences between the diffusion coefficients for the analyzed substance and the titrant.

Examples of titration curves in Fig. 40 are as follows:

Curve A. Titration of copper by cupferron[7] at pH 5–6 and a potential at which Cu(II) is reduced (-0.5 volt versus S.C.E.) and cupferron is not.

Curve B. Titration of magnesium with 8-hydroxyquinoline at pH 9.5 at a potential of -1.6 volts (versus S.C.E.) at which magnesium ion is not reduced and the oxine is.

Curve C. Titration of lead by chromate at the potential of -1.0 volt (versus S.C.E.) at which lead and chromate ions are reduced.

Curve D. Titration of ferric ion in tartrate medium of pH 7 with titanous chloride at a potential of -0.6 volt (versus S.C.E.) at which Fe(III) is reduced and Ti(III) is oxidized.

b. *Influence of the Solubility of the Precipitate.* Experimental titration curves often do not exhibit a sharp angle at the equivalence point because the reaction is not completely quantitative. This is shown in Fig. 41 for the titration of lead nitrate ($5 \times 10^{-3} M$, $10^{-3} M$, and $5 \times 10^{-4} M$) with sulfate, dilution being neglected. The residual current is assumed to be equal to zero for the sake of simplicity. Since the solubility product S_{PbSO_4} is 1.3×10^{-8}, the concentration[8] of Pb^{++} ions at the equivalence point is $\sqrt{S_{PbSO_4}}$ or $1.14 \times 10^{-4} M$, and the current at the equivalence point is relatively large when $\sqrt{S_{PbSO_4}}$ is not negligible (perhaps more than a few per cent) in comparison with the initial concentration of lead ion. This conclusion should be kept in mind in the selection of reagents. Likewise, the reagents in oxidation-reduction titration should give a quantitative reaction (see Section 3–9a for a criterion).

The solubility of a precipitate can be decreased, whenever necessary, by the addition of an organic solvent miscible with water (ethyl alcohol, dioxane, etc.). This procedure is applied, for instance, in the titration of sulfate with lead nitrate, and about 20 per cent (by volume) of ethyl

---

[7]Ammonium salt of nitrosophenylhydroxylamine.

[8]Actually, the activity of Pb^{++} ions is obtained if the solubility product is given for infinite dilution.

alcohol is added to the solution being titrated. The solubility of sparingly soluble substances can also be decreased by changing the temperature. The titration of chloride with silver nitrate, for example, is carried out at

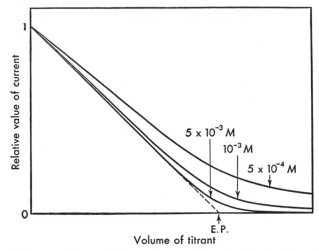

Fig. 41.   Influence of the solubility of the precipitate in the titration of Pb(II) with sulfate for three initial concentrations of Pb(II).

0^0 when low concentrations of chloride are to be determined ($S_{AgCl} \approx 10^{-10}$).

It is possible to develop equations for titration curves in which equilibrium considerations (solubility) are taken into account, but this material will not be presented here since one generally selects reagents which give a virtually quantitative reaction. Reference is made to Kolthoff and Lingane[9] for a detailed mathematical analysis.

c. Experimental Methods.   Polarographic H cells (Fig. 38, Chapter 4) are generally utilized in amperometric titrations with one polarized electrode. The unpolarized electrode is a saturated calomel electrode or any other similar reference electrode. It is convenient to use a silver-silver chloride electrode as reference electrode because of the simplicity of construction; the electrode is made of a silver wire (helix) coated with silver chloride and is immersed in a 0.1 molar potassium chloride solution. The area of the wire should be large enough to avoid concentration polarization for the current at which the polarized electrode functions. Diffusion from one compartment of the cell to the other is virtually prevented by an agar-agar plug.

The compartment of the cell in which the polarized electrode (dropping

[9]I. M. Kolthoff and J. J. Lingane, *Polarography*, 2nd ed., 2 vols., Interscience, New York, 1952, pp. 898–901.

mercury electrode, rotated electrode, etc.) is immersed may have a capacity of approximately 100 ml. Relatively large volumes of solution (50 to 75 ml) are preferred because dilution during titration must be minimized. If there is a marked dilution during titration, diffusion or limiting currents do not vary linearly with the volume of titrant (see Fig. 17 in Chapter 3), and the graphic extrapolation of the equivalence point is difficult. In practice the ratio of the initial volume of solution, v_0, to the volume of titrant at the equivalence point, q, should be of the order of 10 to 20 or a correction should be made for dilution. If $q = 5$ ml (10 ml burette), one has $v_0 = 50$ ml for $v_0/q = 10$. It is of course possible to have much smaller values of v_0/q whenever necessary.

Cells of various designs have been proposed[10] for amperometric titrations.

Oxygen interferes in titrations carried out at potentials ($E < 0$ volt versus S.C.E. on a dropping mercury electrode) at which this substance is reduced. This is generally the case for titrations in which the dropping mercury electrode is the polarized electrode. Oxygen is removed by the methods described in Section 4–10a and especially by bubbling nitrogen through the solution. The gas is bubbled for a short time (1 min) after each addition of titrant in order to stir the solution and to avoid any local excess of titrant. The small amount of oxygen dissolved in the titrant added to the solution is also removed in this operation.[11] *Bubbling of nitrogen should be interrupted during the measurement of the current when a dropping mercury electrode is utilized;* diffusion currents are otherwise erroneous.[12] A moderate continuous flow of nitrogen is permissible when the polarized electrode is a rotated microelectrode.

If the titrant is added with a 5- or 10-ml burette, the formation of drops must be avoided, for example, by adjusting at the tip of the burette a platinum wire which dips in the solution being titrated; drops of titrant flow along this wire. Burettes in which the titrant is kept under nitrogen have been designed, but in most cases an ordinary burette can be utilized.

Currents are measured with a manual polarograph (Section 4–10c). Readings of the current after each addition of titrant are taken only after a stable value of the current is reached. This may require several minutes in the vicinity of the equivalence point in some titrations because of variations in the solubility of the precipitate (growth of particles; see quantitative analysis text).

The equivalence point is determined by graphical extrapolation of the

[10]I. M. Kolthoff and J. J. Lingane, *loc. cit.*, pp. 901–913.

[11]In the analysis of rather dilute solutions (below 5×10^{-4} molar) it may be necessary to bubble nitrogen for more than 1 min after each addition of titrant. Traces of oxygen interfere in this a case.

[12]A cell in which nitrogen can be bubbled continuously has been designed by H. A. Laitinen and L. W. Burdett [*Anal. Chem.*, **22**, 833 (1950)].

linear segments of the titration curve. Three points before the equivalence point and three current readings beyond this point are often sufficient in routine work.

5-3. AMPEROMETRIC TITRATIONS WITH TWO POLARIZED ELECTRODES—"DEAD-STOP END POINTS"

a. Titration Curves. Titrations in which two stationary platinum electrodes (wire) in a stirred solution are polarized have been developed (dead-stop end point). A voltage of small amplitude (from 0.01 to 0.1 volt) is applied to the electrodes by means of a manual polarograph, and the current through the cell is measured during titration. The equivalence point is deduced from the plot of current against volume of titrant. Titration curves will be discussed for the specific case of the titration of iodine by thiosulfate, which involves the reactions[13]

$$I_2 + 2e \longrightarrow 2I^- \tag{5-5}$$

$$S_4O_6^{--} + 2e \longleftarrow 2S_2O_3^{--}. \tag{5-6}$$

The concentration of iodine decreases during titration and that of iodide increases. If current-potential curves were determined during titration with a cell composed of a platinum electrode and an unpolarized electrode,

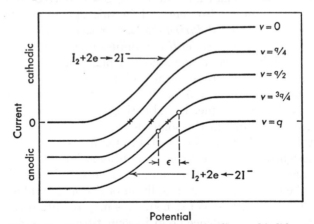

Potential

Fig. 42. Current-potential curves for mixtures of iodine and iodide as obtained with a cell composed of one polarized electrode (platinum wire in stirred solution) and an unpolarized electrode; v volume of titrant, and q, volume of titrant at the equivalence point.

such as a saturated calomel electrode, the results of Fig. 42 would be obtained (see problem 1 in Section 5–6). Two identical platinum electrodes are actually utilized in the titration, and the voltage ϵ applied across these two electrodes is rather small, say, 0.01 volt. Iodine is reduced on the

---

[13]Iodine exists mainly as I_3^- in presence of an excess of iodide.

cathode and iodide is oxidized on the anode. The cathodic and anodic currents, which must have the same absolute value, can be determined readily from the curves of Fig. 42. From the analysis of curves similar to those of Fig. 42 at various stages of titration, one concludes that the current through the titration cell for a given voltage exhibits a maximum and decreases as the equivalence point is approached. It can be shown (see problem 1, Section 5–6) that the maximum is observed at the midpoint of the titration when the reaction occurring at the electrode is symmetrical, as for a reaction symbolized by the equation $O + ne = R$. The current beyond the equivalence point is virtually equal to zero, as will now be shown.

Current-potential curves obtained beyond the equivalence point with a polarized electrode (platinum wire) and an unpolarized electrode (saturated calomel electrode) are shown in Fig. 43. The concentration of iodine

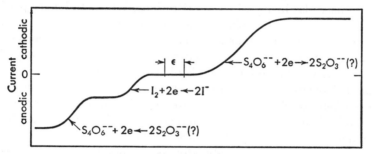

Potential

Fig. 43. Current-potential curve for the titration of iodine with thiosulfate at a given stage of titration beyond the equivalence point.

is practically equal to zero, and the corresponding cathodic current can be neglected. However, an anodic current for the oxidation of iodide is observed. An excess of thiosulfate is present, and the anodic current for the oxidation of this ion to tetrathionate is also observed.[14] Finally, tetrathionate is present at a concentration comparable to that of iodide, and a cathodic current for the reduction of tetrathionate to thiosulfate is observed. The iodine-iodide and tetrathionate-thiosulfate couples have the same equilibrium potential, since these species are in equilibrium. However, the thionate-thiosulfate couple is very irreversible (see Section 2–10b and Section 4–5), and the current remains virtually equal to zero for several tenths of a volt on either side of the equilibrium potential. It is seen in Fig. 43 that the current through the cell composed of two identical polarized electrodes (platinum wire) is practically equal to zero when a small voltage ϵ (0.01 to 0.1 volt) is applied to these electrodes. The current

[14]The electrolytic reduction of tetrathionate and the electrolytic oxidation of thiosulfate involve side reactions which are neglected for the sake of simplicity.

through the titration cell is thus practically equal to zero after the equivalence point.

The foregoing analysis was concerned with the titration of a reversible couple (iodine-iodide) with an irreversible one (tetrathionate-thiosulfate). In the opposite case, i.e., in the titration of an irreversible couple by a reversible one, the current is practically equal to zero before the equivalence point and it increases rapidly beyond this point. In the titration of a reversible couple by another reversible couple the equivalence point is indicated by a sharp minimum.

The above qualitative reasoning can be expressed mathematically; see the specialized literature in Section 5–5.

b. Experimental Methods. Each electrode is generally made of platinum wire (5 mm long) sealed in a glass tube, but two dropping mercury electrodes may also be used in some titrations. When stationary platinum electrodes are utilized, the solution must be stirred with a propeller driven by a motor in an open cell, or by a magnetic stirrer for titrations carried out in air-free medium. Dissolved oxygen should be removed only if this substance is reduced at the potentials of the polarized electrodes.

A manual polarograph is convenient for the electrical measurements. Currents often are of the order of 5 to 20 μa if the solutions are not too dilute, and an inexpensive microammeter may be substituted for the galvanometer (commercial unit from Sargent).

The addition of titrant can be stopped automatically[15] at the equivalence point by substituting a sensitive relay for the galvanometer of the manual polarograph. The stopcock of the burette is replaced by a magnetic valve, which is operated by the relay. The rapid decrease or increase of current through the cell in the immediate vicinity of the equivalence point triggers the relay and stops the addition of titrant. An instrument based on this principle is manufactured in the United States. (Beckman).

5–4. APPLICATIONS

a. Amperometric Titrations with One Polarized Electrode. It is interesting to compare amperometric titrations using one polarized electrode with the direct polarographic or voltammetric method. The accuracy of amperometric titrations is primarily determined by the error made in the titrimetric operations. This error is small, perhaps 0.2 per cent, and amperometric titrations generally yield more accurate results than polarography. The sensitivity is somewhat higher than in polarography because amperometric titrations can still be performed (in most cases) when the direct determination of a limiting current is quite uncertain due to ex-

[15]H. A. Frediani, *Anal. Chem.*, **24,** 1126 (1952).

treme dilution of reagents (see problem 4, Section 5–6). The selectivity of amperometric titrations is about the same as in polarography.

Substances which are not reducible or oxidizable cannot be analyzed directly by polarography, but they often can be determined by amperometric titration with a reducible or oxidizable reagent. A classical example is the titration of magnesium with 8-hydroxyquinoline; magnesium, which does not yield any satisfactory diffusion current, is not reduced in the titration, but the oxine is reducible. It is sometimes possible to devise an amperometric titration even when both the analyzed substance and the titrant are not reducible. Consider the titration of calcium with fluoride and a dropping mercury electrode as the polarized electrode. The potential of this electrode is adjusted at a value at which calcium ion is not reduced, and since fluoride ion is not reduced either no current is detected during titration. Assume now that a *polarographic indicator*[16] (ferric ion in this case) is added to the solution of calcium ions, and that the potential of the dropping mercury electrode is such that ferric ion is reduced, but that the very stable complex ion FeF_6^{-3} is not. The diffusion current for ferric ion remains constant until the equivalence point is reached; thereafter it decreases. The equivalence point is obtained by extrapolation. Actually, the titration curve does not exhibit a sharp angle at the equivalence point, but the current varies progressively in the vicinity of this point (nonquantitative reaction).

Most amperometric titrations reported thus far involve precipitation rather than oxidation-reduction reactions, but there are titrations of the latter type; such as the titration of mercaptans with iodine or the titration of unsaturated hydrocarbons (styrene $C_6H_5CH = CH_2$, for example) with potassium bromate. The latter titration is carried out in acid solution in presence of a large excess of bromide, and bromine, which is easily reduced, appears then in solution beyond the equivalence point. A rotated platinum electrode must be used in this case because mercury is oxidized by the titrant.

There are numerous amperometric titrations involving precipitation[17] reactions, especially with organic reagents: α-benzoinoxime (Cu), dimethylglyoxime (Ni), dipicrylamine (K), 8-hydroxyquinoline (Bi, Cd, Cu, Fe, Mg, Zn), α-nitroso-β-naphthol (Co, Cu), picrolonic acid (Ca), quinaldinic acid (Cu, Zn), salicylaldoxime (Cu). Examples of inorganic reagents are as follows: chromate (Pb, Ba), fluoride (Al, Ca, Mg) with ferric ion as indicator, lead ion (SO_4^{--}), silver ion (Cl^-, Br^-, I^-, and mercaptans), uranyl acetate (PO_4^{-3}).

It may be concluded that amperometric titrations with one polarized electrode are quite useful. Accurate results can be obtained by a simpler

[16]A. Ringbom and B. Wilkman, *Acta Chem. Scand.*, **3**, 22 (1949).
[17]For a detailed discussion see Kolthoff and Lingane, *loc. cit.*, pp. 913–953.

experimental method involving inexpensive equipment, and application to routine analysis can be made readily.

b. Amperometric Titrations with Two Polarized Electrodes. Only a few applications of amperometric titrations with two polarized electrodes have been made, but the equivalence point of many oxidation-reduction titrations could undoubtedly be determined by this method. Potentiometry (Chapter 3) can be applied in most of these titrations, but amperometry with two polarized electrodes may be advantageous in some cases because the electrode system is very simple and no reference electrode is needed. This is particularly advantageous in titrations involving anhydrous organic media; as, for instance, in the Karl Fisher titration of water.[18] The dead-stop end point may also be more advantageous than potentiometry when the electrode potential is sluggishly established at zero current. Potentials readily acquire their steady value when a current (not too low) flows through the cell, and the application of an amperometric end point may result in an appreciable saving of time.

The titration of iodine with thiosulfate, bromometric titrations, various titrations with ceric, permanganate, ferrous and titanous ions have been reported thus far as applications of the dead-stop end point.

5-5. BIBLIOGRAPHY

a. Amperometric Titrations with One Polarized Electrode

The monographs on polarography listed in Section 4-13 give general coverage of amperometric titrations. The following reviews on recent developments are very useful for orientation:

I. M. Kolthoff, *Anal. Chim. Acta*, **2**, 606 (1948).

N. Konopik, *Oster. Chem.-Ztg.*, **54**, 289, 325 (1953); **55**, 127 (1954).

N. Konopik, article in *Fortschritte der physikalischen Chemie*, W. Jost, Ed., Steinkopff, Darmstadt (in press).

H. A. Laitinen, *Anal. Chem.*, **21**, 66 (1949); **24**, 46 (1952); **28**, 666 (1956).

b. Amperometric Titrations with Two Polarized Electrodes and Other Newer Voltammetric Titrations

G. Charlot and D. Bézier, *Méthodes Electrochimiques d'Analyse*, Masson, Paris, 1954. A brief but systematic discussion of electroanalytical chemistry. The chapter on newer voltammetric titrations is particularly recommended.

P. Delahay, *New Instrumental Methods in Electrochemistry*, Interscience, New York, 1954. See detailed discussion of the dead-stop end point and other newer voltammetric titrations.

Furman has included sections on voltammetric titrations in his last periodic

---

[18]For a review see J. Mitchell and D. M. Smith, *Aquametry*, Interscience, New York, 1948, pp. 86–93.

review in *Analytical Chemistry*,[19] The general paper by Kolthoff[20] should be consulted for classification and comparison of the various methods.

5-6. PROBLEMS

a. Extension of Theory.

1. The equation of current-potential curves (Fig. 42) for an electrode reaction of the type $O + ne = R$ is (25°)

$$E = E_{1/2} + \frac{0.0591}{n} \log \frac{i_{l,c} - i}{i_{l,a} + i}$$

where the i_l's are the cathodic and anodic limiting currents. This equation is established in problem 6 of Chapter 4 for the case of the dropping mercury electrode, and it can also be applied to a stationary electrode in a stirred solution. Apply this equation to the derivation of the current through the titration cell in an amperometric titration with two polarized electrodes for the titration of a reversible couple by an irreversible one. Determine the volume of titrant at which the curent is maximum, and plot the ratio i/i_{max} against the volume of titrant.

Note: Identify the current-potential curve with its tangent at $i = 0$.

b. Survey of Literature

2. Discuss the various procedures which have been developed for the amperometric titration of the following elements: Al, Ca, Cl, Cu, Fe, Mg, Ni, Pb, Zn.

3. Survey the applications of the dead-stop end point.

4. Discuss the amperometric titration of micromolar solutions: see J. G. Nikelly and W. D. Cooke, *Anal. Chem.*, **28**, 243 (1956).

[19]N. H. Furman, *Anal. Chem.*, **26**, 84 (1954); see also C. N. Reilley, *ibid.*, **28**, 671 (1956).

[20]I. M. Kolthoff, *Anal. Chem.*, **26**, 1685 (1954).

6

Electrogravimetry, Electrolytic Separations, and Coulometric Methods

6–1. ELECTROGRAVIMETRY

a. Reactions at Electrodes. Electrolysis can be applied in a very simple manner to the separation and analysis of certain elements. For example, in the electrolysis of an aqueous solution of copper sulfate with two platinum electrodes, copper is deposited on the cathode and oxygen[1] is evolved on the anode; the electrolysis is continued until virtually all the copper is removed from solution, and then the amount of copper initially present is calculated from the increase of weight of the cathode. This method is somewhat similar to gravimetry, but the analyzed substance is now deposited on an electrode instead of being precipitated by addition of a reagent. This *electrogravimetric* method was suggested as a qualitative tool more than a century ago,[2] and the first quantitative determination, namely, that of copper, was made independently by Wolcott Gibbs[3] and Luckow[4] about 1860. The method was developed during the second half of the nineteenth century especially by Classen and his students (Fischer, and more recently Schleicher) in Aachen, Germany. E. F. Smith at the University of Pennsylvania contributed much to the development of electrogravimetry in the United States, as did Lassieur in France. Further

---

[1]The evolution of oxygen occurs more easily than the oxidation of sulfate to peroxydisulfate $S_2O_8^{--}$. However, the latter can be prepared by anodic oxidation of sulfate.

[2]W. Cruikshank, *Ann. Physik*, **7**, 88 (1801).

[3]W. Gibbs, *Z. Anal. Chem.*, **3**, 327 (1864).

[4]See, for example, C. Luckow, *Dinglers Polytechn. J.*, **177**, 231 (1865); *Chem. Zentr.*, 735 (1865).

historical details on a modified form of electrogravimetry, i.e., electrolysis at controlled potential, will be found in Section 6–2a.

Although electrogravimetry appears very simple, its discussion requires the knowledge of some of the ideas developed in Chapter 4, and for this reason this chapter follows the treatment of voltammetry and polarography.

Electrolysis may be carried out by two methods, depending on whether the current through the cell or the potential of the working electrode is constant. One could also control the voltage across the cell, but this is a way of electrolysis at controlled potential. We shall first consider the method at constant current.

Electrolysis is carried out with the apparatus schematically represented in Fig. 44. A power supply B (storage battery, transformer-rectifier unit, etc.) is connected to a potentiom-eter P whose output voltage is applied to cell C. The electrolysis current is read on ammeter A, and the voltage applied to the cell is measured with voltmeter V. The solution is mechanically stirred to increase the rate of mass transfer of reagents toward the electrodes. Adjustments of the potentiometer

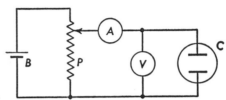

Fig. 44. Schematic diagram of apparatus for electrogravimetry.

to maintain the current at an approximate constant value are made by the operator during electrolysis. Rather large variations (perhaps 50 per cent) of current are permissible in practice, and the expression "constant current electrolysis" is, in this case, somewhat a misnomer.

The reactions occurring at the working electrode can be conveniently discussed by considering current-potential curves for this electrode at various stages of electrolysis (Fig. 45). The limiting current, which is pro-

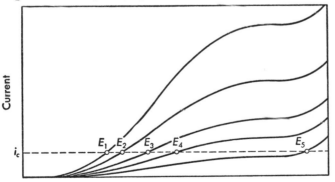

Potential of working electrode

Fig. 45. Current-potential curves for an electrode reaction at various stages of an electrolysis at constant current.

portional to the concentration of reducible or oxidizable substance, decreases during electrolysis. Actually, one does not record current-potential curves, but electrolyzes the solution at a current i_c, which is assumed to be essentially constant throughout electrolysis. Because of the decrease in the limiting current, the potential of the working electrode (E_1, E_2, . . .) varies toward more cathodic (anodic) values during electrolysis. When the limiting current becomes smaller than the current i_c through the cell, the potential varies to a value E_5, at which a new electrode reaction occurs (hydrogen evolution, deposition of another metal). If ions of only one metal are present in solution, no harm results from the shift of potential to E_5; hydrogen is evolved, but the metal deposition continues to virtual completion. Erroneous results are obtained if a second metal is deposited at potential E_5. Deposition of this second metal can sometimes be prevented by engaging its cations in a stable complex ion which is more difficult to reduce than hydrogen ion. Another method is to electrolyze the solution at controlled potential (Section 6–2).

It was assumed above that metal deposition occurs at a potential less cathodic than that at which hydrogen is evolved at an appreciable rate. The respective positions of the current-potential curves for these two reactions can be determined as follows:

The potential for the electrode reaction $M^{+n} + ne = M$, as given by the Nernst equation at 25°, is [see equation (2–4)]

$$E = E^0 + \frac{0.0591}{n} \log f_{M^{+n}} C_{M^{+n}}, \tag{6–1}$$

where E^0 is the standard potential, $f_{M^{+n}}$ the activity coefficient of ion M^{+n}, and $C_{M^{+n}}$ the concentration. We shall assume that $f_{M^{+n}} = 1$, for the sake of simplicity. If one assumes that 99.99 per cent of ions M^{+n} initially present are removed, the potential of the working electrode should be at least as negative as

$$E^0 + \frac{0.0591}{n} \log \frac{100 - 99.99}{100} C^0,$$

C^0 being the initial concentration of the cation to be analyzed. The error due to incomplete deposition is only 0.01 per cent under these conditions. The concentration C^0 is perhaps of the order of 10^{-2} molar, and the potential E should thus be as negative as ($E^0 - 0.36$) volt for $n = 1$, or ($E^0 - 0.18$) volt for $n = 2$, to remove metal M almost completely from the solution.

The potential for hydrogen evolution, as calculated from the Nernst equation, is (Section 2–8b)

$$E = -0.0591 \, pH, \tag{6–2}$$

at 25° and for 1 atm. Actually, hydrogen evolution is markedly irreversible on most metals at the current densities generally utilized in electrogravimetry, as one can ascertain from the overvoltage (see Section 4–5) values listed[5] in Table VII. Since standard potentials for most metals are rather negative (see Table I in Chapter 2), deposition of these metals would be virtually impossible if it were not for the large overvoltage re-

TABLE VII
Overvoltage for Evolution of Hydrogen in 1 N Hydrochloric
Acid at 10^{-3} Amp cm^{-2} and $25°$[a]

METAL	OVERVOLTAGE	METAL	OVERVOLTAGE
Ag	−0.59	In	−0.80
Au	−0.12	Ni	−0.32
Be	−0.63	Pb	−0.85
Cd	−0.99	Pd	−0.09
Cr	−0.42	Pt	−0.27
Cu	−0.50	Ta	−0.20
Fe	−0.40	Tl	−0.80
Ga	−0.68	W	−0.11
Hg	−1.03	Zn	−0.80[b]

[a]From P. Rüetschi and P. Delahay, *J. Chem. Phys.*, **23,** 195 (1955), except for Zn. These are data compiled from the literature.
[b]Estimated from results quoted in footnote 5.

quired for hydrogen evolution. Even so, the deposition of certain metals (K, Na, Ba, Mg, etc.) from aqueous solution is impossible on a platinum electrode[6] because the standard potentials are too negative; hydrogen is evolved at a very high rate even before traces of metal are deposited. It should be noted that it is the overvoltage for evolution of hydrogen on the metal to be deposited which is important and generally not the overvoltage for platinum. This is because the electrode no longer behaves as a platinum electrode when a few atomic layers of deposit are formed.

Abundant evolution of hydrogen during deposition may cause the formation of a spongy deposit because of the occlusion of gas bubbles. Deposits obtained under such conditions do not adhere well to the platinum working electrode, and a serious error may result from the loss of metal during the washing of the electrode prior to its weighing.

The above comparison of the potentials at which a metal is deposited and hydrogen evolved is made on the assumption that metal deposition involves no appreciable overvoltage. This is true for all practical purposes for many common metals, but there are exceptions (nickel, iron, manganese, etc.). The overvoltage at the current density at which the metal is deposited must then be added algebraically to the potential calculated from the Nernst equation (see Section 4–5).

[5]For a critical compilation, see article by J. O'M. Bockris in *Electrochemical Constants*, National Bureau of Standards, Circular 524, 1953, pp. 243–262.
[6]However, deposition is possible on a mercury electrode (polarography) because of the very large overvoltage for hydrogen evolution on this metal and the large free energy change for amalgam formation.

The reaction at the auxiliary electrode depends on the polarity of this electrode and the nature of the medium. Most metals are deposited in a cathodic process, and the auxiliary electrode then functions as the anode. Oxygen often is evolved at the anode, but other anodic products may be formed, depending on the composition of the solution (for instance, chlorine is evolved in chloride solutions). When the anodic product (chlorine) interferes an easily oxidizable substance is added to the electrolyte. Hydrazine, N_2H_4, and hydroxylamine, NH_2OH, which are oxidized, according to the reactions[7]

$$N_2 + 4H^+ + 4e \leftarrow N_2H_4 \qquad \text{(acid or neutral medium)}$$
$$N_2O + 4H^+ + H_2O + 4e \leftarrow 2NH_2OH \text{ (acid medium)},$$

are sometimes utilized.

The auxiliary electrode may function as the cathode, as in the analysis of lead by anodic oxidation of plumbous ion to lead dioxide, PbO_2, in nitric medium. Since nitrate ion is more easily reduced than hydrogen ion, hydrogen is not evolved on the auxiliary electrode. The reduction of nitrate proceeds to nitrous acid or even to ammonium ion, depending on the conditions of electrolysis.

b. Experimental Methods. The power supply for electrogravimetric determinations can be assembled from simple parts generally available in the laboratory: battery, rheostat, etc. In commercial units (Cenco, Eberbach, Fisher, Sargent in the United States) the power supply is an autotransformer (Variac) connected to a rectifier and filtering network; thus, cumbersome storage batteries are avoided.

Electrolysis is carried out in tall beakers having a capacity of 150 to 250 ml. Electrodes are made of platinum gauze to increase their area. This construction is advantageous because limiting currents are larger than those with electrodes made of platinum foil of the same size, and therefore the duration of analysis is shortened. Concentric cylindric electrodes are generally preferred. The inner cylindric electrode (generally the auxiliary electrode) is rotated to stir the solution. Vigorous stirring is essential to obtain high rates of mass transfer and consequently to shorten the electrolysis (20 min, perhaps). Heating of the solution decreases the duration of electrolysis because of increase in mass transfer. A higher temperature is also beneficial in increasing rates of irreversible reactions, and consequently, in facilitating the deposition of certain metals such as nickel, cobalt, etc. This is why commercial units are generally equipped with electrical heaters. Cells and electrodes of varied design are described in the literature (see Section 6–6 for references).

---

[7] The reactions may be more complicated.

The working electrode is acid-cleaned (nitric acid, etc.) of any previously deposited metal and then it is dried and finally weighed.[8] The completion of electrolysis is verified if necessary by a spot test on a drop of solution. The stirrer is stopped and the electrodes are removed from solution (lower beaker or lift electrodes) *while they are still connected to the power supply.* If the electrolysis circuit is opened before removal of the electrodes from solution, there is danger of redissolution of the deposit. The working electrode is rapidly washed with distilled water, rinsed with acetone, and allowed to dry in an oven slightly above 100° for a few minutes.

Smooth deposits are advantageous because errors resulting from loss of metal or from occlusion of some material are minimized. Smoothness of the deposit can be improved by the addition of organic substances (gelatin) and/or the use of complexing agents. The phenomena accounting for improvement of the deposit will not be discussed here, since much speculation and few firmly established ideas would be involved.

Fairly concentrated solutions of sulfuric, nitric, and other inorganic acids often are selected as electrolytes for Ag, Au, Bi, Cd, Cu, Pb, Zn, etc. Ammoniacal solutions and other complexing agents (cyanide, tartrate) are sometimes utilized (Co, Ni, etc.).

c. Applications. Many metals can be determined by deposition on platinum electrodes. Various constituents of quite a few commercial alloys can be determined by electrogravimetry (brass, bronze, lead-tin alloys, zinc base die-casting alloys, etc.). In a few rare cases metals are deposited anodically as oxide, as in the determination of lead as lead dioxide. Detailed instructions can be found in the monographs listed in Section 6–6.

Results in electrogravimetry can be accurate within 0.2 per cent in careful work, but the method is not very selective. Application to routine analysis is immediate, and the cost of equipment is moderate. In conclusion, electrogravimetry has been, and still is, a very valuable tool in the control laboratory.

d. Internal Electrolysis. Electrogravimetric determinations can be made without power supply by using as anode a metal which is more readily oxidized than the metal to be deposited. Consider, for example, a cell composed of a platinum electrode in a solution of silver nitrate and a copper electrode in a cupric sulfate solution. The solution has to be analyzed for silver. The cell is short-circuited, and the reactions $Ag^+ + e \rightarrow Ag$, and $Cu^{++} + 2e \leftarrow Cu$, occur until the potentials of the two couples are

---

[8] In the deposition of metals that alloy with platinum (Pb, Zn), it is necessary to plate the working electrode with another metal, such as copper, prior to deposition of the metal to be analyzed. If this precaution is not taken, the surface of the electrode becomes quite rough after dissolution of the deposit.

the same. If one assumes that the platinum electrode is covered with silver, one has for 25°

$$E_{Ag}^0 + 0.0591 \log a_{Ag^+} = E_{Cu}^0 + \frac{0.0591}{2} \log a_{Cu^{++}},$$

or (see Table I)

$$0.7991 + 0.0591 \log a_{Ag^+} = 0.337 + \frac{0.0591}{2} \log a_{Cu^{++}}.$$

If $a_{Cu^{++}} = 0.1$ (0.1 M solution), the activity of silver ion at the end of electrolysis is $10^{-8.3}$, and removal of silver is virtually complete for initial concentrations of silver larger than $10^{-4}\ M$.

The method is very simple from the experimental point of view and applications have been developed. Details can be found in the monographs of Lingane and Schleicher (Section 6–6).

6–2. ELECTROLYSIS AT CONTROLLED POTENTIAL

a. Principle. It was pointed out in the discussion on electrogravimetry that there may be danger of simultaneous deposition in the analysis of solutions containing several metals. This difficulty can sometimes be overcome by the use of complex forming substances, but a more general solution is to control the potential of the working electrode. This method at controlled potential was developed independently by Sand[9] and Fischer[10] in 1907. Several years before, Haber[11] had pointed out the importance of control of potential. However, the necessity of controlling the potential manually was a strong deterrent to the general application of this method in the analytical laboratory. Automatic control of potential was first used by Hickling[12] in 1942, and electrogravimetry at controlled potential came of age shortly afterwards. Lingane, Diehl, and others have advocated a more widespread application of this method in the recent years.

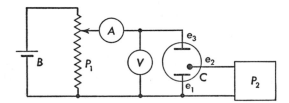

Fig. 46. Schematic diagram of apparatus for electrolysis at controlled potential.

The electrolysis circuit is the same as in classical electrogravimetry, but the potential of the working electrode e_1 (Fig. 46) with respect to a refer-

[9]H. J. S. Sand, *J. Chem. Soc.*, **91**, 373 (1907).
[10]A. Fischer, *Z. angew. Chem.*, **20**, 134 (1907).
[11]F. Haber, *Z. Elektrochem.*, **4**, 506 (1898).
[12]A. Hickling, *Trans. Faraday Soc.*, **38**, 27 (1942).

ence electrode e_2 (saturated calomel electrode, etc.) is controlled. The voltage applied to the cell is adjusted by means of P_1 until the potential of e_1, as determined with potentiometer P_2, has the correct value.

The experimental methods are the same as in the classical method. The electrolysis is prolonged until the current for the deposition of a given metal has virtually dropped to zero. The solution is saved, if necessary, for the deposition of other metals. In the analysis of solutions containing several metals it is sometimes possible to utilize again the working electrode without removing the first deposit; the number of weighings and cleaning operations is decreased and time is saved.

The selection of the potential of the working electrode can be discussed by considering the electrolysis of a solution containing ions of two metals 1 and 2, of which 1 is the easier to deposit. The potential of the working electrode must be such that at the end of electrolysis the concentration of metal 1 in solution is negligible in comparison with its initial concentration. By a reasoning similar to the one in Section 6–1a, one obtains for 25° the condition

$$E \leqslant E_1^0 + \frac{0.0591}{n_1} \log 10^{-4} C_1^0, \tag{6-3}$$

where C_1^0 is the initial concentration of metal 1, and n_1 is the number of electrons involved in the electrode reaction. Metal 2 should not be deposited, and consequently one must have

$$E > E_2^0 + \frac{0.0591}{n_2} \log C_2^0. \tag{6-4}$$

These conditions determine the limits between which E can be varied. Condition (6–3) can be made slightly less stringent by replacing 10^{-4} with 10^{-3}; the deposition of metal 1 is thus 99.90 per cent completed, instead of 99.99 per cent.

EXAMPLE. Prescribe the potential at which silver is to be removed at 25° from a $10^{-2} M$ solution of one of its salts in presence of $2 M$ copper sulfate.

One deduces from conditions (6–3) and (6–4) (see Table I in Chapter 2)

$$E \leqslant 0.779 + 0.0591 \log 10^{-4} \times 10^{-2}$$
$$\leqslant 0.425 \text{ Volt}$$

$$E > 0.34 + \frac{0.0591}{2} \log 2$$
$$> 0.35 \text{ Volt}$$

The potential should be maintained between 0.425 and 0.35 volt, and thus one should select, for instance, 0.38 volt for the separation of silver.

The potential of the working electrode is adjusted at a value at which the concentration of ions of the metal being deposited is negligible at the end of the electrolysis. This potential corresponds to a point in the upper plateau of the current-potential curve, and the limiting current flows through the cell during electrolysis. The rate of removal of the metal from solution is proportional to the limiting current and consequently is also proportional to the concentration of metal ions. It can be shown that the current decreases exponentially with time under such conditions[13] (see problem 1 in Section 6–7). Thus,

$$i = i_0 e^{-pt}, \tag{6-5}$$

where i_0 is the current at time $t = 0$, and p is a constant for a given system. The current decreases continuously during electrolysis and approaches zero for sufficient long times of electrolysis. If the efficiency of stirring is improved, the limiting current for a given concentration of metal is increased, and the metal is then removed more rapidly from solution. In practice the electrolysis is stopped when the current has dropped to a negligible fraction of its initial value, say, less than 0.1 per cent. The resulting error for incomplete deposition is negligible.

It has sometimes been pointed out that electrogravimetry with controlled potential is more time consuming than conventional electrogravimetry because the current is held constant in the latter method, whereas it decreases progressively in the constant potential method. This is not correct because the current in the classical method is used only partially in the deposition of the metal (Fig. 45) at the end of the deposition. Furthermore, the actual current for metal deposition cannot, at any rate, exceed the limiting current which flows through the cell in the method at controlled potential.

b. Instrumentation.   The working and auxiliary electrodes (e_1, e_3 in Fig. 46) are the same as in classical electrogravimetry. The reference electrode e_2 is generally a calomel or silver-silver chloride electrode whose tip is placed in the immediate vicinity of electrode e_1. Electrolysis currents are quite large, perhaps 0.1 amp or even more, and the ohmic drop easily exceeds 0.1 volt if the distance between the working electrode and the tip of the reference electrode exceeds 1 or 2 mm.

A single electrode cannot fulfill the functions of auxiliary (e_3) and reference (e_2) electrodes for two reasons: (1) the distance between these electrodes exceeds several millimeters and the ohmic drop in solution would affect the potential by a serious error; (2) the potential of such an auxiliary reference electrode would not be known with certainty because of

---

[13]A similar situation is encountered in radioactive decay where the number of disintegrations at a given time is proportional to the number of radioactive atoms present in the sample.

rather high currents through the cell and the concomitant danger of polarization. When a separate reference electrode is utilized, the potential of the auxiliary electrode is unimportant.

The apparatus of Fig. 46 with "manual" control of potential is satisfactory when only a few experiments are to be performed, but it is hardly suitable for routine work. Instruments called *potentiostats*, according to a term coined by Hickling,[12] have been developed which automatically maintain the working electrode at a preset potential. Details about these instruments can be found in the specialized literature, and only the simple instrument designed by Lingane[14] will be described. The galvanometer of potentiometer P_2 (Fig. 46) is replaced by a sensitive relay which is essentially a galvanometer whose needle oscillates between two contacts, a and b. When the needle touches contact a, the circuit of a reversible motor, which moves the sliding contact of P_1, is closed. Conversely, when the needle touches contact b the circuit of this reversible motor is also closed, but the direction of rotation is the opposite of that for contact a. When the working electrode e_1 has the potential corresponding to the voltage set on potentiometer P_2, the needle of the relay does not touch contacts a and b. If the potential of e_1 changes, the circuit of contact a or b is closed; the motor moves the sliding contact of P_1 and causes the voltage across the cell to change until the potential is readjusted at its proper value. A storage battery can be utilized as power supply, but a transformer-rectifier unit is more convenient. This unit should have an excellent filter network to eliminate the alternating component of the output voltage (ripple voltage).

Commercial instruments for electrolysis at constant potential are available: Aminco,[15] Fisher,[16] and Analytical Instruments Inc., Bristol, Conn.

c. Applications. Electrolysis at controlled potential is useful in the electrogravimetric analysis of solutions containing more than one metal. If only one metal is present, there is, of course, no danger of codeposition. A few examples of analysis of mixtures will be given for orientation purposes: determination of copper, bismuth, lead, and tin in alloys; determination of nickel in the presence of aluminum, zinc, and iron; determination of antimony in the presence of tin; and determination of silver in the presence of copper. Details may be found in the specialized literature (Diehl, Lingane, Sand, Schleicher; see Section 6–6). Two other types of applications of electrolysis at constant potential are discussed in Sections 6–3 and 6–4.

[14]J. J. Lingane, *Ind. Eng. Chem., Anal. Ed.*, **17**, 332 (1945); J. J. Lingane and S. L. Jones, *Anal. Chem.*, **22**, 1169 (1950).

[15]A version of the instrument described by M. L. Greenough, W. E. Williams, Jr., and J. K. Taylor, *Rev. Sci. Instruments*, **22**, 484 (1951).

[16]This instrument was described (abstract) by J. D. Bode, S. W. Levine, and R. W. Kress, *Anal. Chem.*, **25**, 518 (1953).

The accuracy is the same as in the electrogravimetric classical method (error as low as 0.2 per cent), but the selectivity is much better because of the control of potential. The method can be adapted readily to routine analysis.

6–3. *ELECTROLYTIC SEPARATIONS AND ELECTROGRAPHY*

In the analysis of mixtures it is often necessary to separate certain substances prior to analysis. Separation can be achieved by a variety of methods (precipitation, extraction, distillation, etc.), including electrolysis. Electrolytic separations are carried out without or with control of potential, but the latter method is preferable when there is danger of codeposition.

The first application of electrolysis as a means of separation was reported by Wolcott Gibbs[17] in 1880, and the method was progressively developed by various investigators, among whom E. F. Smith in the United States and Böttger in Germany should be particularly noted. Electrolytic separations at controlled potential and the combination of this method with polarography were pioneered by Lingane.[18]

Mercury cathodes are generally utilized because the overvoltage for hydrogen evolution is much larger than for platinum. The cell designed by Melaven[19] is often used when there is no need for control of potential. A modified form of this cell for separations at controlled potential is shown in Fig. 47. The anode e_3 is a platinum electrode of the type used in classical electrogravimetry; a helix made of platinum wire having a diameter of at least 1 mm could also be utilized. The reference electrode is a silver-silver chloride electrode in a sleeve containing 0.1 molar potassium chloride.[20] The end of this sleeve is closed by a disk of fritted glass covered by a plug of agar-agar; mixing of the solutions in the sleeve and the cell is thus avoided. Solution and mercury are stirred by a propeller partially immersed in mercury. Concentration polarization in solution is thus minimized, and the formation of a concentrated amalgam at the surface of mercury is avoided. The cell is connected to a potentiostat, and the electrolysis is continued until the current is negligible in comparison with its initial value. Mercury is then

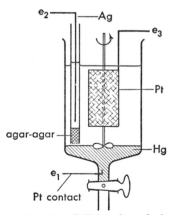

Fig. 47. Cell for electrolytic separations at controlled potential.

[17]W. Gibbs, *Chem. News*, **42**, 291 (1880); see abstract in *Z. Anal. Chem.*, **22**, 558 (1883).
[18]For further historical details see J. A. Maxwell and R. P. Graham, *Chem Revs.*, **46**, 471 (1950).
[19]A.D. Melaven, *Ind. Eng. Chem., Anal. Ed.*, **2**, 180 (1930).
[20]According to a suggestion in Lingane's monograph; see reference in Section 6–6.

drained from the cell *before the electrodes are disconnected*, and the solution is ready for further treatment. It is essential to leave the cell in the circuit when removing mercury because some metals may otherwise be partially redissolved. Some metals such as iron and nickel, which are virtually insoluble in mercury, form a film at the surface of mercury during electrolysis. The amalgam is sometimes saved for further use, and metals are then removed from mercury by treatment with dilute acid. This is an elegant method of extracting traces of certain metals from a large volume of solution. Application to the analysis of uranium salts has been made.[21]

The potential at which separation of a metal is to be carried out can be determined from current-potential curves. The potential is deduced from polarographic waves[22] when a mercury working electrode is utilized. If substance 1 is to be separated from a mixture of substances 1 and 2, the potential for separation is adjusted in the upper plateau of the wave for substance 1.

Commercial instruments especially designed for rapid separations, but without control of potential, are available (Eberbach, Precision Scientific Co.).

Perhaps the most important application of electrolytic separation is the removal of iron prior to analysis for aluminum and the alkaline earth and alkaline metals. Many other applications, however, have been developed, and numerous references can be found in the review of Maxwell and Graham.[18] The method is particularly valuable in the polarographic analysis of a substance in presence of a large excess of other more easily reducible substances. The latter substances then are removed by electrolysis before polarographic analysis. Electrolysis is also applied in the separation of radiotracers, and the corresponding experimental and theoretical problems involved in the electrolytic deposition of less than a monolayer of metal have been investigated by Haissinsky, Rogers, and others.[23]

Electrolysis can also be applied to remove traces of elements from the surface of metallic samples by *electrography*. In this method, which was invented independently by Fritz[24] and Glazunov,[25] the specimen to be examined is pressed against a sheet of filter paper wetted with electrolyte. An aluminum cathode is pressed on the other side of the filter paper and the resulting cell is connected to a power supply. The specimen is oxidized anodically, and the filter paper becomes impregnated with metal ions. After a few minutes of electrolysis, the "imprint" on the filter paper is

[21]N. H. Furman, C. E. Bricker, and B. Duffie, *J. Wash. Acad. Sci.*, **38**, 159 (1948).
[22]J. J. Lingane, *J. Am. Chem. Soc.*, **67**, 1916 (1945).
[23]References in Section 6–6 and the review of L. B. Rogers in *Rec. Chem. Progress*, **16**, 197 (1955).
[24]H. Fritz, *Z. Anal. Chem.*, **78**, 418 (1929).
[25]A. Glazunov, *Chim. et Ind.*, Spec. No. 425 (1929).

developed with a reagent producing a colored product with the metal ions. Surfaces can be studied from the pattern obtained on the filter paper.

Details on this valuable microchemical method can be found in the review of Hermance and Wadlow, and Lingane gives an outline of the method in his text (see references in Section 6–6).

Commercial instruments are on the market (Fisher, Thomas).

6–4. COULOMETRY AT CONTROLLED POTENTIAL

a. Principle. According to Faraday's law, the quantity of electricity involved in the electrolysis of one equivalent of substance is one faraday or 96,494 coulombs. The weight corresponding to one equivalent of the substance being electrolyzed is its gram atomic weight or gram molecular weight divided by the number of electrons involved in the electrode reaction. It follows from this law that the weight W of substance consumed or produced in an electrolysis involving Q coulombs is

$$W = \frac{W_m Q}{96,494n}, \tag{6–6}$$

where W_m is the gram atomic weight or gram molecular weight of the substance being electrolyzed, and n is the number of electrons involved in the electrode reaction.

Equation (6–6) is applicable, provided that *the current efficiency is 100 per cent;* consequently only one reaction should occur on the electrode. For example, in the deposition of copper from cupric sulfate solution, only the reduction of Cu(II) to metallic copper should take place at the exclusion of any other reaction, such as the reduction of Cu(II) to Cu(I)[26] or the evolution of hydrogen.

Analytical methods based on the measurement of a quantity of electricity and the application of equation (6–6) are designated by the generic term of *coulometry*—a term derived from "coulomb," which is a unit commonly used to express quantities of electricity.

The first application of coulometry to analytical chemistry was made by Grower[27] in 1917, almost a century after Faraday (1834) had established the law expressed by equation (6–6). Growers' paper remained buried in the literature, and so did a fundamental investigation of Szebelledy and Somogyi.[28] It is only since about 1945 that interest has arisen in coulometry, thanks to the pioneering efforts of Lingane (coulometry at constant potential), Swift (coulometric titrations), and others.

b. Experimental Methods. According to Lingane's suggestion,[22] apparatus for electrogravimetry at controlled potential can be adapted to

[26]This reaction may occur in chloride medium.
[27]G. G. Grower, *Proc. Am. Soc. Testing Materials*, **17**, 129 (1917).
[28]L. Szebelledy and Z. Somogyi, *Z. Anal. Chem.*, **112**, 313 (1938).

coulometric determinations by inserting in the circuit of the cell a *coulometer* or *current-time* integrator. The electrolysis is continued until virtual completion, and the result of the analysis is computed from equation (6–6). A water coulometer (Fig. 48) in which water is electrolyzed with evolution of hydrogen (cathode) and oxygen (anode) is convenient because the quantity of electricity can be readily calculated from the volume of gas.[22] The coulometer is surrounded by a water jacket with a thermometer to maintain the hydrogen-oxygen mixture at a known temperature. The electrolyte (K_2SO_4 or Na_2SO_4) should not contain any substance (iron salts, etc.) which is reduced or oxidized with the formation of a soluble species. For example, ferric iron would be reduced at the cathode, and the resulting ferrous ions would be oxidized subsequently at the anode. This cycle of reactions resulting from the presence of iron as impurity can involve an appreciable quantity of electricity, and a serious error may result.

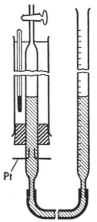

Fig. 48. Water coulometer.[22]

The experimental volume of gas must be corrected for the vapor pressure of the solution and for departure from standard conditions (pressure of 760 mm of mercury at 0°C). See problem 2, Section 6–7.

Titration coulometers can also be utilized; for example, the iodine coulometer in which iodine is generated by anodic oxidation of iodine. The amount of generated iodine is determined by titration with a standard solution of thiosulfate, and the quantity of electricity is calculated from the volume of titrant at the equivalence point.

Since a current expresses the quantity of electricity through a circuit per unit of time, the quantity of electricity consumed in an electrolysis at *constant* current of duration τ sec is $i\tau$. If the current is a function of time, as in electrolysis at constant potential, the quantity of electricity is

$$Q = \int_0^{\tau} i \, dt. \tag{6–7}$$

The integration can be performed graphically by measuring the area under the current-time curve or automatically by means of a mechanical current-time integrator. Another solution is to perform the integration in equation (6–7) by replacing the current by its value from (6–6) (see problem 3 in Section 6–7). However, a departure from the theoretical behavior causes an error when the latter method is applied.

A current-time integrator is available from Analytical Instruments, Inc., Bristol, Conn.

c. Applications. The coulometric method yields results which can be as good as those obtained by electrogravimetry, and errors are as low as

0.2 to 0.5 per cent in careful work. Substances yielding soluble electrolysis products can be determined by coulometry, while this is obviously not the case in electrogravimetry. Numerous applications could be made, and in general, substances which can be determined by polarography or voltametry could be analyzed by coulometry. Adaptation to routine work seems entirely feasible, and the cost of equipment is relatively low.

An interesting application of coulometry at constant potential is the determination of the number of electrons, n, involved in electrode reactions. A known weight of substance is electrolyzed and the number n is computed from equation (6–6). The number n can also be computed from the Ilkovic equation (see Section 4–3), provided that all the other factors in this equation, and in particular the diffusion coefficient of the substance being electrolyzed, are known. When n is quite large ($n > 2$), or when there are kinetic complications, the calculation of n from the Ilkovic equation is uncertain, and the coulometric method is preferable. Such determinations of n are of interest primarily in organic electrochemistry.

The following *microcoulometric method* can also be used in the determination of n. The electrolysis is carried out in a micropolarographic cell (see Fig. 38C in Chapter 4), and the quantity of electricity is measured with a current-time integrator.[29] A water coulometer is not suitable because quantities of electricity to be measured are too small for this instrument. The depletion of the substance being electrolized is practically complete after 1 or 2 hr. A second microcell with a known amount of a substance, whose mechanism of reduction or oxidation at the dropping mercury electrode is well known, may be used as coulometer. The quantity of electricity then is computed from the difference in wave height before and after electrolysis[30] (see problem 5, Section 6–7). In another procedure only one microcell is utilized, and the number of electrons is determined from the variations of current during electrolysis (see problem 6 in Section 6–7).

6–5. COULOMETRIC TITRATIONS

a. Principles. The idea of generating a titrant by electrolysis was advanced by Szebelledy and Somogyi[28] in 1938, but it was a decade later before the method was developed as a practical analytical tool by Swift[31] and others.

The principle of the method will be discussed by considering the titration of ferrous ions with generated ceric ions.[32] The solution of ferrous ions is placed in cell C of Fig. 49, and the platinum anode e_1, having an

[29]S. Bogan, L. Meites, E. Peters, and J. M. Sturtevant, *J. Am. Chem. Soc.*, **73**, 1584 (1951).

[30]T. De Vries and J. L. Kroon, *J. Am. Chem. Soc.*, **75**, 2484 (1953).

[31]J. W. Sease, C. Niemann, and E. H. Swift, *Anal. Chem.*, **19**, 197 (1947). This is the first of a series of papers by Swift and co-workers in this field.

[32]N. H. Furman, W. D. Cooke, and C. N. Reilley, *Anal. Chem.*, **23**, 945 (1951).

area of a few square centimeters, is immersed in the cell. The solution in the anodic compartment is stirred mechanically. The cathode e_2 is in a separate compartment to prevent mixing of the solutions from one compartment to the other. The solution in the cathodic compartment, is for instance, 0.1 molar sulfuric acid. The electrolysis circuit is closed with switch S which also starts the electric timer T, and the current through the cell is maintained rigorously constant regardless of the processes which occur at the electrodes. We shall see below how this result is achieved. Since the current i_c through the cell is constant, the

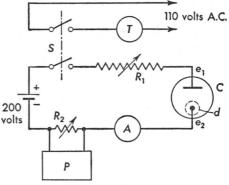

Fig. 49. Schematic diagram of apparatus for coulometric titrations at constant current with internal generation of titrant.

quantity of electricity consumed during electrolysis is $i_c\tau$, where τ is the duration of electrolysis read on timer T.

We shall first consider the case in which no cerium salt is added to the ferrous solution in cell C. The behavior of the anode is similar to that of the working electrode in electrogravimetry (Section 6–1a), and the results of Fig. 45 can readily be applied here. However, it is to be noted that Fig. 45 was constructed for a cathodic process, while we deal now with an anodic process, namely, the oxidation of ferrous ion; the sign of the current must be reversed. The anode potential varies progressively and acquires the value of E_5 when the limiting current for the oxidation of ferrous ion is smaller than the current flowing through the cell. A new anodic reaction must then take place, and in this case, oxygen is evolved at the anode.[33] Oxygen does not react appreciably with the remaining ferrous iron, and the current efficiency for the oxidation of ferrous ion is thus smaller than 100 per cent. The quantity of ferrous ions initially present in solution cannot be computed from Faraday's law under such conditions. This difficulty is avoided when cerous ions are added in large excess with respect to ferrous ions. There is no reaction between cerous cerium and ferrous ions, but cerous ions are oxidized more easily than water.[34] The resulting ceric ions readily react with the remaining ferrous iron, according to the reaction

$$Ce^{+4} + Fe^{++} = Ce^{+3} + Fe^{+3},$$

and the oxidation of ferrous ions proceeds with 100 per cent efficiency.

[33]E^0 for $Fe^{+3} + e = Fe^{++}$ is 0.77 volt.

E^0 for $O_2 + 4H^+ + 4e = 2H O$ is 1.229 volts; this reaction involves an overvoltage of at least a few tenths of a volt even at very low current densities.

[34]Oxygen evolution involves a large overvoltage; see footnote 33.

Side reactions are avoided at the generating electrode when there is not complete depletion (at the electrode surface) of the substance involved in the generation of titrant. The concentration of generating substance thus depends on the current through the cell, the area of the generating electrode, and the rate of stirring. This concentration is generally between 0.01 and 0.1 M.

In the preceding example it is only toward the end of electrolysis that ceric ions are produced at the anode, but there are cases in which the titrant is generated during the whole titration. Consider for instance the titration of thiosulfate by generated iodine. Thiosulfate is oxidized to tetrathionate, according to the reaction

$$S_4O_6^{--} + 2e \leftarrow 2S_2O_3^{--},$$

which requires a large overvoltage on a platinum anode and involves complications resulting from side reactions. If iodide is added to the solution, the reaction

$$I_2 + 2e \leftarrow 2I^-$$

occurs, and the resulting I_2 readily reacts with thiosulfate. The direct electrolytic oxidation of thiosulfate virtually does not occur under these conditions.

The titrant, iodine, in the preceding example, is produced by electrolytic oxidation instead of being added with a burette in the usual manner. This is why the method is referred to as a *coulometric titration with internal generation of titrant*. The qualification "internal" indicates that generation takes place in the titration cell, in opposition to a method in which the generation cell is outside the titration cell. The cell schematically represented in Fig. 50 is used for *external generation* of titrant.[35] The solution consumed in the generation of titrant flows in a T-tube in which two platinum electrodes are sealed. The titrant is generated at one of these electrodes, and the resulting solution is collected in the titration vessel. For example, a solution of potassium iodide is used in the titration of thiosulfate, and the iodine solution formed at the anode flows in the titration cell. External generation is applied whenever internal generation fails; for example, because of interference of the substance to be titrated with the generation reaction.

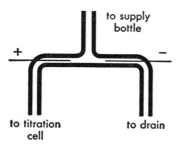

Fig. 50. Cell for coulometric titrations at constant current with external generation of titrant.

[35]D. D. DeFord, J. N. Pitts, and C. J. Johns, *Anal. Chem.*, **23**, 938 (1951).

b. Experimental Methods. An example of cell for titrations with internal generation of titrant is shown in Fig. 51. Generation occurs on the platinum electrode e_1, having an area of a few square centimeters to allow relatively large generation currents with moderate stirring. The other electrode, e_2, is placed in a sleeve whose bottom is a fritted glass disk, d. Mixing of solutions from one compartment to the other is further prevented by a plug of agar-agar or gelatinous silicic acid (add a drop of acid to a solution of sodium silicate). It is essential to separate the two electrodes to obtain 100 per cent current efficiency at the generating electrode. Consider, for example, the generation of iodine by oxidation of iodide on electrode e_1, and assume that electrode e_2 is directly immersed in solution. Iodine would then be produced at e_1 and partially reduced at electrode e_2 in a cyclic process, and the coulometric determination would be erroneous.

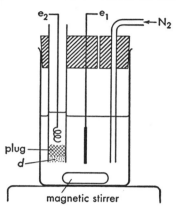

Fig. 51. Example of cell for coulometric titrations at constant current with internal generation of titrant.

The solution is stirred mechanically and is freed from oxygen if the generation reaction occurs at a potential at which oxygen is reduced. Nitrogen is then bubbled for 10 to 15 min. before titration to remove oxygen.

The generation current is kept constant by connecting the cell in series with a large resistance R_1 to a power supply (dry cells, etc.) having a constant output voltage of the order of 100 to 200 volts (Fig. 49). The current through the cell is read on ammeter A, and more precise values of the current are obtained by using a student potentiometer to measure the ohmic drop in an adjustable calibrated resistance, R_2. This resistance is adjusted at a value for which the ohmic drop is of the order of 1 volt. Since resistance R_2 is easily accurate within 0.05 per cent and the ohmic drop is measured within 1 mv, the error on the current does not exceed about 0.1 per cent.

The current is not rigorously constant during titration, but the variation is quite small, as can be seen from the following considerations. The current is

$$i_c = \frac{V_p - V_c}{R_1 + R_2 + R_a} \tag{6-8}$$

where V_p is the output voltage of the power supply (100 to 200 volts), V_c is the voltage across the cell (1 to 2 volts), R_1 and R_2 are the resistances in Fig. 49, and R_a is the resistance of ammeter A. The voltage V_c varies during electrolysis by perhaps 0.5 volt. If V_c is, for example, 1 volt before electrolysis and 1.5 volts at the end of the titration, the relative variation of current is

$$\frac{\Delta i_c}{i_c} = \frac{0.5}{V_p - V_c},$$ (6-9)

or, since $V_p \gg V_c$,

$$\frac{\Delta i_c}{i_c} \approx \frac{0.5}{V_p}.$$ (6-10)

If $V_p = 200$ volts, the variation of current is only 0.25 per cent and quite negligible. More rigorous control of the current can be achieved by electronic regulation, but the simple circuit of Fig. 49 is adequate in most cases.

The end point is detected by means of a color indicator or an instrumental method such as potentiometry, amperometry, photometry (see Chapter 9). Instrumental methods are generally preferred to indicators because of their greater sensitivity. Generation of titrant is interrupted periodically, and readings of the quantity which serves as indicator are taken. A plot of this quantity against time yields the equivalence point. The time between consecutive generation periods is increased in the vicinity of the equivalence point to avoid errors resulting from sluggishness of the titration reaction. Generation times generally are of the order of 200 to 300 sec, but much shorter times are involved when very dilute solutions are titrated. Readings can be made on an electric timer with an accuracy of 0.1 to 0.01 sec, and consequently the error on, say, 200 sec is negligible. The order of magnitude of the current and generation time to be selected for titration can be calculated from equation (6-6) and the relationship $Q = i_c \times \tau$, provided that the quantity of substance to be titrated is known approximately.

Instruments in which the generation circuit is automatically open at the equivalence point are described in the literature.[36] These instruments are based on a principle similar to that of the titrimeter of Fig. 24, discussed in Section 3-10c. A commercial unit is available (Fisher).

c. Applications.   Quantities of electricity corresponding to very small amounts of substances can be measured with precision, and coulometric titrations can still be performed in cases in which small volumes of an extremely dilute titrant would be required. For instance, 0.1 ml of a 10^{-6} M solution contains $0.1 \times 10^{-3} \times 10^{-6}$ mole, that is, 10^{-10} mole. In view of Faraday's law, this amount of substance corresponds to $10^{-10} \times$ 96,494 $\times$ n coulombs, n being the number of electrons involved per mole-

[36]D. D. DeFord, C. J. Johns, and J. N. Pitts, *Anal. Chem.*, **24**, 941 (1951); W. N. Carson, Jr., *ibid.*, **25**, 226 (1953); E. N. Wise, P. W. Gilles, and C. A. Reynolds, Jr., *ibid.*, **25**, 1344 (1953).

cule of electrolyzed substance. If n equals one and a generation time of 10 sec is selected, the generation current i_c is

i.e.,
$$i_c \times 10 = 10^{-10} \times 96{,}494,$$

$$i_c = 0.964 \ \mu a.$$

Such a current can be easily measured and coulometric titrations are thus applicable to trace analysis. Application of conventional titrimetric procedures to the determination of very small amounts of substance involves very serious difficulties because it is virtually impossible to store standard solutions of low concentration, say, below $10^{-3} M$. No problem of this type is encountered in coulometric titrations since the titrant is immediately consumed as it is being generated. This major advantage of coulometric titrations accounts for the favor with which this rather new method has been received by analytical chemists. Another advantage is the possibility of generating titrants which are readily oxidized by air and are therefore difficult or impossible to use in conventional titrimetry. For example, titanous ion or cuprous copper can be readily generated electrolytically but as reagents are easily oxidized by air. A third advantage of coulometric titrations is the possibility of devising simple automatic instruments. These instruments are somewhat simpler than conventional "autotitrimeters" because it is easier to control a current than to handle a liquid.

Summarizing, coulometric titrations are primarily interesting in the titration of small amounts of substance under conditions in which ordinary titrimetric procedures fail. It should be emphasized that in such applications the main difficulty and source of error is the detection of the end point, and not the measurement of the quantity of electricity consumed in the titration.

Only rather inexpensive equipment is required, and application in the control laboratory appears entirely feasible.

It is a relatively simple matter to generate the most common reagents of titrimetric analysis. Quite a few applications have already been reported, as one can deduce from the following list of titrants and titrated substances. Many other applications are also possible.

H^+: OH^-

OH^-: H^+

Cl_2: As(III)

Br_2: As(III), CNS^-, Cu(I), I^-, N_2H_4, NH_2OH, Sb(III), Tl(I), U(IV), thiodiglycol, mustard gas, 8-hydroxyquinoline, aniline

I_2: As(III), $S_2O_3^{--}$

Ce(IV): Fe(II)

Fe(II): $Cr_2O_7^{--}$, MnO_4^-, vanadate

Cu(I): $Cr_2O_7^{--}$, vanadate

Ti(III): Fe(III)

Hydrogen and hydroxyl ions are generated by electrolysis of water

$$1/2\,O_2 + 2H^+ + 2e \longleftarrow H_2O \text{ (anode)}$$

$$H_2O + e \longrightarrow 1/2\,H_2 + OH^- \text{ (cathode)}.$$

The halogens are generated by anodic oxidation of the corresponding potassium or sodium halides. The other titrants in the above list are generated by oxidation [for instance, Ce(III) to Ce(IV)] or reduction (for example, TiO^{++} to Ti^{+3}) of a salt of the element in another oxidation state.

An ingenious application of coulometry at controlled current has been made to the continuous analysis of gases. A short description of this method may be prepared as an exercise (problem 19 in Section 6–7).

Coulometry at constant current can also be applied to the determination of the thickness of corrosion films on metallic surfaces. The film (oxide, sulfide, etc.) is reduced at constant current, and the end of dissolution is indicated by a rapid variation of potential. The thickness of the film is calculated from the quantity of electricity consumed in electrolysis (problem 20, Section 6–7).

6–6. BIBLIOGRAPHY

a. Books and Articles in Monographs

N. A. Bonner, article in *Radioactivity Applied to Chemistry*, A. C. Wahl and N. A. Bonner, Eds., Wiley, New York, 1951. See references for the electrolytic separation of traces of radioactive elements, pp. 460–465.

W. Böttger, article in *Physikalische Methoden der Analytischen Chemie*, W. Böttger, Ed., Vol. 2, Akademische Verlagsgesellschaft, Lepizig, 1936. Authoritative review with very detailed bibliography.

A. Classen and H. Danneel, *Quantitative Analyse durch Elektrolyse*, 7th ed., Springer, Berlin, 1927. A classic in electrogravimetry.

W. D. Cooke, article in *Organic Analysis*, J. Mitchell, Jr., I. M. Kolthoff, E. S. Proskauer, and A. Weissberger, Eds., Vol. 2, Interscience, New York, 1954. A discussion of coulometric methods.

P. Delahay, *New Instrumental Methods in Electrochemistry*, Interscience, New York, 1954. See chapters on coulometric methods and electrolysis at controlled potential.

H. Diehl, *Electrochemical Analysis with Graded Cathode Potential Control*, The G. Frederick Smith Chemical Co., Columbus, Ohio, 1948. A short monograph on electrogravimetry at controlled potential; contains detailed instructions for applications.

M. Haissinsky, *Electrochimie des Substances Radioactives et des Solutions Extrêmement Diluées*, Hermann, Paris, 1946. A good review of the theory and applications of electrolytic separation of traces.

A. Hollard and L. Bertiaux, *Analyse des Métaux par Electrolyse*, 4th ed., Dunod, Paris, 1930. Valuable in the control laboratory.

H. W. Hermance and H. V. Wadlow, article in *Physical Methods in Chemical Analysis*, W. G. Berl, Ed., Vol. 2, Academic Press, New York, 1951. Authoritative and detailed discussion of electrography.

A. Lassieur, *Electroanalyse Rapide*, Presses Universitaires de France, Paris, 1927. An early monograph on electrogravimetry at constant potential.

J. J. Lingane, *Electroanalytical Chemistry*, Interscience, New York, 1953. See detailed discussion of electrolysis at controlled potential and coulometry.

H. T. S. Sand, *Electrochemistry and Electrochemical Analysis*, Chemical Publishing Co., Brooklyn, N.Y., 1940–42. See Vol. 2 for a discussion of electrogravimetry at controlled potential by the inventor of the method.

A. Schleicher, *Elektroanalytische Schnellmethoden*, 3rd ed., Enke, Stuttgart, 1947. Rather recent monograph in electrogravimetry with detailed bibliography.

G. W. Slomin, *Rapid Quantitative Electrolytic Methods of Analysis*, available from E. H. Sargent and Co., Chicago. Instructions for a wide variety of electrogravimetric determinations.

E. F. Smith, *Electroanalysis*, 6th ed., Blakiston, New York, 1918. A classic in electrogravimetry.

b. Reviews

S. E. Q. Ashley, *Anal. Chem.*, **21,** 70 (1949); **22,** 1379 (1950); **24,** 91 (1952). Review of recent literature on electrogravimetry and electrolytic separations.

D. D. DeFord, *Anal. Chem.*, **26,** 135 (1954); **28,** 660 (1956). Review of recent literature on electrogravimetry, electrolytic separations, and coulometric methods.

N. H. Furman, *Anal. Chem.*, **22,** 33 (1950); **23,** 21 (1951); **26,** 84 (1954); see sections on coulometric titrations. *J. Electrochem. Soc.*, **101,** 19 C (1954); a survey of coulometric and related methods.

J. A. Maxwell and R. P. Graham, *Chem. Revs.*, **46,** 471 (1950). Detailed review of separations with the mercury electrode.

P. S. Tutundzic, *Anal. Chim. Acta*, **8,** 182 (1953). A survey of coulometric analysis (in German).

6-7. PROBLEMS

a. Extension of Theory

1. Derive the current-time relationship [equation (6–5)] for electrolysis at controlled potential.

Note that $i = KN/V$ and $i = nF \, dN/dt$, where K is a proportionality factor [see equation (4–41)], N the number of moles of the substance being electrolyzed at time t, V the volume of solution, n the number of electrons involved in the electrode reaction, and F the faraday.

Apply the result to the following problem: 100 ml of a $1.2 \times 10^{-3} M$ solution of lead nitrate are electrolyzed on a mercury cathode of 5.20 cm^2 at a potential of -0.7 volt (versus S.C.E.). The solution is also 0.1 molar in potassium nitrate (supporting electrolyte). Mechanical stirring is such that the thickness of the diffusion layer, which is assumed to remain constant during electrolysis, is 0.025 mm. The diffusion coefficient of lead ion in this medium is 9×10^{-6} cm^2 sec^{-1}. Calculate enough values of the current to plot a current-time curve. At which time does the concentration of lead ions drop to one-thousandth of its original value?

2. A volume of 27.13 ml of hydrogen-oxygen mixture was measured in a water coulometer in a coulometric determination of lead at constant potential. The temperature of the gas was 23.0° and the barometric pressure in the room was 751 mm of mercury. Calculate the quantity of lead intially present in the electrolytic cell. The water vapor pressure of the 0.1M sodium sulfate solution in the coulometer is as follows:

t (degrees centigrade)	20	21	22	23	24	25
p (mm Hg)	17.5	18.6	19.2	21.0	22.3	23.7

Calculate the theoretical volume of hydrogen-oxygen mixture per coulomb for standard conditions, and compare it with the experimental value of 0.1739 ml per coulomb. Use the latter value in the calculation of the result of the analysis.

3. Derive the value of the quantity of electricity Q consumed in electrolysis at constant potential by integrating the current over the duration of electrolysis. Show that the quantities necessary for the calculation of Q can be determined from an experimental plot of the logarithm of current against time.

Note: Apply equations (6–6) and (6–7).

4. Calculate the relative error which is made by stopping an electrolysis at controlled potential at a given time τ. Plot the error against τ for the particular case in which the current has dropped to 0.1 per cent of its initial value after 2 hr. Limit the graph to values of τ corresponding to errors from 5 to 0.005 per cent.

Note: Integrate equation (6–5) from 0 to ∞ and from 0 to τ.

5. A 2-millimolar solution of nitrobenzene buffered at pH 3 is electrolyzed at -0.50 volt (versus S.C.E.), i.e., at a potential in the upper pleateau of the first of the two polarographic waves that this compound yields ($E_{1/2} = -0.34$ volt and $E_{1/2} = -0.86$ volt at pH 3). The volume of solution is 0.37 ml. After electrolysis the height of the first wave is 50 per cent of its original value. A second microcell containing 0.44 ml of 3.14 millimolar cadmium is inserted in series with the first cell. The height of the cadmium wave was 173 mm before electrolysis and 93 mm after completion of electrolysis. Calculate the number of electrons involved in the electrode reaction and write the equation for this reaction.

6. The average height of a polarographic wave is

$$\bar{h} = nF \frac{dN}{dt}$$

where n is the number of electrons involved in the electrode reaction, F the faraday, and N the number of moles of the electrolyzed substance in the polarographic cell. One also has

$$\bar{h} = KC$$

where C is the concentration of electrolyzed substance, and K a proportionality constant embodying the various factors of the Ilkovic equation. K can be determined experimentally for a known value of C. Finally, one has

$$N = Cv$$

where v is the volume of solution.

On the basis of these three equations show that the number of electrons n can be deduced from a plot of log $\bar{h}$ against time.

b. Application of Theory

7. Fifty milliliters of a zinc sulfate solution are transferred to an electrolytic cell with mercury cathode, and enough solid potassium nitrate is added to make the solution approximately 0.1 M in this salt. The potential of the cathode is adjusted at -1.3 volts (versus S.C.E.), and the electrolysis is carried out to virtual completion. The quantity of electricity, as read on a mechanical current-time integrator, is 241 coulombs. Calculate the initial concentration of zinc ion.

8. One hundred milliliters of a $2.15 \times 10^{-3}\,M$ buffered solution (pH 8.9) of selenite (SeO_3^{--}) are reduced on a mercury pool at -1.80 volts (versus S.C.E.). The following current readings were made during electrolysis:

t (sec)	0	72	180	360	720	1080	1440	1800	2520	3600
i (milliamp)	173	156	135	105	63.7	39.5	23.4	14.2	5.23	1.17

Calculate by graphic integration the quantity of electricity consumed in electrolysis, and deduce the number of electrons involved in the electrode reaction. Write the equation for this reaction. Plot log i against time and explain the result.

9. Many metals (Al, Cu, Fe, Mg, Zn, etc.; see quantitative analysis text) can be determined by precipitation with 8-hydroxyquinoline. The result of the analysis is computed by weighing the precipitate according to usual gravimetric procedures. In another method the precipitate is dissolved after suitable washing in an acid solution, and the oxine is titrated with a bromate solution in presence of an excess of bromide, according to the reaction

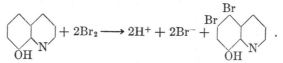

When small amounts (1 mg or so) of oxine are involved, coulometric titration with generated bromine is of interest [W. N. Carson, Jr., *Anal. Chem.*, **22**, 1565 (1950)]. Bromine is generated by anodic oxidation of bromide.

This method was applied to the analysis of magnesium, and the following measurements were made during the coulometric titration.

> Generation time: 247.4 sec
> Ohmic drop in calibrated resistance: 0.934 volt
> Calibrated resistance: 100 ohms

Calculate the amount of magnesium present in the sample.

Note: Two molecules of oxine are precipitated per atom of magnesium.

10. The following measurements were made in a coulometric titration of ferric ions with generated titanous ions.

> Generation time: 116.3 sec
> Ohmic drop in resistance: 1.213 volts
> Calibrated resistance: 100 ohms

Calculate the amount of iron present in the sample.

c. Survey of Literature

11. Make a critical analysis of the electrogravimetric analysis of copper.

Note: Use as a source the paper by S. Skowronski, *ASTM Bull.*, No. 174, pp. 60–65, (1951).

12. Prepare instructions for the electrogravimetric determination of the following elements: Ag, As, Bi, Co, Ni, Pb, Sb, Sn, Zn.

Note: See Slomin's monograph as a main source. Consult also the classical works listed in Section 6–6.

13. Prepare instructions for the following electrogravimetric determinations: Cd in presence of Zn; Cu in presence of Bi; Cu in presence of Ag; Cu in presence of Pb; Ni in presence of Zn; Sn in presence of Sb.

Note: See remark in problem 12.

14. Prepare instructions for the following electrogravimetric determinations at controlled potential: Bi in presence of Pb, Sn, Sb; Rh in presence of Ir; Pb in presence of Cd, Ni, Sn, Zn.

Note: See Lingane's monograph listed in Section 6–6.

15. Prepare a survey of the applications of electrogravimetry with internal electrolysis.

Note: See Schleicher's or Lingane's monograph (Section 6–6).

16. Prepare instructions for coulometric titrations with generated bromine for the following determinations: As(III), Cu(I), I$^-$, Sb(III), Tl(I), U(IV).

Note: For references, see Cooke's article and Lingane's or Delahay's monographs (Section 6–6).

17. Prepare instructions for coulometric titrations with generated ferrous ions for the following determinations: dichromate, permanganate, vanadate.

Note: See remark in problem 16.

18. Discuss criteria for the design of an automatic instrument for coulometric titrations at constant current.

Note: See W. N. Carson, Jr., *Anal. Chem.*, **25**, 226 (1953).

19. Prepare a discussion of continuous coulometric titration of gases at controlled current.

Note: See remark in problem 14. A commercial instrument is available. (Titrilog from Consolidated Engineering Co., Pasadena, Cal.)

20. Prepare a discussion of the coulometric determination of the thickness of corrosion films.

Note: See remark in problem 16.

21. Discuss the determination of traces of metals by electrolysis followed by anodic stripping. See S. S. Lord, R. C. O'Neill, and L. B. Rogers, *Anal. Chem.*, **24**, 209 (1952); K. W. Gardiner and L. B. Rogers, *ibid.*, **25**, 1393 (1953); J. G. Nikelly and W. D. Cooke, *ibid.*, in course of publication.

7

Conductometry and High-Frequency Methods

7-1. HISTORICAL

The current through an electrolytic cell depends on the transport of electricity in solution and the phenomena occurring at the electrode. The voltage across the cell is thus the sum of the voltage drops at each electrode and in solution. In the preceding chapters we were interested in electrode processes, and we generally neglected the voltage drop in solution for the sake of simplicity. We now examine the transport of electricity in solution and application of this phenomenon to chemical analysis.

The transport of electricity in electrolytes and conductance phenomena have been investigated since about 1800. Many distinguished contributions were made by Hittorf, Kohlrausch, Arrhenius, Ostwald, and others in the nineteenth century. A new impetus was given in the 1920's by the theoretical work of Debye, Onsager, Hückel, Falkenhagen, and others. Methods for the very precise measurement of conductances were developed by Kohlrausch in the second half of the nineteenth century, and by Jones, Shedlovsky, and others in the 1930's.

Since the conductance of a solution of electrolyte is related to the concentration of electrolyte, analytical applications of conductance are possible. Conductance measurements can also be applied to the determination of the equivalence point of certain titrations, as was first shown by Dutoit[1] in 1910. Many conductometric titrations were developed by Kolthoff, Britton, Jander, Pfundt, and others, particularly in the 1920's.

[1]P. Dutoit, *J. chim. phys.*, **8**, 12 (1910).

As we shall see in Section 7–4, the conductance of electrolytes is measured with alternating current at frequencies of the order of 1000 cps and with a cell in which two platinum electrodes are immersed. The possibility of making measurements at high frequency (5 megacycles per second for instance) and with the electrodes outside the cell was recognized by Blake[2] in 1933, but there was not a general awareness or understanding of the possibility of the high-frequency method until Jensen and Parrack[3] presented their interesting results in 1946.

7–2. CONDUCTANCE AND CONCENTRATION

Consider a solution of a *completely ionized* electrolyte M_pA_q in an ideal cell in which are immersed two plane electrodes, each having an area of 1 sq cm. The interelectrode distance is 1 cm, and the cross section of the solution path between electrodes is 1 sq cm. A voltage of E volt is applied across the electrodes, and experimental conditions are such that the sum of the voltage drops at the two electrode-solution interfaces is equal to zero.

The current through the cell is the sum of the absolute values of the charges transferred toward each electrode per unit of time. Each mole of salt M_pA_q produces upon dissolution p moles of cations M^{+n_c}, which carry a total positive charge of pn_cF coulombs, n_c being the valency of the cation, and F the faraday, i.e., 96,494 coulombs (see Faraday's law in Section 6–4). Likewise, the total negative charge is qn_aF. Because of electroneutrality, pn_cF and qn_aF are equal and can be set equal to νF. If C_m is the molar concentration, $\nu FC_m/1000$ charges of each sign are produced per cubic centimeter. If the cation migrates in a field of 1 volt per centimeter with a *mobility* of u cm per second, and the anion has a mobility v under the same conditions, the current is

$$ I = \frac{F\nu C_m}{1000}(u + v)E, \qquad (7\text{–}1) $$

or in an abridged form,

$$ I = \kappa E \qquad (7\text{–}2) $$

with

$$ \kappa = \frac{F\nu C_m(u + v)}{1000}. \qquad (7\text{–}3) $$

There, κ is the *specific conductivity* of the electrolyte, i.e., the conductivity of a cell having a length of 1 cm and a cross section of 1 sq cm. It follows from equation (7–2) that Ohm's law is obeyed by electrolytes, at least in the ideal case considered here.

It is convenient to introduce the *equivalent conductance* $\Lambda = \kappa V$, where V is the volume in cubic centimeters which contains one equivalent of electrolyte. One has $\nu C_m = 1000/V$, where the factor 1000 results from the use of

[2] G. G. Blake, *J. Roy. Soc. Arts London*, **82**, 154 (1933).
[3] F. W. Jensen and A. L. Parrack, *Ind. Eng. Chem., Anal. Ed.*, **18**, 595 (1946).

cubic centimeters (practically millimeters) for expressing V, and moles per liter for C_m. Equation (7-3) can now be written as

$$\Lambda = F(u + v) \tag{7-4}$$

or

$$\Lambda = \lambda_+ + \lambda_- \tag{7-5}$$

where the λ's are the *ionic equivalent conductances*.

Since νC_m is the normality N of the solution, it follows from equation (7-5) and the definition of $\Lambda(\Lambda = \kappa V)$ and from the relationship $\nu C_m = 1000/V = N$ that the specific conductance is

$$\kappa = 10^{-3}N(\lambda_+ + \lambda_-), \tag{7-6}$$

for a single electrolyte. By analogy, one has for a mixture of electrolytes,

$$\kappa = 10^{-3} \Sigma N_i\lambda_i, \tag{7-7}$$

where N_i is the normality of ion i and λ_i its ionic equivalent conductance.

The foregoing treatment is based on a rather drastic simplification of actual conditions because interactions between ions in solution are neglected. These interactions are taken into account in modern treatments of conductance, but such material is not within the scope of this book, and the reader is referred to electrochemistry and physical chemistry texts (see references in Section 2-11a).

Because of interactions, the equivalent conductance Λ depends on the electrolyte concentration and tends toward the *equivalent conductance at*

TABLE VIII
Equivalent Ionic Conductances at Infinite Dilution at 25°[a]

CATIONS	λ^0_+	$\dfrac{1}{\lambda^0_+}\dfrac{d\lambda^0_+}{dT}$	ANIONS	λ^0_-	$\dfrac{1}{\lambda^0_-}\dfrac{d\lambda^0_-}{dT}$
H+	349.82	0.0142	OH−	198.0	0.0160
K+	73.52	0.0189	Br−	78.4	0.0187
NH4+	73.4		I−	76.8	0.0186
Ag+	61.92		Cl−	76.34	0.0188
Na+	50.11	0.0209	NO3−	71.44	0.0180
Li+	38.69	0.0226	ClO4−	68.0	
Pb++	73		CH3CO2−	40.9	
1/2 Ba++	63.64	0.0206	1/2 SO4−−	79.8	0.0196
1/2 Ca++	59.50	0.0211	1/2 C2O4−−	70	
1/2 Sr++	59.46				
1/2 Mg++	53.06	0.0218			

[a]Mainly from J. J. Lingane. *Electroanalytical Chemistry*, Interscience, New York, 1953, p. 147.

infinite dilution Λ^0 as the concentratoin approaches zero. Likewise, λ_+ and λ_- tend toward limiting values λ_+^0 and λ_-^0. A few typical values of equivalent ionic conductances at infinite dilution and their corresponding temperature coefficients are listed[4] in Table VIII.

[4]Numerous data are given by H. S. Harned and B. B. Owen, *The Physical Chemistry of Electrolytic Solutions*, 2nd ed., Reinhold, New York, 1950.

In addition to ionic interaction, one must take into account, in the case of weak electrolytes, the dissociation of the electrolyte. We shall consider 1-1 weak electrolytes such as, for example, a weak acid HA. Because of incomplete dissociation the conductance of a solution containing C moles of acid per liter is smaller than the value one would expect on the assumption of complete dissociation. The concentrations of ions H^+ and A^- are the same and equal to αC, α being the degree of dissociation of the acid. Hence, the equivalent conductance Λ at the concentration C is $\alpha \Lambda^0$, where Λ^0 is the equivalent at infinite dilution. The degree of dissociation may be readily calculated, provided that Λ^0 is known and Λ is determined from experimental conductances. The dissociation constant of the weak acid[5] may then be deduced from α and C (problem 1, Section 7–8).

7–3. CONDUCTOMETRIC TITRATIONS

Conductance measurements can be applied to the determination of the equivalence point of titrations involving acid-base neutralization or precipitation reactions. Application is seldom made to titrations involving oxidation-reduction reactions. The latter titrations are often carried out in the presence of a large excess of hydrogen ions, and the conductance does not vary appreciably during titration.

The principle of conductometric titrations can be conveniently discussed by considering the titration of a strong acid with a strong base; for instance, hydrochloric acid with sodium hydroxide,

$$H^+ + Cl^- + Na^+ + OH^- = H_2O + Cl^- + Na^+.$$

In view of equation (7–7), the specific conductance of the solution is ($\nu = 1$)

$$\kappa = 10^{-3} \Sigma N_i \lambda_i.$$

Hydrogen ions are replaced by sodium ions before the equivalence point, and the conductance decreases because $\lambda_{Na^+}(\lambda_{Na^+}^0 = 50.11$ at $25°)$ is smaller than $\lambda_{H^+}(\lambda_{H^+}^0 = 349.82$ at $25°)$. The conductance increases after the equivalence point because sodium hydroxide is added to the solution. If the reaction is quantitative and the volume of titrant consumed at the equivalence point is much smaller than the volume of solution being titrated, the concentrations vary linearly during titration (see Fig. 18 and Section 3–5). The conductance, then, is a linear function of the volume of titrant[6], and the titration curve is composed of two segments of straight lines (Fig. 52A). In practice, one determines three points on each side of the equivalence point and obtains the latter by extrapolation.

[5]The ionization constant is the value of the dissociation constant extrapolated at zero concentration.

[6]This is not rigorous because Λ varies somewhat with concentration.

Various types of titration curves can be obtained for titrations involving strong or weak acids and bases. These curves are shown in Fig. 52 for conditions under which dilution during titration can be neglected. The curve of Fig. 52B corresponds to the titration of a strong acid with a weak base.

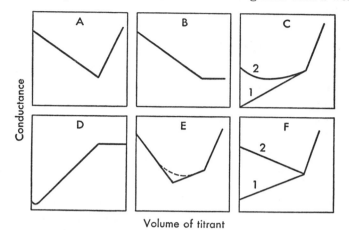

Fig. 52. Types of conductometric titration curves: (A) strong acid by a strong base, or vice versa; (B) strong acid by a weak base; (C) weak acid by a strong base; (D) weak acid by a weak base, or vice versa; (E) titration of a mixture of strong acid and a very weak acid with a strong base; and (F) titration of a salt of a weak acid and a strong base with a strong acid. See text for precipitation reactions.

Since the titrant is a weak electrolyte, the conductance remains virtually constant after the end point. However, if very dilute solutions are involved, the ionization of the weak base is appreciable, and the conductance may increase after the equivalence point. The conductance increases throughout the titration of a weak acid by a strong base (Fig. 52C, curve 1), but the increase is more rapid after the equivalence point because of the high ionic equivalent conductance of hydroxyl ions. If the concentrations are very low and the acid not too weak, ionization of the weak acid is not negligible, and curve 2 of Fig. 52C is obtained. Finally, the conductance increases before the equivalence point in a titration involving a weak acid and a weak base because of the production of a completely ionized salt (Fig. 52D). The conductance near the origin is not entirely negligible because of ionization of the weak electrolyte.

The titration of a mixture of a strong acid and a very weak acid with a strong base yields the curve of Fig. 52E. The minimum indicates the neutralization of the strong acid, and the break in the curve corresponds to the neutralization of the weak acid. When the acid is not a very weak one, the first equivalence point becomes less pronounced (dotted curve). The curves of Fig. 52F are obtained in the titration of a salt of a weak acid and a strong base with a strong acid or in the corresponding titration involving a salt of a weak base. Curve 1 is observed when the anion of the titrant (acid) has a larger mobility than the anion of the salt, and curve 2 corresponds to the opposite case.

The equivalence point of titrations involving the formation of a precipitate, according to the reaction

$$\underset{\substack{\text{solution being}\\\text{titrated}}}{AB} \quad + \quad \underset{\text{titrant}}{CD} \quad = \quad \underset{\text{precipitate}}{AC} \quad + BD,$$

can also be determined by conductometry. Since ions A disappear from solution and are replaced by D, the conductance decreases before the equivalence point when $\lambda_A > \lambda_D$ (Fig. 52A). Conversely, the conductance increases from the beginning of the titration when $\lambda_A < \lambda_D$ (Fig. 52C curve 1). The acuteness of the angle at the equivalence point is not so pronounced as in this schematic diagram. If the titrant is an organic reagent, the conductivity remains virtually constant after the equivalence point, provided that the reagent is nonionic (Fig. 52B). However, if an alcoholic solution of reagent is utilized, the addition of titrant after the equivalence point results in an increase in alcohol concentration and a concomitant decrease in conductivity.

A detailed mathematical analysis of titration curves can be made for the general case in which equilibrium considerations are taken into account (see problems 3 and 4 in Section 7–8).

7–4. *EXPERIMENTAL METHODS*

a. Cells. It was pointed out in Section 7–2 that the sum of the voltage drops at the electrodes of a conductance cell must be equal to zero. This condition is fulfilled when two identical reversible electrodes are utilized. For instance, the conductance of a potassium chloride solution can be measured by immersing two silver-silver chloride electrodes in the solution. The voltage of this cell is equal to zero, since the two electrode potentials are equal. Ohm's law is obeyed under such conditions, and the conductance of the cell can be determined by measuring the current through the cell for a given voltage. Such measurements with direct current are seldom made, and the alternating-current method discussed below is preferred.

The electrodes of a conductance cell are made of platinum foil covered with finely divided platinum (platinized platinum). This deposit is obtained by electrolysis of a solution of chloroplatinic acid. Polarization of the electrodes is avoided by periodic reversal of the current; for instance, at a frequency of 1000 cps. In cells used in precise measurements[7] (Fig. 53A), the two leads and filling tubes are far apart to minimize capacitance effects. Cells of the immersion type (Fig. 53B) are particularly convenient,

[7]G. Jones and G. M. Bollinger, *J. Am. Chem. Soc.*, **53**, 411 (1931).

but the capacitance between the leads is not entirely negligible. This cell can be used whenever data need not be very accurate, i.e., when a relative error of 0.1 per cent is unimportant, as is generally the case in conducto-metric titrations. Quite a few other designs have been proposed, and the

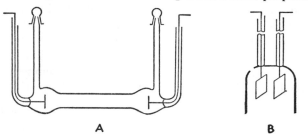

A   **B**

Fig. 53. Conductance cells.

reader is referred to an article by Shedlovsky (see Section 7–7) for a detailed description.

The geometry of actual cells does not correspond to the ideal cell of Section 7–2, in which the cross-sectional area is uniform and equal to 1 sq cm and the distance between electrodes is 1 cm. If the cross section is A and the interelectrode distance l, the resistance of the cell filled with a solution of specific conductivity κ is

$$R = \frac{1}{\kappa}\frac{l}{A}. \tag{7-8}$$

Equation (7–8) expresses that R is proportional to the interelectrode distance and inversely proportional to the cross section of the cell. In practice, the cross section A is not uniform, but one can determine a *cell constant* l/A from equation (7–8) by measuring R for a solution of known specific conductance κ. Solutions of potassium chloride of known concentration are utilized for this purpose. The specific conductance of these solutions was determined once and for all with a cell in which the cross-sectional area was uniform and known with accuracy.

Incidentally, it is seen from equation (7–8) why a conductance, i.e., $1/R$, is expressed in ohms^{-1}, while a specific conductance is expressed in units of ohms^{-1} cm^{-1}.

The conductance of water must be taken into account in precise measurements. The specific conductance of the very pure water prepared by Kohlrausch and Heydweiler[8] after numerous distillations was 6×10^{-8} ohm^{-1} cm^{-1} at 25°. The equation

$$\kappa = \kappa_{\text{experimental}} - \kappa_{H_2O} \tag{7-9}$$

can be applied for the correction of the conductance of water, but there are cases in which this equation cannot be used. These cases, which are not

[8] F. Kohlrausch and A. Heydweiler, *Z. physik. Chem.*, **14**, 317 (1894).

important from the point of view of chemical analysis, will not be discussed here. The correction of equation (7–9) need not be made in most analytical work when the specific conductance exceeds 10^{-4} ohms^{-1} cm^{-1}.

The conductance of electrolytes varies with temperature because ionic mobilities are temperature dependent (variation of viscosity, etc.). The temperature coefficient is of the order of 2 per cent per degree at room temperature (see Table VIII), and control of temperature is thus essential in precise work. The temperature need not be controlled in conductometric titrations, but it is not advisable to allow variations of temperature of more than 1 degree during titrations to avoid distortion of titration curves.

b. Bridges. The resistance of a conductance cell can be determined by measuring the alternating current through the cell for a given applied voltage. This direct method does not yield accurate results because of the errors made on the current and voltage, and far more precise results are obtained with a Wheatstone bridge. The bridge (Fig. 54) is connected to a generator of alternating current (OSC) having a output voltage of a few volts. The choice of the frequency is not critical, but a frequency of 1000 cps is generally adopted. The cell is placed in one arm of the bridge, and the variable resistance R_3 and capacitor C are adjusted until no current flows through the diagonal BD. The balance indicator BI is not an ordinary galvanometer, since this instrument is not sensitive to alternating current at the frequencies at which the bridge operates. A telephone with preamplifier can be utilized, but cathode-ray oscilloscopes and electron tubes (magic eyes) are preferred nowadays. An inexpensive and very sensitive ($40\mu v$) balance indicator is available from General Radio (Cambridge, Mass.).

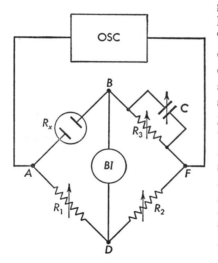

Fig. 54.   Conductance bridge.

The condition of balance will be established for the particular case in which the cell behaves as a pure resistance, i.e., for C set at zero. This is not so in practice, but the treatment is a little simpler[9] than for the case in which capacitances are taken into account. Since the voltage between B and D is equal to zero at balance, one has

$$i_1 R_x = i_2 R_1, \tag{7–10}$$

$$i_1 R_3 = i_2 R_2, \tag{7–11}$$

[9]For students who have not had a course in alternating currents.

where i_1 and i_2 are the currents in the upper and lower arms, respectively. Hence,

$$R_x R_2 = R_1 R_3, \qquad (7\text{--}12)$$

and the product of the resistances in opposite arms of the bridge are equal. Equation (7–12) can also be written in the form

$$R_x = R_3 \frac{R_1}{R_2}, \qquad (7\text{--}13)$$

which shows that a wide range of resistances can be covered by adjustment of the *bridge ratio* R_1/R_2. This ratio is kept equal to unity whenever possible, because this condition is the most favorable to precise measurements.

The cell actually behaves as a pure resistance in parallel with the small capacitance between the electrodes and the leads, and capacitor C must be properly adjusted to balance the bridge. One can show by a reasoning similar to the one above that the condition

$$C_x = C \frac{R_1}{R_2} \qquad (7\text{--}14)$$

must be satisfied at balance, C_x being the capacity of the cell.

The simple bridge of Fig. 54 has been improved by Jones and co-workers[10] to minimize errors resulting from stray capacitances, etc. The "Jones bridge" is available commercially (Leeds and Northrup) and so are less precise bridges (Leeds and Northrup, Industrial Instruments Co., in the United States). Finally, it might be useful to remember that the student potentiometer manufactured by Leeds and Northrup can be utilized, with additional components, as a conductivity bridge.

7–5. HIGH-FREQUENCY METHODS

a. Titration Curves. In high-frequency methods the vessel with the sample to be analyzed is placed in a coil (or between the plates of a capacitor) which is part of the circuit of a high-frequency generator functioning at a few megacycles per second or even higher frequencies. Results obtained with instruments of the "capacitor" type are easier to interpret than those obtained with the "coil" type, and we shall limit our discussion to the former type of instrument.

A simple cell may be composed of two metallic plates sealed on the wall of a rectangular container (Fig. 55A). This cell may be represented by the equivalent circuit of Fig. 55B, where C_1 is the capacitance of the capacitor having the glass wall as dielectric; C_2 is the capacitance of the capacitor whose dielectric is the solution; and R is the resistance of the solution. The resistance of the walls of the cell is assumed to be infinite. The circuit of

---

[10]G. Jones and R. C. Josephs, *J. Am. Chem. Soc.*, **50**, 1049 (1928). See Shedlovsky's review (Section 7–7) for additional references.

Fig. 55B is equivalent to a resistance R_p and a capacitance C_p in parallel, (Fig. 55C) having the values[11]

$$\frac{1}{R_p} = \frac{\kappa_c \omega^2 C_1^{\,2}}{\kappa_c^{\,2} + \omega^2 (C_1 + C_2)^2} \tag{7-15}$$

$$C_p = \frac{C_1 \kappa_c^{\,2} + \omega^2 (C_1^{\,2} C_2 + C_1 C_2^{\,2})}{\kappa_c^{\,2} + \omega^2 (C_1 + C_2)^2}. \tag{7-16}$$

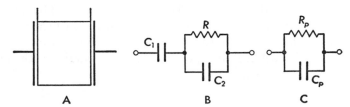

Fig. 55. High-frequency cell and equivalent circuits.

There, $\omega = 2\pi f$, f being the frequency, and κ_c the conductance of the solution as measured with an ordinary cell having the same geometry as the high-frequency cell. In view of equation (7–8) one has $\kappa_c = \kappa A / l$, where κ is the specific conductance of the solution in the cell, l is the distance inside the cell between the walls adjacent to the plates, and A is the area of these walls. This relation between κ_c and κ holds only for cells with the ideal geometry of Fig. 55A.

The derivation of equations (7–15) and (7–16), which involves ordinary calculations of the theory of alternating currents, will not be given here for the sake of simplicity. The elements R_p and C_p, which characterize the behavior of the high-frequency cell, can be determined with a bridge similar in principle to that of Fig. 54. The elements R_3 and C in this diagram would then be the resistance R_p and the capacitance C_p.

The variations of the high-frequency conductance $1/R_p$ with the low-frequency conductance κ_c are shown in Fig. 56A. When κ_c is very small, the term in $\kappa_c^{\,2}$ in the denominator of equation (7-15) can be neglected, and $1/R_p$ is simply proportional to κ_c. Conversely, the term $\omega^2 (C_1 + C_2)$ becomes negligible when κ_c is very large and $1/R_p$ is inversely proportional to the low-frequency conductance κ_c. Hence, the conductance $1/R_p$ decreases when κ_c is sufficiently large. It follows from these two extreme cases that the curve $1/R_p$ against κ_c exhibits a maximum. The value of κ_c at the maximum increases with frequency, as one can ascertain by setting

[11]Equivalent circuits have been used by the following authors: W. J. Blaedel, H. V. Malmstadt, D. L. Petitjean, and W. K. Anderson, *Anal. Chem.*, **24**, 1240 (1952); J. L. Hall, *ibid.*, **24**, 1236 (1952); C. N. Reilley and W. N. McCurdy, Jr., *ibid.*, **25**, 86 (1953). Our treatment follows that of the latter authors, but in a simplified fashion; see also P. H. Sherrick, G. A. Dawe, R. Karr, and E. F. Ewen, *Manual of Chemical Oscillometry*, published by Sargent, Chicago, 1954.

$d(1/R_p)/d\omega = 0$ and solving for ω. Furthermore, the high-frequency conductance at the maximum increases with frequency.

The high-frequency capacitance C_p increases with the low-frequency conductance κ_c and approaches the limiting value C_1 when κ_c tends to

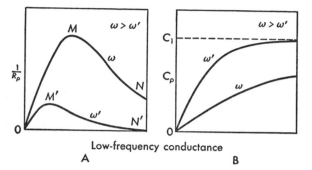

Fig. 56. Variations of $1/R_p$ and C_p with the low-frequency conductance of solution.

infinity (Fig. 56B). The increase of C_p with κ_c is more rapid as the frequency is decreased.

Plots of $1/R_p$ and C_p against κ_c are most valuable in the analysis of high-frequency titration curves. When the high-frequency conductance is measured, the three types of titration curves in Fig. 57 may be obtained

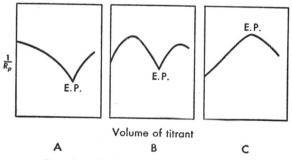

Fig. 57. High-frequency titration curves.

for a V-shaped titration curve at low frequency. Curve A of Fig. 57 is observed when the low-frequency conductance varies in the ascending part of the plot $1/R_p$ versus κ_c (Fig. 56A, segment OM). Titration curves of the type C (Fig. 57) correspond to the descending part MN in Fig. 56. Finally, titration curves with two maxima and one minimum (curve B, Fig. 57) are obtained when κ_c passes through the maximum (Fig. 56A) of the plot $1/R_p$ versus κ_c before and after the equivalence point.

The foregoing analysis can be transposed to titrations in which the high-frequency capacitance C_p [equation (7–16)] is measured. Since the plot of

C_p against κ_c does not exhibit a maximum, "inversions" of the type in Fig. 57B and Fig. 57C are not observed. When C_p approaches its limiting value C_1, the detection of the equivalence point becomes very uncertain.

It should be emphasized that the sensitivity of the high-frequency method is not better than in conventional conductometry. Consider for instance the variations of R_p with κ_c [equation (7–15)]. In the most favorable case, i.e., when κ_c is low, one has

$$\frac{1}{R_p} \approx \kappa_c \frac{C_1{}^2}{(C_1 + C_2)^2} \tag{7–17}$$

where the factor $C_1{}^2/(C_1 + C_2)^2$ is obviously smaller than unity. The amplitude of variations of κ_c is multiplied by a factor smaller than unity. High-frequency methods, however, may be much easier to apply than the ordinary method. An interesting feature of high-frequency titrations is the absence of electrodes in solution and the elimination of errors resulting from coating of the electrodes by a precipitate and other surface phenomena. High-frequency methods may also be useful in titrations with nonaqueous solvents (low conductance).

b. *Analysis of Binary Mixtures.* High frequency methods are sometimes applicable under conditions in which conventional conductometry fails; for example, in the case of liquids having a very low conductance. The capacitance C_p of equation (7–16) is then

$$C_p \approx \frac{C_1 C_2}{C_1 + C_2}, \tag{7–18}$$

or

$$\frac{1}{C_p} \approx \frac{1}{C_1} + \frac{1}{C_2}, \tag{7–19}$$

and the cell behaves as two capacitors of capacitances C_1 and C_2 in series. The capacitance of a capacitor formed by two parallel plates is proportional to the dielectric constant of the medium between the plates and is inversely proportional to the distance between the plates (see a physics text). Since capacitance C_2 is proportional to the dielectric constant, ϵ, of the liquid in the cell, equation (7–19) may be written as

$$C_p \approx \frac{p\epsilon C_1}{C_1 + p\epsilon}, \tag{7–20}$$

with

$$C_2 = p\epsilon \tag{7–21}$$

p being the proportionality factor between C_2 and ϵ. The capacitance C_p increases less rapidly than ϵ because of the term $p\epsilon$ in the denominator of equation (7–21). However, C_p is almost proportional to ϵ when the capacitance C_1, associated with the glass as a dielectric, is high. Since the capacitance of a parallel plate condenser is inversely proportional to the thickness of the dielectric medium, C_p is essentially proportional to ϵ when the cell walls are as thin as possible. In practice there always is some departure from linearity, but a linear plot can be obtained by introducing an inductor in series with the cell. This procedure will not be discussed here; details can be found in the review of Sherrick *et al.* (see Section 7–7).

The measurement of C_p is very useful in the analysis of mixtures of two miscible liquids having different dielectric constants. Consider for example the analysis of ethanol-water mixtures. The dielectric constant of this mixture is comprised between those of ethanol ($\epsilon = 24.30$ at 25°) and water ($\epsilon = 78.54$ at 25°), and the composition of the mixture can be deduced from the value of ϵ, i.e., from the capacitance C_p. The procedure is very simple, since the results can be read directly from a calibration curve showing C_p against composition[12] (per cent water in ethanol). Application of this method in the control of streams in industrial plants has been made.[13]

TABLE IX
Dielectric Constants of Various Liquids[a]

Substance	ϵ	T	Temperature Coefficient[b]
n-pentane	1.844	20	0.0016
n-octane	1.948	20	0.0013
Cyclohexane	2.023	20	0.0016
Carbon tetrachloride	2.228	20	0.0020
p-xylene	2.270	20	0.0016
Benzene	2.274	20	0.0020
m-xylene	2.374	20	0.0019
Toluene	2.379	25	0.0024
o-xylene	2.568	20	0.0027
Carbon disulfide	2.641	20	0.0027
Chloroform	4.806	20	0.0016
Acetic acid	6.15	20	
Acetone	20.7	25	
Ethanol	24.30	25	
Methanol	33.63	25	
Nitrobenzene	34.82	25	
Glycerol	42.5	25	0.002
Water	78.54	25	

[a]From P. H. Sherrick *et al.*, *Manual of Chemical Oscillometry*, published by E. H. Sargent, Chicago, 1954, pp. 32–33.

[b]Note that $\epsilon_{T'} = \epsilon_T - (T' - T) \times$ temperature coefficient.

The dielectric constants of a few liquids are listed in Table IX and additional data can be found in the literature.[14]

c. Instrumentation. We considered so far the rather ideal case in which the resistance R_p and capacitance C_p of equations (7–15) and (7–16)

[12]P. W. West, T. S. Burkhalter, and L. Broussard, *Anal. Chem.*, **22**, 469 (1950); P. W. West, P. Senise, T. S. Burkhalter, *ibid.*, **24**, 1250 (1952).

[13]B. W. Thomas, F. J. Faegin, and G. W. Wilson, *Anal. Chem.*, **23**, 1750 (1951).

[14]See *Circular* **514** of the National Bureau of Standards, and the review of Sherrick *et al* (Section 7–7).

are measured with a bridge. Such measurements are possible and are very valuable for the interpretation of the behavior of high-frequency cells, but direct-reading instruments are generally employed in control work. The combined effect of R_p and C_p is measured by these instruments and this complicates the interpretation of data, particularly with instruments of the coil type. However, the rather empirical results obtained in this manner can be very useful from a practical point of view.

Cells of instruments of the capacitor type follow the general design of Fig. 55. Cells in instruments of the coil type are simply test tubes.

A variety of instruments are described in the literature and discussion of them is beyond the scope of this text. In one of these instruments, the Oscillometer of Sargent, the cell C is in parallel with a calibrated adjustable capacitor C_a. The cell and the capacitor are in the circuit of an oscillator whose variations of frequency from a fixed value can be detected. The frequency of the oscillator with an empty cell is adjusted by means of C_a at some prescribed value (5 megacycles per second in the Sargent instrument). When the sample is placed in the cell the capacitance across the terminals of the oscillator changes and the frequency varies accordingly. Capacitor C_a is then adjusted to a value at which the frequency recovers its initial value. The difference in readings of C_a is a measure of the effect of the sample in the cell. The Sargent instrument is primarily designed to measure capacitances, although it can also be applied to titrations. Two other commercial instruments (Beckman, Fisher[15]) are also available in the United States.

7–6. APPLICATIONS

a. Direct Conductometric Methods. Analytical applications of direct conductometry are rather limited in scope because of the lack of selectivity. The method is useful only when an approximate value of electrolyte contents is needed; as, for example, in the analysis of water, sugar, etc. It is current practice to measure the conductivity of the water used in boilers. Likewise, the mineral contents of sugar can be evaluated from the conductivity of a solution of the sugar sample; the conductivity of a solution of pure sucrose is approximately the same as for pure water. In these applications one generally expresses the salt contents by assuming that only one metal is present in solution; calcium, for instance (see problem 7 in Section 7–8).

The solubility of sparingly soluble salts can be determined from conductance measurements, provided that the necessary equivalent ionic conductances are known. Equation (7–6) is applied and the correction for the conductivity of the solvent is made. A somewhat similar application is the

[15]Based on the instrument described by J. L. Hall, *Anal. Chem.*, **24**, 1244 (1952).

determination of the ionization constants of weak electrolytes (see Section 7–8). For a detailed discussion of this and other applications in physical chemistry, see electrochemistry texts, and in particular, MacInnes' book.[16]

The water contents of organic solvents can be determined from the conductance of the liquid, which is saturated with a sparingly soluble salt. Results are computed from a calibration curve showing water contents against conductance. However, high-frequency methods seem preferable in this case because the water contents may be obtained more simply by direct reading and without the addition of salts.

b. Conductometric Titrations. Quite a few conductometric titrations involving acid-base and precipitation reactions have been studied, as one can ascertain by consulting the monographs of Kolthoff, Britton, and Kolthoff and Laitinen (see Section 7–7). Conductometric titrations are possible only when electrolytes, which are not involved in the titration reaction, are not present in large excess. Since conductance measurements are rather precise, a change of a few per cent in conductance during titration is sufficient.

A few titrants and examples of titration will be quoted for orientation purposes.

$$AgNO_3: Cl^-, Br^-, I^-, CN^-, CrO_4^{--}$$
$$Pb(NO_3)_2: I^-, SO_4^{--}, C_2O_4^{--}$$
$$Ba(CH_3CO_2)_2: CO_3^{--}, CrO_4^{--}, SO_4^{--}$$
$$Li_2C_2O_4: Ca^{++}$$

Conductometric titrations can also be applied to the study of complex ions. The metal ion is titrated with the complexing agent, and the nature of the complex ions thus formed can sometimes be determined from the titration curve.

In conclusion, conductometric titrations are of rather limited scope, but analytical chemists have perhaps disregarded too often the limited but nevertheless real potentialities of the method.

c. High-Frequency Methods. Some potential uses of high-frequency methods were mentioned in Section 7–5. The method is interesting primarily when ordinary conductometry fails. This is generally not the case for aqueous solutions, at least when precipitation reactions are not involved. Conventional conductometry is then preferable because experimental results are more accurate and less difficult to interpret than in high-frequency methods.

Some typical applications of high-frequency methods are the analysis of binary organic mixtures, the determination of moisture contents in a

[16]D. A. MacInnes, *The Principles of Electrochemistry*, Reinhold, New York, 1939.

variety of materials, the control of the purity of distilled alcohol, and the study of the kinetics of various reactions. For a detailed bibliography, see the reviews of Reilley and Sherrick *et al.* (Section 7-7).

7-7. BIBLIOGRAPHY

G. G. Blake, *Conductometric Analysis at Radio-Frequency*, Chapman and Hall, London, 1950. Deals primarily with the author's pioneering work on high-frequency titrations.

H. T. S. Britton, *Conductometric Analysis*, Chapman and Hall, London, 1934. A classical work.

H. T. S. Britton, article in *Physical Methods in Chemical Analysis*, Vol. 2, W. G. Berl, Ed., Academic Press, New York, 1951.

G. Jander and O. Pfundt, *Die visuelle Leitfähigkeitstitration*, Enke, Stuttgart, 1934. A detailed review with applications.

G. Jander and O. Pfundt, article in *Physikalische Methoden der Analytischen Chemie*, Vol. 2, W. Böttger, Ed. Akademische Verlagsgesellschaft, Leipzig, 1936. Reprinted by Edwards Brothers, Inc., Ann Arbor, 1943. See also Vol. 3, 1939. Detailed review with abundant references.

I. M. Kolthoff, *Konduktometrische Titrationen*, Steinkopff, Dresden, 1923. The first book on conductometric titrations and a classic in the field.

I. M. Kolthoff and H. A. Laitinen, *pH and Electro Titrations*, Wiley, New York, 1941. See introductory treatment of conductometry and its applications.

J. J. Lingane, *Electroanalytical Chemistry*, Interscience, New York, 1953. Reviews of the fundamentals and brief discussion of high-frequency methods.

C. N. Reilley, chapter in P. Delahay, *New Instrumental Methods in Electrochemistry*, Interscience, New York, 1954.

K. Sandera, article in *Physikalische Methoden der Analytischen Chemie*, Vol. 2, W. Böttger, Ed., Akademische Verlagsgesellschaft, Leipzig, 1936. Reprinted by Edwards Brothers, Inc., Ann Arbor, 1943. See also Vol. 3, 1939. Deals with applications in detail.

T. Shedlovsky, article in *Physical Methods of Organic Chemistry*, A. Weissberger, Ed., 2nd ed., Vol. 1, Part 2, Interscience, New York, 1949. General review with an excellent survey of experimental methods.

P. H. Sherrick, G. A. Dawe, R. Karr, and E. F. Ewen, *Manual of Chemical Oscillometry*, Sargent, Chicago, 1954. Discusses mainly the Sargent Oscillometer, but also contains a good treatment of fundamentals.

The following books and articles, which are concerned with dielectric constants and dipole moments, might be of indirect interest in the discussion of high-frequency methods.

C. J. F. Böttcher, *Theory of Electric Polarization*, Elsevier, Houston, 1952. Detailed monograph giving an excellent account on the classical theory of dielectrics.

P. Debye, *Polar Molecules*, Dover (reprint), New York, 1929. A classic.

R. J. W. Le Fèvre, *Dipole Moments*, Methuen, London, 1939. An introductory treatment.

H. Frölich, *Theory of Dielectrics*, Oxford University Press, Oxford, 1949.
C. P. Smyth, *Dielectric Behavior and Structure*, McGraw-Hill, New York, 1955.
C. P. Smyth, article in *Physical Methods in Organic Chemistry*, A. Weissberger, Ed.,
 Vol. 1, Part 2, Interscience, New York, 1949. See also complement by J. G.
 Powell and C. P. Smyth in Vol. 1, Part 3, 1954.
A. R. von Hippel, *Dielectrics and Waves*, Wiley, New York, 1954.
A. R. von Hippel, *Dielectric Materials and Applications*, Wiley, New York, 1954.

7-8. PROBLEMS

a. Extension of Theory

1. The specific conductance of a solution of a weak acid HA at the concentration of C moles per liter is κ. Calculate the dissociation constant of the weak acid from these data and the equivalent ionic conductances λ_H^0 and λ_A^0 at infinite dilution.

2. Calculate the conductance of pure water at 25° from the equivalent ionic conductances of H^+ and OH^- ions (Table VIII) and the ionic product of water ($\approx 10^{-14}$ at 25°).

3. One hundred milliliters of $10^{-4}\,M$ acetic acid are titrated with $10^{-2}\,M$ sodium hydroxide. Calculate the conductance after the addition of the following volumes of titrant: 0, 0.1, 0.2, 0.4, 0.6, 0.8, 0.9, 0.95, 1.0, 1.05, 1.1 ml. Ionization constant: $K_a = 1.8 \times 10^{-5}$ at 25°.
Note: Neglect dilution, but take into account the partial ionization of the acid.

4. Solve the same problem as in (3), but for the titration of 100 ml of ammonium chloride with 0.1 M sodium hydroxide. Ionization constant of ammonium hydroxide: $K_b = 1.8 \times 10^{-5}$ at 25° C.

b. Application of Theory

5. Calculate the solubility product of lead sulfate at 25° from the specific conductance of a saturated aqueous solution of this salt: $\kappa = 3.72 \times 10^{-5}$ ohms^{-1}cm^{-1}. The specific conductance of the water used in preparing the solution was 2.2×10^{-6} ohms^{-1}cm^{-1}.
Note: Use equivalent ionic conductances at infinite dilution.

6. Neglecting the ionization of the weak electrolyte or the solubility of the precipitate, plot the titration curves for the following conductometric titrations: (a) sodium hydroxide with nitric acid (titrant); (b) magnesium sulfate with barium acetate (titrant); (c) magnesium sulfate with barium chloride (titrant); (d) ammonium hydroxide with acetic acid (titrant); ammonium nitrate with sodium hydroxide.
The concentration of the substance to be titrated is $10^{-2}\,M$, and the concentration of titrant is 1 M.
Note: Calculate κ for the following volumes of titrant: 0, 0.5, 1, 1.1, 1.2 ml.

7. The conductance of a cell containing a 0.1 M solution of potassium chloride is 0.193 ohms^{-1} at 25°. This cell is used in the analysis of a water containing calcium sulfate. A conductance of 1.83×10^{-4} ohms^{-1} was measured with the water at 25°.

Calculate the concentration of calcium in parts per million on the assumption that calcium and sulfate ions are the only ionic species present.

Note: Use equivalent ionic conductance at infinite dilution.

8. The characteristics of a high-frequency cell similar to that of Fig. 55A are as follows: wall thickness 1.17 mm, distance between electrodes 2.03 cm, electrode area 4.61 cm². The two electrodes have the same area. The cell is filled with a sodium hydroxide solution of varied concentration. Calculate the resistance of the parallel circuit of Fig. 55C at 10 Mc per second and for the following concentrations of hydroxide: $10^{-4} M$, $5 \times 10^{-4} M$, $10^{-3} M$, $5 \times 10^{-3} M$, $10^{-2} M$, $5 \times 10^{-2} M$, $10^{-1} M$. Dielectric constants: solution, 78.5; glass, 4.86.

Equivalent conductance of sodium hydroxide at 25° and for different concentrations: 248 (Λ_0), 245 (0.001 N), 237 (0.01 N), and 221 (0.1 N).

Note that the capacitance of a parallel plate condenser in farads is

$$\frac{1}{9 \times 10^{11}} \frac{\epsilon A}{4 \pi d}$$

where ϵ is the dielectric constant of the medium between the plates, A the area of the plates in square centimeters, and d the distance between the plates in centimeters. This formula holds when the effect of the edges of the plates can be neglected. This is strictly not the case here, but the approximation will suffice.

9. The cell of problem 8 is filled with the following pure liquids at 25°: benzene, acetic acid, ethanol, methanol, glycerol, and water. Calculate the capacitance C_p of Fig. 55C for these liquids, and plot C_p against the dielectric constant of the liquid in the cell. Plot on the same diagram the relationship between C_p and dielectric constant for the case in which the glass wall is infinitely thin.

c. Survey of Literature

10. Find in the literature two actual titrations for each of the diagrams in Fig. 52.

Note: Use mainly the books of Kolthoff and Britton and the review of Jander and Pfundt (Section 7–7) as sources.

11. Give a discussion (with references to the literature) of the conductometric titration of sulfate with barium acetate.

12. Prepare instructions for the conductometric determination of mineral impurities in sugars.

Note: See Sandera's review (Section 7–7).

13. Prepare a review of some typical high-frequency titrations.

Note: Use mainly the reviews of Reilley and Sherrick et al (Section 7–7).

14. Discuss the application of high-frequency methods in the control of industrial streams in plant control work.

Note: See B. W. Thomas, F. J. Faegin, and G. W. Wilson, *Anal. Chem.*, **23**, 1750 (1951).

8

Emission Spectroscopy

8–1. INTRODUCTION

Analytical methods based on the emission or absorption of electromagnetic radiation are discussed in this and the subsequent five chapters. This chapter deals with emission spectrochemical analysis.

The origin of spectroscopy[1] can be traced to the work of Newton, who dispersed solar light with a prism (1672). However, it was not until 1802 that the first determination of wave length in the solar spectrum was made by Young.[2] The first spectroscope was constructed somewhat later (1817) by Fraunhofer.[3] The fundamental idea that elements have characteristic spectra was progressively developed by J. E. W. Herschel, Talbot, and others during the first half of the nineteenth century, and the first application of emission spectroscopy to chemical analysis was made by Bunsen and Kirchhoff[4] in 1860. Spectroscopy was soon to be recognized as a powerful qualitative tool. Thirteen new elements were discovered by application of spectroscopy during the second half of the nineteenth century and the early 1900's: cesium and rubidium (Kirchhoff and Bunsen, 1861), thallium (Crookes, 1861), and several rare earth metals (von Welsbach, de Boisbaudran, Urbain). Much more recently spectroscopy served in establishing the existence of deuterium (Urey, 1932).

Application of emission spectroscopy to quantitative analysis dates

---

[1]For a detailed historical account, see Twyman's book listed in Section 8–10.

[2]T. Young, *Phil. Trans.*, **92**, 12 (1802).

[3]J. Fraunhofer, *Ann. Physik*, **56**, 264 (1817).

[4]G. Kirchhoff and R. Bunsen, *Pogg. Ann.*, **110**, 161 (1860). See detailed abstract in *Chem. Ztb.*, 657 (1860).

back to the work of Lockyer and Roberts (1873). The principle of the internal standard method, which is most frequently applied nowadays, and other procedures for quantitative determinations were advanced by these investigators. Further pioneering work was done by Hartley (in the 1880's), by De Gramont (early 1900's), and more recently by Twyman, Kayser, Gerlach, and Schweitzer in Europe. Meggers, Harrison, Sawyer, Brode, and many others contributed much to the development of emission spectrochemical analysis in the United States.

Since the 1930's, quantitative emission methods have found numerous applications in control laboratories, especially in the metallurgical industry. Several thousand papers have been published in the field, and emission spectroscopy has become one of the most important instrumental methods of chemical analysis. Several hundred thousand spectral lines of the various elements have been catalogued, and the rather recent study of the spectra of isotopes manufactured in uranium piles has further enriched tables of spectral lines.

Spectroscopes, i.e., instruments in which spectral lines are directly observed, were preferred during the nineteenth century, although photography had been applied to spectroscopy by Becquerel and Draper as early as 1842. It was only at the beginning of this century that the use of spectrographs, in which the spectrum is recorded on a photographic plate, became quite general. Direct-reading *spectrometers*, in which line intensities are measured with photoelectric tubes, became available in the late 1940's.

It is not within the province of this book to discuss the theory of emission spectra, since detailed treatments can be found in physical chemistry texts and specialized books.[5] A few essential terms, however, will be defined.

Electromagnetic radiation can be characterized by its wave length, its wave number, or its frequency. The *wave length* λ for a sinusoidal wave is the distance between two consecutive maxima in the wave train. The *frequency* ν is the number of cycles completed per unit of time, and the *wave number*[6] σ is the number of waves per unit of length. One has the relationships

$$\lambda = \frac{1}{\sigma} \tag{8-1}$$

$$\lambda = \frac{c}{\nu} \tag{8-2}$$

$$\nu = \sigma c \tag{8-3}$$

[5]Particularly G. Herzberg, *Atomic Spectra and Atomic Structure*, 2d ed., Dover, New York, 1944. Good summaries are given in the books of Nachtrieb and Harrison *et al;* see Section 8–10.

[6]The symbol ν has been generally used for frequency and wave number, but it has been recommended [*J. Optical Soc. Am.*, **43,** 410 (1953)] that wave numbers be designated by σ.

where *c* is the velocity of light in the particular medium being considered (3×10^{10} cm sec^{-1} in vacuum).

Wave lengths in spectroscopy are expressed in angstroms[7] (1 A = 10^{-8} cm), in millimicrons (1 mμ = 10^{-7} cm), and in microns (1μ = 10^{-4} cm), according to the range of wave lengths being considered. Thus, the angstrom is utilized in the ultraviolet (30 to 4000 A) and visible ranges (4000 to 7000 A), and the micron in the infrared. The use of the millimicron in absorption spectroscopy in the visible and ultraviolet ranges is quite common.

Frequencies are expressed in vibrations per second, or more frequently in spectroscopy, in *fresnels*,[8] i.e., in units of 10^{12} vibrations per second. Wave numbers are in reciprocal centimeters or in *kaysers*.[9]

When a substance is placed in an electric arc, for instance, its atoms collide with electrons in the arc, and this results in *transitions* of electrons in the outer orbitals of the atoms to levels of higher energy (*excitation*). As an electron falls back to a lower energy level, a quantum of light is emitted at a frequency ν which depends on the energy change ΔE between the two electronic levels. The frequency ν is given by

$$\nu = \frac{\Delta E}{h} \tag{8-4}$$

where *h* is Planck's constant (6.62×10^{-27} erg sec).

Changes in energy levels are quantized, i.e., they can only occur by finite increments. In other words ΔE does not vary continuously, but has a series of values for each element. Each value of ΔE for an element corresponds to a *line* of the frequency given by equation (8-4) in the emission spectrum of the element. The number of lines in emission spectra varies greatly from one element to another; hydrogen has a relatively simple spectrum, whereas more that 1000 lines have been reported for some of the transition elements. The number of lines for a given element also depends on the conditions of excitation. For example, excitation by flame produces spectra with fewer lines than spectra obtained with a d-c arc.

Each element has a characteristic emission spectrum, and spectroscopy is applied to qualitative analysis. Quantitative determinations are also possible because the energy emitted for a given line of an element during

[7]A better definition is to refer the angstrom to the spectroscopic standard, which is more reliable than the standard meter. Thus, the angstrom is defined as 1/6438.4696 of the wave length of the calcium red line. This unit of length was named in honor of Angström, the Swedish physicist who made precise measurements of wave lengths in the late 1860's.

[8]From the name of the French physicist who contributed much to physical optics in the nineteenth century.

[9]Term recommended by the Joint Commission for Spectroscopy [*J. Optical Soc. Amer.*, **43**, 410 (1953)]. Kayser is the author of a monumental treatise on spectroscopy (see reference in Section 8-10).

the burning of the sample is proportional to the number of atoms of this element in the sample, provided that excitation conditions are kept constant and the sample composition varies only in a narrow range.

8-2. PRISM SPECTROGRAPHS

The essential components for emission spectroscopy are a source of radiation, a system for dispersing radiation, and a receptor, such as a photographic plate in spectrographs or a set of phototubes in spectrometers. Prisms or gratings are utilized as dispersion elements. Prism spectrographs are discussed here, and grating instruments are covered in Section 8–3.

a. Characteristics of Spectrographs. Dispersion of light by a prism is based on the property of light to travel in a substance, such as glass, with a velocity which varies with wave length. When a parallel beam of *monochromatic light*, i.e,. radiation of a single wave length, impinges on a prism, the emerging beam is deflected from the direction of the incident beam. The angles i and r in Fig. 58 are related by Snell's law, $(\sin i / \sin r) = n$,

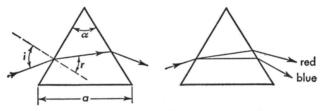

Fig. 58. Refraction and dispersion by prisms.

where n is the *index of refraction* of the material of the prism. It is assumed that the prism is placed in vacuum in the above definition of the index of refraction. The index of refraction is equal to unity for vacuum, but is slightly larger for air.

The index of refraction of a substance decreases with increasing wave length λ in the range of wave lengths in which the prism material does not absorb radiation[10] (Fig. 59). It follows from Snell's law that the angle r becomes smaller as λ decreases, and consequently a beam of red light at 7000 A is deflected less than a beam of blue light at 4500 A (Fig. 58). This property of prisms can be characterized by the *angular dispersion*, which is the limit of $\Delta\theta / \Delta\lambda$, as $\Delta\lambda$ approaches zero, where $\Delta\theta$ is the deflection corresponding to a small change of wave length $\Delta\lambda$. In other words the angular dispersion is defined as the derivative $d\theta/d\lambda$. The larger the angular

[10]There may also be anomalous dispersion, but one need not go into the matter here. For a discussion of the dependence of the index of refraction on wave length, see a text on physical optics; for instance, F. A. Jenkins and H. E. White, *Fundamentals of Optics*, 2nd ed., McGraw-Hill, New York, 1950, pp. 462–485.

dispersion, the easier it is to separate spectral lines which differ only slightly in wave length. Thus, good spectrographs generally have a large angular dispersion. In practice, spectrographs are characterized by their

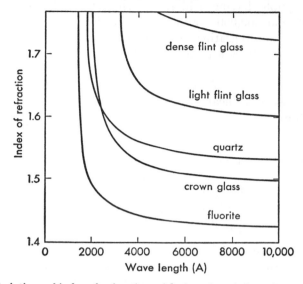

Fig. 59. Variations of index of refraction with wave length for a few materials. (After F. A. Jenkins and H. E. White, *Fundamentals of Physical Optics*, 2nd ed. McGraw-Hill, New York, 1950, p. 463.)

linear reciprocal dispersion (also called *plate factor*) which is the difference in wave length, as measured on the photographic plate in the instrument, of two lines separated by one unit of length. The linear reciprocal dispersion is often but incorrectly called the dispersion of the spectrograph.[11] Good spectrographs have a low linear reciprocal dispersion; for instance, 1 A per millimeter.

Because of the shape of the curves representing the index of refraction against wave length, the linear reciprocal dispersion increases with wave length (see problem 1 in Section 8–11), and the distance between two lines corresponding to a given difference in wave length decreases with increasing wave length.

Prisms made of different materials are utilized to cover different ranges of the spectrum; for instance, all other conditions being equal, a spectrograph with a prism made of light flint glass has a lower linear reciprocal dispersion in the range 4000 to 5000 A than the same instrument with a quartz prism (see Fig. 59).

The *resolving power* is another important characteristic of spectrographs,

[11]See Nachtrieb (reference in Section 8–10), who prefers the expression "linear reciprocal dispersion" to the term *dispersion*.

which is defined as the ratio $\lambda/\Delta\lambda$ where $\Delta\lambda$ is the smallest difference in wave length for which separation of two adjacent spectral lines of wave lengths $\lambda - (\Delta\lambda/2)$ and $\lambda + (\Delta\lambda/2)$ is still possible. It is advantageous to select spectrographs having a high resolving power. In general, $\lambda/\Delta\lambda$ is between 5000 and 200,000 for most commercial instruments, the upper value corresponding to grating instruments. A resolving power of 200,000 indicates that two lines separated by 0.025 A can still be resolved at 5000 A.

It can be shown (see problem 2 in Section 8–11) that the resolving power for the ideal case of a linear source of radiation having an infinitesimal narrow width is

$$\frac{\lambda}{\Delta\lambda} = a\,\frac{dn}{d\lambda},\tag{8-5}$$

where a (Fig. 58) is the basis of the prism (isosceles triangle) of the spectrograph. Since the derivative $dn/d\lambda$ at a given wave length is solely determined by the material of the prism, the resolving power depends on the size of the prism. This explains why instruments with high resolving power have large prisms (see problem 3 in Section 8–10).

b. Optical Systems. In addition to the dispersing element, prism spectrographs also have a suitable focusing system, a slit, and a camera for the photographic plate, or a set of phototubes in direct-reading instruments.

The source of radiation is focused on a narrow *slit* whose width may vary from 0.005 to 1 mm. Either the slit width can be varied continuously by moving one or both jaws or a set of slits having different widths can be utilized.

The three optical systems of Fig. 60 are most frequently utilized with prisms, but more involved systems, such as multiprisms, have also been described. Optical components are generally made of quartz for the ultraviolet range because glass absorbs quite strongly below 3500 A and quartz is transparent down to about 2000 A. Since quartz is birefringent,[12] lenses and prisms made of this material must be cut in the proper direction with respect to the optical axis.

The Cornu mounting (Fig. 60A) is advantageous only in small spectrographs, because other mountings are less cumbersome when high resolving power is desired. To avoid doubling of image the prism is composed of two pieces of right-hand and left-hand quartz[13] glued together. The distance between the camera lens and the plate is the *focal length* and is indicative of the size of the spectrograph. Cornu spectrographs (and also the Littrow instruments described below) are corrected for various errors

[12]This means that the index of refraction varies according to the direction of the incident beam; for details see a text on physical optics.[10]

[13]See text on physical optics for details; for instance, reference in footnote 10.

such as aberration and astigmatism. Details on these possible errors can be found in texts of optics.[14]

The Littrow mounting (Fig. 60B) is less cumbersome than the Cornu type and is most frequently adopted. By comparing Fig. 60A and 60B one

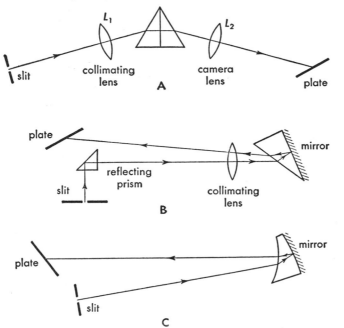

Fig. 60.   Optical systems for prism spectrographs.

readily sees that the length of a Littrow spectrograph is approximately one-half that of a Cornu instrument having the same characteristics. The same lens serves as collimator and camera lens. Radiation is reflected on the mirror on the back of the prism and passes twice through the same optical elements. The effect of birefringence thus cancels. In large Littrow spectrographs only a fraction of the spectrum in the visible and ultraviolet ranges can be covered on a single plate, and the instrument must be adjusted for the various wave length ranges by rotation of the prism. Prisms of different materials are also utilized according to wave length.

The Féry mounting (Fig. 60C) is seldom used in emission spectroscopy, but it finds application in the far ultraviolet (below 2000 A) where absorption by the optical components is very pronounced. The prism in this type of mounting also serves as collimator, and the number of optical components is thus reduced to a minimum. The distance between plate and prism can also be relatively short, and the spectrograph is rather compact.

[14]See for example, J. Valasek, *Introduction to Theoretical and Experimental Optics*, Wiley, New York, 1949.

8-3. GRATING SPECTROGRAPHS

a. Diffraction by Gratings. A grating is essentially a piece of metal or glass with numerous parallel and identical grooves—as many as 30,000 grooves per inch. Two types of gratings can be distinguished, depending on whether diffracted radiation is transmitted through the grating or is reflected. Reflection gratings are preferred because there is no absorption of light by the material of the grating. Diffraction is discussed here for transmission gratings, and transposition of the reasoning to reflection gratings is immediate.

Reflection gratings are generally made of aluminum. Speculum, an alloy of copper and tin, was often used in the past, but aluminum, which has a higher reflectivity, is now preferred. The grating is ruled with a diamond on a coating of aluminum on glass rather than on a block of aluminum because it is much easier to polish glass than aluminum. Numerous precautions must be taken, and only a few laboratories (John Hopkins University, University of Chicago, etc.) have the equipment for the production of high quality gratings. Inexpensive *replica gratings* of good quality have now become available. These are made of plastics and are not much inferior to the original grating from which they are cast.

The interpretation of diffraction phenomena was developed during the nineteenth century by Young, Fraunhofer, Fresnel, and others. This material is covered in detail in books on physical optics, and only the fundamental equation for transmission gratings will be discussed here. The schematic diagram of Fig. 61 represents an ideal grating formed by a series of parallel slits. The distance between consecutive slits is constant and equal to d. A parallel beam of monochromatic radiation of direction MP and of wave length λ impinges on the grating and is diffracted in the direction PQ. The two consecutive fronts of the wave trains before and after diffraction are MS and SQ. The angle θ is such that the condition

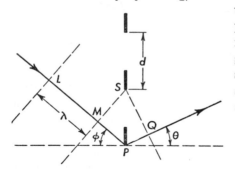

Fig. 61. Diffraction by a transmission grating.

$$MP + PQ = \lambda \qquad (8\text{-}6)$$

is satisfied, since the intensity is then reinforced in the direction PQ. One deduces from Fig. 61

$$MP = d \sin \varphi \qquad (8\text{-}7)$$

$$PQ = d \sin \theta, \qquad (8\text{-}8)$$

and in view of equation (8-6),

$$\lambda = d(\sin \varphi + \sin \theta). \qquad (8\text{-}9)$$

If the incident beam is not monochromatic, the angle θ has a different value for each wave length, and a spectrum is observed. Since the angles φ and θ generally exceed several degrees, the sum $\sin \varphi + \sin \theta$ is perhaps between 0.1 to 1, and it follows from equation (8–9) that the distance between consecutive slits or grooves must be of the order of the wave length. For instance, if $\sin \varphi + \sin \theta = 0.5$, one has for $\lambda = 5000$ A $d = 5000 \times 10^{-8}/0.5$ cm, i.e., 10^{-4} cm or about 25,000 grooves per inch.

The spectrum for which condition (8–6) is fulfilled is said to be of the *first order*. Higher-order spectra are observed when the condition

$$MP + PQ = m\lambda \qquad (8\text{--}10)$$

is satisfied, where m is the order of the spectrum. Thus,

$$m\lambda = d(\sin \varphi + \sin \theta). \qquad (8\text{--}11)$$

It follows from equation (8–10) that the angle θ is the same for incident beams of wave lengths λ, $\lambda/2$, $\lambda/3$, etc. Gratings are generally ruled in such a manner that the first order spectrum has a much greater intensity than spectra of higher order.

The angular dispersion, (which is defined as $d\theta/d\lambda$, as for the prism) is in view of equation (8–11)

$$\frac{d\theta}{d\lambda} = \frac{m}{d \cos \theta}. \qquad (8\text{--}12)$$

It follows from equation (8–12) that the angular dispersion $d\theta/d\lambda$ is inversely proportional to the distance d between adjacent slits (or grooves). Conversely, the reciprocal linear dispersion, which is defined as the difference in wave length on the plate of the spectrograph for two lines separated by one unit of length, decreases with the distance between slits (or grooves). When θ does not vary appreciably, say, a few degrees, the term $\cos \theta$ in equation (8–11) is almost constant, and the angular dispersion is virtually independent of wave length. This is a definite advantage of grating spectrographs over prism instruments.

The resolving power of grating spectrographs is defined, as for prism instruments, by the ratio $\lambda/\Delta\lambda$ where $\Delta\lambda$ is the minimum difference in wave lengths for two lines of wave lengths $\lambda - \lambda/2$ and $\lambda + \lambda/2$ that still can be resolved. It can be shown that the resolving power is proportional to the *total* number of grooves on the grating (see problem 4 in Section 8–10). Hence, instruments with high resolving power have large gratings.

An important advance in the design of grating spectrographs was the development of *concave gratings* by Rowland[15] in 1882. Such gratings are ruled on a concave mirror which also focuses the spectrum on the plate of the spectrograph. The above discussion of plane gratings can be transposed to concave gratings, and the foregoing conclusions about dispersion and resolving power are also valid for a concave grating. No lens is required in

[15]H. A. Rowland, *Phil. Mag.*, **13**, 469 (1882); **16**, 197, 210 (1883).

spectrographs with a concave grating, and investigations in the far ultra-violet (below 2000 A) and the far infrared (above 40 μ) were thus made easier. Observations in these regions of the spectrum were very difficult before the invention of concave gratings because of absorption of radiation by optical components.

b. Mounting of Gratings. Rowland discovered that the slit and diffraction spectrum are on a circle which is tangent to the grating and has a radius equal to one-half the grating radius of curvature (Fig. 62). This

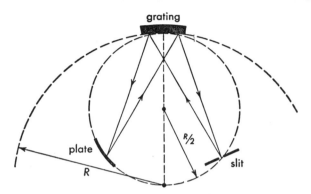

Fig. 62. Rowland's circle and mounting of Paschen and Runge.

important property of concave gratings is applied in all mountings except the Wadsworth mounting. In the Rowland mounting (Fig. 63A) the grating and the plate are on two perpendicular beams, and the slit is at the intersection of the beams. Various regions of the spectrum are studied by varying the positions and orientations of the grating and the plate. The moving parts must be machined with high precision, and the rails in which they move should be rigid. Because of these mechanical difficulties, Rowland mountings are seldom utilized nowadays.

In the mounting of Paschen and Runge[16] (1902) the grating and slit are fixed (Fig. 62), and the plate is moved along the Rowland circle to change the range of wave lengths. This mounting is often used in modern spectrographs, especially for research instruments, but it requires more space than the Eagle and Wadsworth mountings described below.

The grating and the plate in the Abney[17] mounting (1886) are fixed on the Rowland circle, but the position of the slit is changed to vary the wave-length range. This is a disadvantage because of the necessity of moving the rather bulky equipment by which radiation is focused on the slit. The Abney mounting is seldom used, although one commercial instru-

[16]C. R. Runge and F. Paschen, *Abh. d. K. Akad. d. Wiss. Z. Berlin*, Anhang 1 (1902).
[17]W. de W. Abney, *Phil. Trans.*, **177**, 457 (1886).

ment with this mounting is on the market (Applied Research Laboratories).

In the Eagle[18] mounting (1910), which is inspired from the Littrow prism spectrograph (Fig. 63B), the incident beam is reflected by a prism *P* before impinging on the grating. The grating and plate are on the

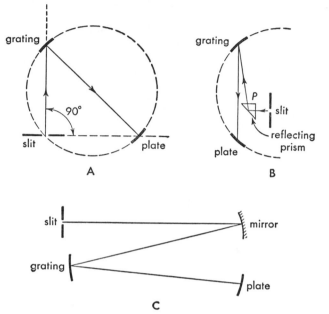

Fig. 63. Different mountings in grating spectrographs: (A) Rowland; (B) Eagle; (C) Wadsworth.

Rowland circle. The wave-length range is adjusted by changing the positions and orientations of the grating and the plate. This mounting is compact and is adopted in small instruments, but it requires rather delicate adjustments for changing the wave-length range.

In the Wadsworth[19] mounting (1896), which does not make use of the Rowland circle, a beam of parallel radiation produced by means of a concave mirror impinges on the grating (Fig. 63C). The wave-length range is changed by rotation of the grating and displacement of the plate. The Wadsworth mounting gives sharp spectral lines and is often adopted in spectrographs for chemical analysis.

A rather recent innovation in spectrographic instrumentation is the prism-grating dispersion system developed by Harrison.[20] The principle of this two-coordinate deflection system is shown in the self-explanatory

[18]A. Eagle, *Astrophys. J.*, **31**, 120 (1910).
[19]F. L. O. Wadsworth, *Astrophys. J.*, **3**, 54 (1896).
[20]G. R. Harrison, *J. Optical Soc. Am.*, **39**, 522 (1949).

diagram of Fig. 64. The linear reciprocal dispersion can easily be as low as 0.5 A per millimeter. A commercial instrument is available (Bausch and Lomb).

Excellent grating spectrographs, as well as prism instruments, are com-

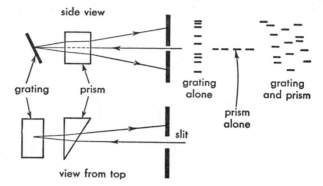

Fig. 64. Principle of the prism-grating dispersion system.

mercially available: Applied Research Laboratories, Baird Associates, Bausch and Lomb, Gaertner Scientific Corporation, Jarrell-Ash, National Spectrographic Laboratories in the United States; Hilger and Zeiss among others in Europe. The focal length of some of these instruments is as long as 4 to 5 meters. A comparison of several commercial instruments has been made by Churchill[21] in a review which is quite old by now, but which still gives a good idea of the criteria to be considered in comparing instruments from the point of view of the analytical chemist.

8–4. SOURCES, ELECTRODES, AND HANDLING OF SAMPLES

a. Sources. There are essentially five different sources in emission spectroscopy: the flame, the d-c arc, the a-c arc, the spark, and the discharge tube (for gases). The flame is a simple source suitable for the excitation of certain elements. Details on flame photometry will be reserved for Section 8–8.

Direct-current arcs are fed by a power supply such as a motor-generator group or a transformer-rectifier unit. The electrodes of the arc are in series with an ammeter, a variable resistance for adjustment of the current, and a choke to prevent transients in the arc circuit. The current is adjusted at 5 to 15 amp with a voltage across the arc of approximately 40 to 60 volts.

Electrons emitted by the cathode bombard the anode and raise its temperature (perhaps to 6000°K) with the resulting emission of positive ions from the electrode material. These ions migrate toward the cathode where they form a space charge around the electrode. This *cathodic layer* has a

[21]J. R. Churchill, *Ind. Eng. Chem., Anal. Ed.*, **16**, 653 (1944).

much greater (10 to 20 times) luminous intensity than the other zones of the arc, probably because of the high density of atoms and ions. This is why the image of the cathodic layer rather than any other zone of the arc is sometimes focused on the slit of the spectrograph. Spectra of d-c arcs mainly correspond to the excitation of neutral atoms.

The d-c arc has the advantages of being simple and inexpensive. It produces very rich spectra and is particularly advantageous in qualitative analysis. Application to quantitative analysis has been made (see Ahrens' book, Section 8–10), but good reproducibility may not be easy to achieve. The zone of burning is not distributed over the whole area of the electrode tip and this results in a certain instability of the arc. This difficulty can be eliminated to a certain extent by continuous rotation (600 rpm) of the electrode, but this complicates the electrode assembly. It is simpler in quantitative work to feed the arc with alternating current, as was first shown by Duffendack and Wolfe.[22]

An a-c arc source is essentially composed of a transformer having an output voltage of 2000 to 5000 volts and a variable inductance in the primary and/or a variable resistance in the secondary of the transformer. The arc current of 1 to 5 amp is adjusted by means of the resistance or the inductance. The transformer is fed with the line voltage at 60 cps, and the arc extinguishes itself 120 times per second. The relatively high voltage of 2000 to 5000 volts must be applied to the arc to cause self-ignition. As soon as the arc is ignited the voltage across its terminals drops to perhaps 40 to 60 volts (Fig. 65A) because of the resistance in series with the arc

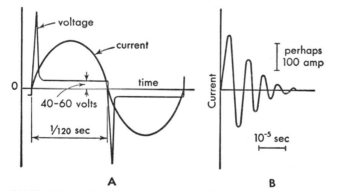

Fig. 65.   (A) Variations of voltage and current with time for an a-c arc. (B) Current-time variations in the condensed spark.

or the inductance in the primary of the transformer. Since the electrical field for a given voltage changes with the distance between electrodes, the electrode gap should be kept constant in comparative measurements.

[22]O. S. Duffendack and R. Wolfe, *Ind. Eng. Chem., Anal. Chem.*, **10**, 161 (1938).

Emission spectra obtained with a-c arcs are composed of lines for the excitation of neutral atoms and molecules, and are not so rich as for the d-c arc.

Higher excitation energies than those obtained with the arc are generated in the *condensed spark*. The electrodes in series with an inductance (50 to 5000 μh) are connected to a capacitor (0.001 to 0.02 μf), which is charged up to 10,000 to 100,000 volts by means of a d-c power supply, or more simply, a transformer. A resistance (0–500 ohms) is inserted between the capacitor and the transformer to limit the charging current. Oscillations of high amplitude but of short duration because of damping by resistance are generated at each discharge (Fig. 65B). The current is large (perhaps 100 amp) because of the low impedance of the electrode circuit.[23]

If the capacitor is charged with a transformer, as is often the case, there may be as many as 10 to 20 discharges during each half-cycle of the output voltage of the transformer. The reproducibility is improved when the number of discharges is controlled during each half-cycle. This can be done by inserting in series with the electrode a commutator driven by a synchronous motor.[24] The number of discharges is then determined by the number of poles and the speed of the commutator. Control is also achieved when a second set of electrodes is inserted in series with the main electrodes. A jet of air is directed on the auxiliary spark gap, and the number of discharges is controlled by varying the velocity of the air jet.[25]

Apparent tenperatures[26] in the spark are as high as 10,000° K, but the electrodes are "cold." Spectra are mainly composed of lines for the excitation of atoms and are not so rich as spectra obtained with a-c arcs. The sensitivity of the condensed spark is not so good as for the a-c arc, but the reproducibility is better. In general, the use of the condensed spark is not advisable when the concentration of the analyzed element is below 0.1 per cent, and the a-c arc is then preferred, perhaps to concentrations as low as 1 ppm.

Beside its excellent reproducibility, the condensed spark also is more versatile than the a-c arc because of the possibility of adjustment of the capacitance, inductance, and resistance. The intensity of lines increases with capacitance and decreases with the resistance in series with the condenser. An increase of resistance also minimizes the danger of discharge between only limited areas of the electrodes. Decrease of the inductance favors transitions requiring high energies, but it also increases the general background in the spectrum.

[23]For a discussion of current-time curves see H. Kaiser and A. Wallraff, *Ann. Physik*, **34,** 297 (1939).

[24]O. Feussner, *Arch. Eisenhüttenw.*, **6,** 551 (1933).

[25]J. H. Enns and R. A. Wolfe, ASTM *Special Tech. Pub.*, No. **76,** pp. 12–24 (1946).

[26]One refers to an apparent temperature because the thermodynamic definition of temperature does not apply to the conditions in the spark.

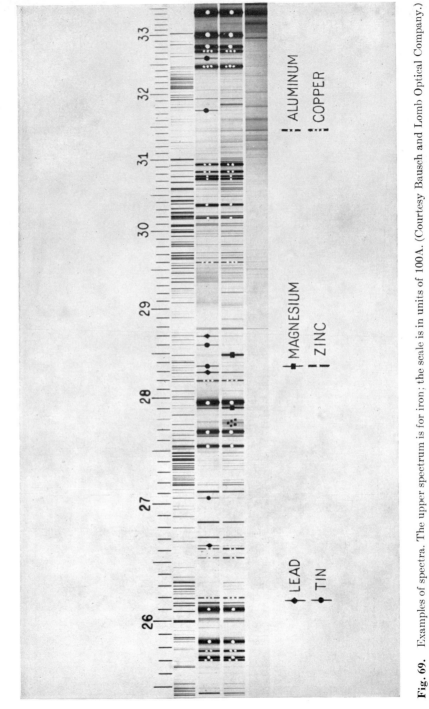

Fig. 69. Examples of spectra. The upper spectrum is for iron; the scale is in units of 100A. (Courtesy Bausch and Lomb Optical Company.)

Commercial units with power supplies for d-c and a-c arcs and for condensed spark are available: Applied Research Laboratories,[27] Baird Associates, National Spectrographic Laboratories in the United States.

Discharge tubes operating at a few thousand volts and at pressures of a few millimeters of mercury are employed in gas analysis. In the Geissler tube the discharge occurs in a constricted section of the tube and is focused on the slit of the spectrograph. The hollow-cathode tube (Fig. 66) developed by Paschen is another possible type of discharge tube. The spectra of gases can also be studied with electrodeless discharge tubes operating at high frequency.

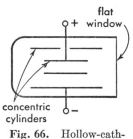

Fig. 66.   Hollow-cathode discharge tube.

b. Electrodes and Handling of Samples. In the analysis of metals and alloys which are available in substantial quantities for sampling it is often possible to utilize *self-electrodes* made of the metal sample. Electrodes (cylinder or disk) are cast or are prepared by pressing the metal powder. Care should be taken to have a homogeneous sample. The electrodes are made of two rods of the metal being analyzed, or in the case of flat specimens, a graphite rod and the metal sample. In the latter case the sample is placed on a platform which is connected to one of the terminals of the power supply (Petrey stand).

Electrodes are generally made of graphite rods of high purity for nonmetallic samples and in the analysis of metal samples available only in small quantities. The end of the graphite anode is shaped like a small cup in which the sample (powder, pellet, etc.) is placed; the cathode is a pointed graphite rod. Solutions can be evaporated in the anode cup, or the electrodes may be impregnated with the solution or liquid to be analyzed. Metallic electrodes (copper) also can be used for the analysis of solutions.[28]

The intensity of a line of a given element varies during the burning of the sample, as shown in Fig. 67. Different curves are obtained for each element in the sample because of differences in volatility, and there is *fractional distillation* of the sample. A serious error may result from this effect unless the sample is burned completely. Fractional distillation, however, may serve a useful purpose in the analysis of traces of volatile elements, since the impurities first appear in the spectrum. Application of fractional distillation has been made in the analysis of some impurities in uranium oxides.[29]

[27]Unit described by M. F. Hasler and H. W. Dietert (abstract only), *J. Optical Soc. Am.*, **35**, 802 (1945).

[28]M. Fred, N. H. Nachtrieb, and F. S. Tomkins, *J. Optical Soc. Am.*, **37**, 279 (1947).

[29]B. F. Scribner and H. R. Mullin, *J. Research Nat. Bur. Standards*, **37**, 379 (1946).

Fractional distillation also may cause some error with self-electrodes, but this difficulty can sometimes be overcome by *presparking* the electrodes prior to the actual analysis.

Very rapid vaporization of an element may cause a serious error be-

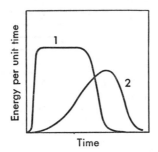
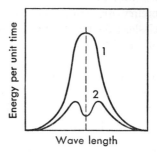

Fig. 67. Variations of line intensity during burning of sample; element 1 is more volatile than 2.

Fig. 68. Energy-wave length profile and self-absorption.

cause of *self-absorption* of lines of this element. The explanation of this effect is as follows. The vapor of an element absorbs radiation at the wave lengths corresponding to the lines (for neutral atoms) of the emission spectrum of the element. Absorption results from the variation between energy levels which is the inverse of the variation corresponding to emission (Fraunhofer lines; see physics text). As a result of self-absorption by the vapor of the element, the line intensity is lower than expected.

Self-absorption may also cause *self-reversal* of a line. The energy wavelength profile of a line normally has the shape of curve 1 in Fig. 68. In case of self-absorption the energies are smaller than for curve 1, and in extreme cases profile 2 with a minimum is obtained. In the latter case it is said that there is self-reversal of the line.

Cyanogen, $(CN)_2$, is formed in an arc between graphite electrodes burning in air. Cyanogen dissociates with production of the group CN which strongly emits radiation in the range 3500 to 4200 A. The resulting *cyanogen bands* may interfere with the determination of some elements unless the intensity of these bands is minimized by proper adjustment of the characteristics of operation (current, voltage, etc.) of the arc. The cyanogen bands are completely eliminated when the arc is surrounded by an atmosphere of hydrogen, argon or helium, as was shown by Paschen.[30] The continuous background upon which the line spectrum is superimposed is also minimized, and the sensitivity is increased. The use of helium was thoroughly reinvestigated by Vallee and Peattie.[31]

[30]F. Paschen, *Ann. Physik*, **12**, 509 (1932).
[31]B. L. Vallee and R. W. Peattie, *Anal. Chem.*, **24**, 434 (1952).

8-5. QUALITATIVE ANALYSIS

Since each element has a characteristic spectrum, an element can be identified by a few lines. In spectrochemical analysis the plate is calibrated in wave-length units. Iron or manganese are generally selected as reference because the spectra of these elements are particularly rich (Fig. 69).

Distances between lines can be measured with a ruler, but much more accurate results are obtained with a *comparator*. In this instrument the plate is set on a platform which can be moved back and forth along the spectrum by means of a calibrated screw. The plate is examined with a microscope attached to the stand of the comparator, and the distance between two lines, 1 and 2, is determined as follows:

The microscope, whose occular is equipped with a cross hair, is focused on the center of line 1, and the reading of the dial of the screw is noted. The same procedure is followed for line 2, and the distance between the two lines is determined from the difference in the dial readings. Instead of moving the plate, one can, of course, keep the plate in a fixed position and move the microscope laterally by means of a calibrated screw.

The wave length of a given line located between two lines, 1 and 2, of known wave lengths can be determined by linear interpolation. This procedure can be applied with grating spectrographs even over a range of several hundred angstroms because the linear reciprocal dispersion is essentially independent of wave length (see Section 8-3a). This is not the case with prism instruments, as was shown in Section 8-2a, and only interpolation over a narrow wave length range is possible, say, 20 A. A better method is to apply the interpolation formula of Hartmann (problem 1 in Section 8-11). Still another method is to use a plot of wave length against distance from a reference line. Determination of wave lengths within one tenth of an angstrom is amply adequate in analytical work.

Since several hundred thousand lines have been reported, tables of wave lengths, and atlases of spectra (see Section 8-10c) are essential tools in the spectrographic laboratory.

As the concentration of an element in a mixture decreases, the number of lines decreases, and finally only the *"raies ultimes"* (ultimate lines, or R.U. lines) are observed. R.U. lines for a large number of elements were determined by De Gramont in a series of investigations extending over a period of more than 20 years (approximately 1900-1920). A powder specimen containing about 50 elements in such proportions that only a few R.U. lines appear per element is available from the Jarrell-Ash Company. Lists of R.U. lines are given in tables of wave lengths and in handbooks of chemistry and physics.

Most qualitative work is done with a *master plate* showing three or four of the most persistent lines of a large number of elements, together with the symbols of these elements. Master plates are commercially available (Applied Research Laboratories).

8-6. QUANTITATIVE ANALYSIS BY THE PHOTOGRAPHIC METHOD

a. Properties of Photographic Emulsions. If the excitation conditions are kept constant and the sample composition is varied over a narrow range, the energy emitted for a given spectral line of an element is proportional to the number of atoms that are excited and consequently to the concentration of element in the sample. The emitted energy is measured by one of the following two methods: (1) the spectrum is photographed, and the concentration of the unknown is determined from the blackening of the plate for certain lines in the spectrum; (2) the energy emitted at given wave lengths is measured directly with a suitable detector (phototube). The photographic method has been applied for many years and still is most frequently used, but direct-reading methods find increased use in large control laboratories. The photographic method will be discussed first and will be introduced by a brief review of the properties of photographic emulsions.

The first problem in the study of photographic emulsions is to determine quantitatively the blackening of plates. This measurement is made with

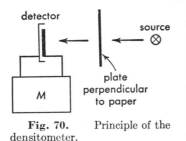

Fig. 70.   Principle of the densitometer.

a *densitometer* (Fig. 70), which is essentially composed of a source of light and a detector for measuring light intensities. One type of detector (phototube) is described in Section 8–7, and another type (barrier layer cell) is discussed in Section 9–4. The intensity of irradiation of the detector is first measured for an unexposed portion of the plate, and a reading I_0 is made on the output meter M of the detector. An exposed area is then interposed between source and detector, and the reading of meter M is I. The *transmission* T of the emulsion is the ratio I/I_0, and the *density* D is log I_0/I. In view of the definition of T and D, one has $D = \log(1/T)$. The transmission varies from 0 to 1, and the density from 0 to infinity.

It was observed by Bunsen and Roscoe[32] that the transmission or the density of an emulsion depends only on the total energy absorbed by the plate, regardless of the intensity and duration of irradiation (*reciprocity law*). If the absorbed energy ϵ is constant during exposure and τ is the exposure time, the transmission or the density depends only on the product $\epsilon\tau$, all conditions being the same except that ϵ and τ are varied in consecutive exposures. If the energy ϵ varies during exposure, the product $\epsilon\tau$ must be replaced by the integral $\int_0^\tau \epsilon \, dt$ over the exposure time. This

[32]R. W. Bunsen and H. E. Roscoe, *Ann. Physik.*, **117**, 529 (1862).

integral is called the *intensity of exposure,* or simply, the *intensity* or the *exposure.* This integrating property of photographic emulsions is most valuable in spectroscopy because the energy output of the source of irradiation varies considerably during the burning of a sample (Fig. 67).

It should be emphasized that the reciprocity law is only approximate, and that this law fails for extreme values of ϵ or τ.

It is observed that the density of photographic emulsions varies linearly with the logarithm of the exposure over a wide range (Fig. 71). Hurter

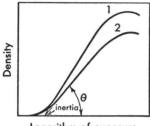

Logarithm of exposure

Fig. 71. H and D curves for photographic emulsions. The development time is longer for curve 1 than for curve 2.

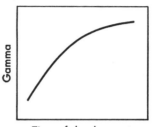

Time of development

Fig. 72. Variations of gamma with development time.

and Driffield[33] were the first to report this relationship, and the corresponding plots therefore are called *H and D curves.* The slope of the linear segment of the H and D curve, i.e., tanθ, is an important characteristic and is called the *gamma* of the emulsion. Emulsions with a high gamma give images with strong contrast because a small difference in exposure causes a large variation in density. The intercept of the linear segment of the H and D curve with the abscissa axis is defined as the *inertia* of the plate.

The gamma of an emulsion increases with development time (Fig. 72), and consequently this time should be controlled in the processing of spectroscopic plates. The inertia, however, is independent of development time (curves 1 and 2, Fig. 71). The gamma and inertia also depend on wave lengths.

Further details on the photographic process can be found in some of books listed in Section 8–10 (Harrison *et al.,* Nachtrieb, Sawyer, etc.) and in the books of Mees[34] or Boucher.[35] Practical information on spectroscopic plates is available.[36]

The processing of spectroscopic plates follows conventional practice

[33]F. Hurter and V. C. Driffield, *J. Soc. Chem. Ind.,* **9,** 455 (1890); *Photography,* **5** supplement, 22 (1893).

[34]C. E. K. Mees, *The Theory of the Photographic Process,* Macmillan, New York, 1942.

[35]P. E. Boucher, *Fundamentals of Photography,* 3rd ed., Van Nostrand, New York, 1956.

[36]*Materials for Spectrum Analysis,* Eastman Kodak Co., Rochester, N.Y., 2nd ed., 1954.

except that the duration of each step (development, fixing, washing) must be controlled. Special care should be taken to stir properly the developer because, otherwise, concentration gradients are set up in the vicinity of spectral lines, where the developer is used more rapidly than in other areas of the plate. The density of lines may be affected by poor stirring of the developing bath (*Eberhard effect*).

b. Measurement of Line Densities. The densitometer utilized in the measurement of the density of emulsions can readily be adopted to the determination of the density of spectral lines. The beam falling on the plate (Fig. 70) must be much narrower than the breadth of spectral lines. The plate is mounted on a calibrated screw, as in the comparator described in Section 8–5, and the plate position is changed by rotation of the calibrated screw. In recording instruments the calibrated screw rotates at a uniform speed, and the detector output is applied to a pen-and-ink recorder (see Section 2–10c). A diagram is obtained in which the ordinate is proportional to the energy measured by detector M and the abscissa is proportional to the distance along the plate. Each line appears on the diagram as a peak, similar to the line profile of Fig. 68 (curve 1). Commercial manual and recording densitometers, or *microphotometers* as they are called sometimes, are available from manufacturers of spectroscopic equipment.

A continuous background is superimposed on the special lines, and a *background correction* must be made. The correction is easily made if one recalls that the corrected exposure is the difference between the exposure of the line (generally the center of the line) and the exposure for the background. The densities D_l and D_b for the line and the background, respectively, are converted to the relative exposures 10^{D_l} and 10^{D_b} in an arbitrary scale. The corrected exposure then is $10^{D_l} - 10^{D_b}$, and the corrected density[37] is $\log(10^{D_l} - 10^{D_b})$.

c. Internal Standard Method. It was pointed out in part *a* of this section that the energy emitted for a given line of an element during the burning of a sample is proportional to the concentration of this element, provided that excitation conditions are kept constant and the sample composition varies over a narrow range. It follows that the plate exposure during the burning of the sample is proportional to the concentration, and the curve showing line density versus concentration has the same shape as the H and D curve for the plate emulsion under the particular conditions prevailing in the analysis. The density of spectral lines therefore can be utilized for quantitative purposes. Other characteristics of lines, such as

[37]The procedure of setting the densitometer output meter at zero in the background range and then make the reading for the line is not correct; see Nachtrieb, pp. 135–139 (reference in Section 8–10).

line breadth,[38] for instance, have been proposed but have not been adopted in general.

The density of spectral lines for given experimental conditions is not very reproducible because several important factors cannot be controlled rigorously: conditions of excitation, processing of the plate, etc. The accuracy is improved by application of the *internal standard method*, which was first described in detail by Gerlach[39] in 1925. This method, which is the key to the application of spectroscopy to quantitative analysis, is based on the comparison of the line density for the element of unknown concentration with the line density of an element of known concentration. Two *homologous lines*, i.e., lines for which the ratio of transmissions is essentially independent of the conditions of excitation, are selected for the standard and the unknown.[40]

In contrast with homologous lines, the ratio of the transmissions for *fixation lines* depends much on conditions of excitation. Fixation pairs are, of course, not selected for analytical determinations but are utilized in the verification of the reproducibility of excitation conditions.

The internal standard can be an element present at a much larger concentration than the unknown. The concentration of the standard is then virtually independent of variations in the sample composition. For instance, a metal being analyzed for small amounts of impurities may serve as internal standard. An alternative to this procedure is to add to the sample a known and generally constant quantity of a derivative of the element selected as internal standard.

A few simple rules should be followed in the selection of the internal standard. Thus,[41] the rates of volatilization of the standard and the unknown should not be very different; the line of the standard should not exhibit self-absorption; the wave lengths of lines for the unknown and the standard should be approximately the same because the variation of the gamma of the emulsion with wave length may otherwise cause some error. Quite obviously, the internal standard should be essentially free of the elements for which the sample is analyzed.

Wave lengths of pairs of homologous lines are listed in the literature for a variety of groups of two elements. If the wave lengths are not listed, they must be determined by trial and error. Diagrams of electronic shifts of the two elements being considered may help in the selection of lines

[38]P. Coheur, *J. Optical Soc. Am.*, **36**, 498 (1946).

[39]W. Gerlach, *Z. Anorg. Chem.*, **142**, 383 (1925). The idea of using an internal standard is, however, much older and may be attributed to Lockyer and Roberts (1873); see Section 8–1.

[40]In its original sense, a "homologous pair" had to fulfill the additional condition of equality of the line densities. This additional restriction is no longer implied at the present.

[41]According to L. H. Ahrens, *Spectrochemical Analysis*, Addison–Wesley Press, Cambridge, Mass., 1950, p. 81.

because homologous lines correspond to electronic transitions having fairly similar characteristics.

d. Preparation of the Calibration and Working Curves. The quantitative analysis of plates involves two essential steps: (1) line densities must be converted to exposures, and (2) exposures must be converted to concentrations. The first step requires the determination of the *calibration curve* for the emulsion, and the second step involves the preparation of a *working curve*.

All that is principally required in the preparation of the calibration curve of an emulsion is a source of known variable intensity. The great variety of methods which have been proposed[42] can be divided into two groups, depending on whether a single or multiple exposures are required. The following methods are most frequently applied: sector methods, the line ratio and "two-line" methods, the inverse square law, and the variable exposure time methods. The latter two procedures, which require mutliple exposures, will be first discussed.

The inverse square law method is based on the relationship between the exposure and the reciprocal of the square of the distance between the source and the photographic plate. This method requires a stable source, and it involves more operations than one-exposure methods. The calibration method based on *variation of the exposure time* is very simple, but it depends on the validity of the reciprocity law.

In single-exposure methods the intensity of illumination along the slit of the spectrograph is varied in a known fashion. This result can be achieved by a number of methods: step-sector disk, logarithmic sector, the line ratio method, and the two-line method. The *sector methods* are very simple. A sector is rotated (several hundred revolutions per minute) in front of the slit, in such a way that the intensity of irradiation varies either logarithmically or step-wisely along the slit. In the step-sector intensities each step corresponds to a decrease in intensity, for instance, 50 per cent. Sector methods were common in the past, but other more accurate methods are now preferred.

In the *line ratio method* the density is measured for a series of lines whose relative intensities are known and essentially independent of the conditions of excitation.[43] The iron spectrum, with lines of relative intensities in the range 1 to 10, is generally adopted (about 10 lines). It is essential that the group of lines used for calibration be in a narrow wave-length band (100 A) because of variations of the gamma of the emulsion with wave length. This condition may seriously restrict the application of the method.

[42]G. R. Harrison, *J. Optical Soc. Am.*, **24,** 59 (1934).
[43]G. H. Dieke and H. M. Crosswhite, *J. Optical Soc. Am.*, **33,** 425 (1943).

The *two-line method* developed by Churchill[44] is probably the simplest and most accurate method for analytical appplications. The densities of two homologous lines of iron are determined for varying conditions of exposure, and the results are interpreted as follows.

The line densities D_I and D_{II} are plotted one against the other (Fig. 73).

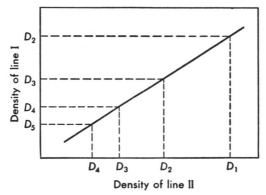

Fig. 73. Plot for the two-line calibration of an emulsion.

A density D_1 of line II, larger than any density expected in the actual analysis, is selected, and the corresponding density D_2 of line I is read on the curve of D_I against D_{II}. The density D_2 is selected as density for line II and the corresponding density D_3 of line I is read on the plot of D_I against D_{II}. The procedure is repeated until the last value of D_p for line I is smaller than any density expected in the analysis. Since the ratio of the intensities for lines I and II is constant, one has

$$\frac{D_2}{D_1} = \frac{D_3}{D_2} = \cdots = \frac{D_p}{D_{p-1}} = k, \tag{8–13}$$

or by multiplication,

$$\frac{D_2 \times D_3 \cdots \times D_{p-1} \times D_p}{D_1 \times D_2 \cdots \times D_{p-2} \times D_{p-1}} = k^{p-1}, \tag{8–14}$$

i.e.,

$$\frac{D_p}{D_1} = k^{p-1}. \tag{8–15}$$

The calibration curve can now be constructed by plotting D_p against k^{p-1} for $p = 2, 3, \ldots$.

The two-line method is particularly advantageous because the relative values of the exposures must not be known. This greatly simplifies the technique and eliminates errors of mechanical or optical nature.

Once the calibration curve has been determined, line densities can be converted to exposures. The final step in the analysis of the plate, then, is

[44]J. R. Churchill, *Ind. Eng. Chem., Anal. Ed.*, **16**, 653 (1944).

the conversion of exposure to the concentration of the unknown by means of a *working curve*. This curve, which is generally plotted in log-log coordinates, is prepared from spectra of standard samples having compositions very similar to that of the unknown. Considerable preliminary work is frequently involved in the preparation of a working curve, and emission spectroscopy therefore is not well adapted to quantitative analysis of single samples of widely varying composition. Conversely, emission spectroscopy is ideally suited to routine analysis.

An example of a working curve is shown in Fig. 74 for the analysis of

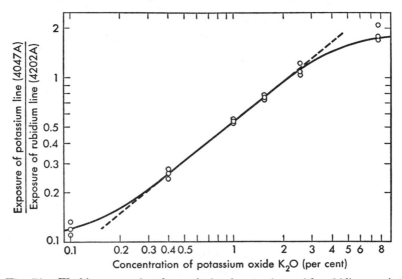

Fig. 74. Working curve for the analysis of potassium with rubidium as internal standard. (From L. H. Ahrens, *Spechrochemical Analysis*, Addison-Wesley, Cambridge, Mass., 1954, p. 134.)

potassium in feldspar with rubidium as internal standard. A marked departure from linearity is observed at high concentrations because of self-absorption and at low concentrations because of pronounced interference by the background.

Quantitative determinations were made by the sector method before the development of the densitometer, and concentrations were deduced from the lengths of lines. Details will not be given, since the method is seldom applied at the present.

8–7. DIRECT-READING SPECTROMETERS

Manipulations in emission spectroscopy are simplified when the photographic process is eliminated and the energy emitted for given lines is measured directly and integrated during the burning of the sample. Direct-reading methods require a very sensitive detector for the measurement of radiation at low intensities. Geiger-Müller counters (see Section 14–2d) were utilized, but *photomultiplier tubes*, which were invented[45] about 1940, proved more sensitive and accurate. The principle of the photomultiplier tube and its precursor, the phototube, will be discussed first, and application to spectrometry will be examined afterwards.

A phototube is essentially composed of two electrodes in an evacuated vessel.[46] The electrodes are connected to a power supply (dry cell, etc.) having an output of 100 to 200 volts, and the current through the tube is measured with a galvanometer *G* (Fig. 75). Electrons emitted by photo-

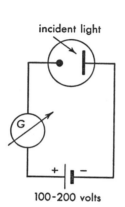

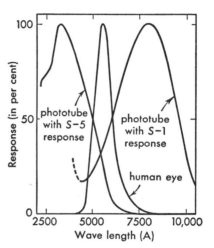

Fig. 75. Schematic diagram of phototube circuit.

Fig. 76. Characteristics of the human eye and two different phototubes. (From data on phototubes in brochure CRPS-102 of Radio Corporation of America; drawing somewhat different from that in the RCA pamphlet).

electric effect under the influence of light are collected by the anode. The resulting current varies linearly with the intensity of radiation, but a very low current (*dark current*) flows through the tube even in complete darkness because of leaks in the circuit and thermal emission of electrons by the cathode.

The current in the electrode circuit varies greatly with the nature of the cathode and the wave length of the incident light (Fig. 76). The alkali metals, particularly potassium and cesium, are generally used because the energy required for electron extraction is lower than for other metals.

[45]V. A. Zworykin and J. A. Rajchman, *Proc. I.R.E.*, **27**, 558 (1939); J. A. Rajchman and R. L. Snyder, *Electronics*, **13**, No. 12, 20 (1940).

[46]There are phototubes filled with a gas, but these need not be described here.

Hence potassium or cesium cells can be used at relatively long wave lengths at which the photoelectric effect is not observed with other metals. In general, phototubes with a cesium coated cathode are employed in the range 5000 to 10,000 A, and potassium cells are utilized mainly in the 2000 to 5000 A range (approximate limits). Tubes for measurements below 3500 A must have a quartz window.

It is observed that the current through a phototube for given conditions of illumination first increases with voltage. A saturation plateau is reached at about 100 volts. All the electrons emitted by the cathode are then captured by the anode, and the current is independent of the voltage across the electrodes. The operating voltage of the tube is adjusted in the saturation plateau.

Galvanometers are too delicate in many applications of phototubes and electronic amplifiers are preferred. The galvanometer in the circuit of Fig. 75 is replaced by a large resistance (perhaps 10^9 to 10^{12} ohms) connected to a vacuum-tube voltmeter. The input tube of this instrument has a very low grid current and generally an electrometer tube is used when low light intensities have to be measured.

The sensitivity of phototubes, which is high, is further increased by a factor of the order of 10^6 in photomultiplier tubes. The anodes of photomultiplier tubes are covered with a material which emits several (2 to 5) electrons for each electron being collected on its surface. The electrons emitted by anode e_2 of Fig. 77 are collected on a third electrode e_3, which is

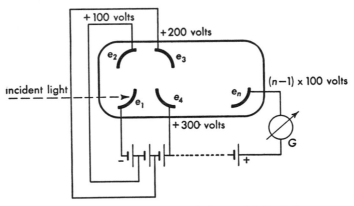

Fig. 77.   Schematic diagram of photomultiplier tube.

about 100 volts more positive than e_2. Electron multiplication again occurs on electrode e_3; up to nine to twelve anodes can be utilized. The current in the circuit of the most positive anode is measured directly or is amplified by a conventional electronic amplifier. Since the amplification factor is between 2 and 5 for each anode, the over-all amplification factor for a ten-anode tube is between 2^9 and 5^9, i.e., between 500 and 2×10^6. Gains of 10^6 are not uncommon for commercial tubes. Tubes with a higher gain are too unstable for practical purposes.

After this digression on photomultiplier tubes we now return to direct-reading spectrometers. In these instruments, photomultiplier tubes are placed at the positions corresponding to the lines used in the analysis of the various elements of the sample. One tube is needed per element and an additional tube is required for the internal standard. The same line of the standard is often utilized for the different elements for which the sample is analyzed. The current of each phototube is integrated over the burning of the sample by means of an electronic integrator. Commercial instruments are also equipped with a computer which expresses directly the result of the analysis in per cent of each element. Results can be accurate within 1 per cent under favorable conditions, and a dozen different elements can be determined simultaneously.

Several direct-reading spectrometers are described in the literature,[47-50] and commercial instruments are available (the *Quantometer* from Applied Research Laboratories, Baird Associates).

8-8. FLAME PHOTOMETRY AND SPECTROMETRY

The idea of using the flame for excitation of emission spectra is as old as spectrochemical analysis but it was not fully exploited in quantitative analysis until about 1930. Lundegardh,[51] who did the pioneering work in this field, applied the conventional photographic method; however, direct-reading instruments are preferred nowadays.

The method of excitation in the flame is as follows:

The sample is dissolved, and a small volume of solution (perhaps 1 ml) is transferred in the cup C of an atomizer (Fig. 78). Air or oxygen and a combustible gas are fed to the atomizer at controlled rates of flow, and the solution is regularly vaporized in a burner. The resulting emission spectrum corresponds to excitation of neutral atoms by collision with the high-velocity atoms or molecules produced in the flame.

The temperature in the flame is between 1000 and 3000° K. Mixtures of ordinary gas and air do not give very hot flames because the heating of nitrogen greatly cools the flame. Hotter flames are obtained with mixtures of oxygen and hydrogen, propane, or acetylene. The highest flame temperature is produced, according to Vallee,[52] with cyanogen-oxygen mix-

[47]E. A. Boettner and G. P. Brewington, *J. Optical Soc. Amer.*, **34**, 6 (1944).
[48]R. O'B. Carpenter, E. DuBois, and J. Sterner, *ibid.*, **37**, 707 (1947).
[49]M. F. Hasler and H. W. Dietert, *ibid.*, **34**, 751 (1944).
[50]J. L. Saunderson, V. J. Caldecourt, and E. W. Peterson, *ibid.*, **35**, 681 (1945).
[51]H. Lundegardh, *Die Quantitative Spektranalyse der Element*, Fisher, Jena, Vol. I (1929), Vol. II (1934).
[52]Article by B. L. Vallee in *Symposium on Trace Analysis*, J. H. Yoe and H. J. Koch, Eds., Wiley, New York (in press).

tures. High temperatures are necessary in the analysis of elements which are not too easily excited.

The photographic method is generally not applied at present in methods involving excitation by flame because more accurate results can be ob-

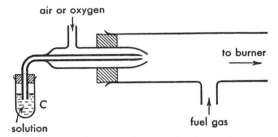

Fig. 78. Schematic diagram of burner for flame photometry.

tained with simple direct-reading instruments. These instruments are of two different types,[53] namely, the *flame photometer* and the *flame spectrometer*.

In the flame photometer, which can be compared to a filter photometer, the intensity of the filtered radiation of the flame is measured with a photoelectric detector. The filter, interposed between the flame and the detector, transmits only a strong line of the element being determined. The width of the band transmitted to the detector can be decreased by substituting for the filter a monochromator, i.e., an instrument which transmits only a narrow band of adjustable wave length (see description in Section 9–5).

Excitation by flame is very stable and measurements without internal standard can be made with errors as low as 1 to 2 per cent. Only one photocell and one filter is then required. In some cases the precision is improved by the use of an internal standard, and two filters, and in general, two photocells (one for the standard and one for the unknown) are utilized. The electric circuit can be devised to give a direct reading of the ratio of the line intensities.

Filter photometers were first developed in Europe[54,55] in the late 1930's and were introduced in the United States by Griggs[56] and Barnes, and co-workers.[57,58] Rather inexpensive commercial instruments with filters

[53]This distinction was made by B. L. Vallee and M. Margoshes, *Anal. Chem.*, **28**, 175 (1956).

[54]W. Schuhknecht, *Angew. Chem.*, **50**, 299 (1937).

[55]L. Schmitt and W. Breitwieser, *Bodenkunde u. Pflanzeuernähr.*, **9-10**, 750 (1938).

[56]M. A. Griggs, *Science*, **89**, 134 (1939).

[57]R. B. Barnes, D. Richardson, J. W. Berry, and R. L. Hood, *Ind. Eng. Chem., Anal. Ed.*, **17**, 605 (1945).

[58]J. W. Berry, D. G. Chappell, and R. B. Barnes, *ibid.*, **18**, 19 (1946).

or monochromators are available (Baird,[59] Barclay, Beckman, Fox,[60] Perkin-Elmer). Accessories[61] are available from Beckman to adapt the spectrophotometers (see Section 9-5) *B* and *DU* to flame photometry.

Flame excitation can be combined with a direct-reading spectrometer for the analysis of several elements. A flame spectrometer having excellent characteristics was described by Vallee and Margoshes[53] for the simultaneous analysis of sodium, potassium, magnesium, calcium, and strontium.

8-9. *APPLICATIONS*

Emission spectroscopy is one of the most important instrumental method of analysis. Its great advantages are: selectivity, sensitivity, short duration of measurements in routine analysis, and the possibility of analyzing samples without prior dissolution. The latter advantage is particularly pronounced in the analysis of such samples as minerals, alloys, and organic substances.

Most elements can be analyzed by spectroscopy, and certain elements can be determined at extremely low concentrations; for instance, 0.01 to 0.1 ppm in the most favorable cases. The sensitivity, however, varies from one element to another. Only small samples of perhaps 10 mg or even less suffice if necessary.

The accuracy is quite good, since errors are as low as 2 per cent with good photographic techniques. Errors are somewhat lower (1 to 2 per cent) with direct-reading instruments and also for good determinations in flame photometry.

Emission spectroscopy is often applied to the analysis of a great variety of materials: salts, plants, animal tissues, food products, etc. Application in forensic chemistry is common. A particularly important application is the control of metal and alloy composition in the metallurgical industry. The amounts of the constituents needed for the adjustment of metal composition must be known continuously during production, and analyses must be performed in a minimum time. Electrodes of the metal or alloy to be analyzed are cast in the plant and are sent by a pneumatic tube to the control laboratory where the analysis is performed by direct-reading spectrometers. Saving in production costs amply justifies the relatively high cost of the installation (50,000 to 100,000 dollars).

Applications of flame photometry and spectrometry are more limited than for methods with arc or spark excitation for two reasons: (1) excitation energies from the flame are too low for certain elements; (2) the sample must be dissolved for flame excitation. The latter condition may

---

[59]Described by J. U. White, *Anal. Chem.*, **24**, 394 (1952).
[60]Described by C. L. Fox, *ibid.*, **23**, 137 (1951).
[61]Described by P. T. Gilbert, Jr., R. C. Hawes, and A. O. Beckman, *ibid.*, **22**, 772 (1950).

be difficult to fulfill with certain samples, or at any rate, may require time-consuming operations. Flame excitation, however, is the most reliable method of excitation. Applications of great practical value have been made, particularly in agricultural, geological, and clinical laboratories. The alkali and alkaline earth metals can be determined easily, and up to now, most applications of flame photometry or spectrometry have dealt with the analysis of these elements. Extension to the analysis of perhaps as many as forty elements may be possible.[61]

8-10. BIBLIOGRAPHY

a. Books and Articles

L. H. Ahrens, *Spectrochemical Analysis*, Addison Wesley Press, Cambridge, Mass., 1950. The d-c arc quantitative method is emphasized.

L. H. Ahrens, *Quantitative Spectrochemical Analysis of Silicates*, Addison Wesley Press, Cambridge, Mass., 1955.

ASTM (Committee E-2) *Methods for Emission Spectrochemical Analysis*, Philadelphia, 1953.

W. R. Brode, *Chemical Spectroscopy*, 2nd ed., Wiley, New York, 1943. Discussion of fundamentals, and numerous tables and data; covers the whole field of spectroscopy. Contains a detailed bibliography.

C. Candler, *Practical Spectroscopy*, Hilger and Watts, London, 1949.

F. L. de Boisbaudran and A. De Gramont, *Analyse Spectrale Appliquée aux Recherches Minérales*, Paris, 1924. A classical work, mainly of historical interest at the present.

H. Dingle, *Practical Applications of Spectrum Analysis*, Chapman and Hall, London, 1950.

W. Gerlach and E. Schweitzer, *Die chemische Emissionsspektral-analyse*, Vol. I, Voss, Leipzig, 1929; English translation from A. Hilger, London. Vol. II by W. Gerlach and W. Gerlach, Voss, Leipzig, 1933; English translation, A. Hilger, London, 1934. Vol. III by W. Gerlach and E. Reidl, Voss, Leipzig, 1936. A classical work.

T. R. P. Gibb, *Optical Methods of Analysis*, McGraw-Hill, New York, 1942. An introductory treatment.

G. R. Harrison, R. C. Lord, J. R. Loofbourow, *Practical Spectroscopy*, Prentice-Hall, 1948. Detailed discussion of instrumentation in the whole field of spectroscopy, including methods for the far ultraviolet and interferometric measurements.

C. E. Harvey, *Spectrochemical Procedures*, Applied Research Laboratories, Glendale, California, 1950. Gives much valuable information of practical interest.

H. Kayser and co-workers, *Handbuch der Spektroskopie*, 8 vols., Hirzel, Leipzig, 1901–1934. Treatise on spectroscopy.

H. Lundegardh, *Die quantitative Spektralanalyse der Element*, Fischer, Jena, Vol. I (1929), Vol. II (1934).

R. Mavrodineanu and H. Boiteux, *L'Analyse Spectrale Quantitative par la Flamme*, Mason, Paris, 1954. Applications of flame photometry

H. Moritz, *Spektrochemische Betriebsanalyse*, 2nd ed., Enke, Stuttgart, 1955. Excellent introductory treatment.

N. H. Nachtrieb, *Principles and Practice of Spectrochemical Analysis*, McGraw-Hill, New York, 1950. Excellent treatment of fundamentals; contains also many details of practical interest.

R. A. Sawyer, *Experimental Spectroscopy*, 2nd ed., Prentice-Hall, New York, 1951. Excellent discussion of spectroscopic instrumentation.

G. Scheibe, article in *Physikalische Methoden der Analytischen Chemie*, Vol. I, W. Böttger, Ed., Akademische Verlagsgesellschaft, Leipzig, 1933. See also the article by A. Henrici and G. Scheibe in Vol. III (1939).

W. Seith and K. Ruthardt, *Chemische Spektranalyse*, Springer, Berlin, 1949.

J. Sherman, article in *Physical Methods in Chemical Analysis*, Vol. I, W. G. Berl, Ed., Academic Press, New York, 1950. Oriented toward metallurgical applications.

F. Twyman, *The Spectrochemical Analysis of Metals and Alloys*, Chemical Publishing Co., Brooklyn, N.Y., 1941. A classical work.

b. Reviews and Index to the Literature

H. K. Hughes *et al.* (18 other co-authors), *Anal. Chem.*, **24**, 1349 (1952). Rather comprehensive list of terms used in spectroscopy and their definition.

W. F. Meggers, *Anal. Chem.*, **21**, 29 (1949); **22**, 18 (1950); **24**, 23 (1952); **26**, 54 (1954); **28**, 616 (1956).

B. F. Scribner and W. F. Meggers, *Index to the Literature on Spectrochemical Analysis:* Part I, 1920–1939; Part 2, 1940–1945; Part 3, 1946–1950; *Am. Soc. Testing Materials*, Philadelphia.

c. Tables of Wave Lengths and Atlases of Spectra

A. Gatterer and J. Junkes, *Atlas der Restlinien*, 3 vols., Specola Vaticana, Citta del Vaticano, Vol. I (1937), Vol. II (1945), Vol. III (1949). Reliable tables of spectral lines; contains spectra for 73 elements.

G. R. Harrison, Ed., *M.I.T. Wave Length Tables*, Wiley, New York, 1939. Gives more than 100,000 wave lengths of lines for 87 elements.

H. Kayser and R. Ritschi, *Tabelle der Hauptlinien aller Elements*, 2nd ed., Springer, Berlin, 1939. See also Kayser's *Handbuch der Spektroskopie*.

C. E. Moore, *An Ultraviolet Multiplet Table*, Circular 488, Part 2 (1952), National Bureau of Standards.

C. E. Moore, *Atomic Energy Levels*, Circular 467, Vol. I (1949), Vol. II (1952) National Bureau of Standards.

See also chemistry handbooks for condensed tables of line wave lengths.

d. Journals

Spectrochimica Acta (founded in 1939), *Bulletin of the Society for Applied Spectroscopy*, and other bulletins published by various groups of spectroscopists.

8-11. PROBLEMS

a. Extension of Theory

1. Calculate the linear reciprocal dispersion of a spectrograph with quartz prism for 2000, 3000, 4000, 5000, and 6000 A. The angle a (Fig. 58) is 60°, and the focal length of the camera lens 150 cm. Plot the results.

Note: One has $d\theta/d\lambda = (d\theta/dn)(dn/d\lambda)$, where n the index of refraction of quartz, and λ the wave length. Furthermore, the linear reciprocal dispersion is $(1/f)/(d\lambda/d\theta)$, where f is the focal length of the camera lens.

It can be shown (see texts in Section 8–10; for instance, Nachtrieb or Sawyer; study the derivation of the formula) that the angular dispersion is given by

$$\frac{d\theta}{dn} = \frac{2 \sin \frac{a}{2}}{1 - n^2 \sin^2 \frac{a}{2}}$$

The index of refraction can be calculated by the empirical Hartmann formula,

$$n = n_0 + \frac{C}{\lambda - \lambda_0},$$

where n_0 must be known for a given wave length λ_0 and C is a constant. The constant C can be evaluated from the following data for quartz,

λ (angstroms)	5086	3034
n	1.5482	1.5769

2. Derive equation (8–5) for the resolving power of a prism spectrograph.

3. By applying equation (8–5) and the Hartmann formula given in problem (1), calculate the basis a (Fig. 58) of the quartz prism of a spectrograph for which the resolving power is 10,000 at 4000 A.

4. The resolving power of a grating spectrograph is given by the formula

$$\frac{\lambda}{\Delta\lambda} = mn$$

where m is the order of the spectrum and n the total number of lines of the grating. Study the derivation of this equation (see the books of Nachtrieb, Sawyer, etc. listed in Section 8–10). Calculate the resolving power ($m = 1$) of a spectrograph having a 4-in. grating with 15,000 lines per inch.

5. Derive the equation of the Rowland circle.

Note: See Sawyer or other texts listed in Section 8–10.

b. Application of Theory and Literature Survey

6. On the basis of Churchill's article (see reference in footnote 21), discuss the important criteria to be considered in the selection of a commercial spectrograph.

7. Discuss the copper-spark method for the analysis of solutions by emission spectroscopy.

See reference in footnote 28.

8. Discuss direct-reading spectrometers. See references in footnotes 47–50; also M. R. Hasler, R. W. Lindhurst, and J. W. Kemp, *J. Optical Soc. Am.*, **38**, 789 (1948).

9. Discuss the spectroscopic determination of trace elements in petroleum. This is a good example of application for which other methods would be very difficult to apply.

References: L. W. Gamble and C. E. Kling, *Spectrochim. Acta*, **4**, 439 (1952); J. H. Karchmer and E. L. Gunn, *Anal. Chim.*, **24**, 1733 (1952); R. F. Meeker and R. C. Pomatti, *Anal. Chem.*, **25**, 151 (1953).

10. Discuss the spectroscopic determination of the halides, sulfur, and selenium. Note that this is an example of application to nonmetallic elements.

Reference (in German): A. Gatterer, *Spectrochim. Acta*, **3**, 214 (1948).

11. Review the spectroscopic determination of transuranium elements.

Reference: F. S. Tomkins and M. Fred, *J. Optical Soc. Am.*, **39**, 357 (1949); D. L. Timma, *ibid.*, **38**, 898 (1949).

12. Prepare an outline for the spectroscopic analysis of stainless steel.

Reference: J. Eeckhout, *Anal. Chim. Acta.*, **3**, 377 (1949); M. F. Hasler, *Iron Age*, **164**, No. 18, 96 (1949); J. F. Young, *ibid.*, **168**, No. 2, 91 (1951).

13. Outline a procedure for the spectroscopic determination of hafnium in zirconium. This is a case in which methods other than spectroscopy may be quite involved.

Reference: D. M. Mortimore and L. A. Noble, *Anal. Chem.*, **25**, 296 (1953).

14. As an example of application of spectroscopy to air pollution, outline a procedure for the spectroscopic determination of traces of beryllium in air.

Reference: W. L. Churchill and A. H. C. P. Gillieson, *Spectrochim. Acta*, **5**, 238 (1952).

15. Discuss an application of spectroscopy in forensic chemistry.

Reference: F. X. Mayer, *Spectrochim. Acta*, **5**, 63 (1952) (in German).

16. Discuss the background interference in the determination of potassium, sodium, magnesium, calcium, and strontium by flame spectrometry. See M. Margoshes and B. L. Vallee, *Anal. Chem.*, **28**, 180 (1956).

17. Discuss the application of atomic absorption spectra to chemical analysis. See A. Walsh, *Spectrochim. Acta*, **7**, 108 (1955).

18. Study how the cathode layer technique enhances the sensitivity in emission spectroscopy. See the paper of F. T. Birks [*Spectrochim. Acta*, **7**, 231 (1956)] for application to sub-microgram quantities of beryllium.

19. Discuss the significance of temperature measurements in spectroscopic arcs. See L. Huldt, *Spectrochim. Acta*, **7**, 264 (1956); in German.

20. Discuss the technique of solution analysis with an immersed rotated graphite electrode. See J. P. Pagliassotti, *Anal. Chem.*, **28**, 1774 (1956).

21. Compare modern methods of plate calibration. See H. T. Shirley, A. Oldfield, and H. Kitchen, *Spectrochim. Acta*, **7**, 373 (1956).

22. Prepare a seminar on flame photometry. Use references in text and V. W. Meloche's review, *Anal. Chem.*, **28**, 1844 (1956).

23. Discuss the spectroscopic determination of oxygen in carbon steel. See V. A. Fassel and R. W. Tabeling, *Spectrochim. Acta,* **8,** 201 (1956).

24. Study the technique for spectroscopic analysis of radioactive materials. Use as a source the paper of F. T. Birks [*Spectrochim. Acta,* **8,** 167 (1956)] on the analysis of alpha-active materials. See also the paper on the spark spectrum of americium by R. P. Thorne, *Spectrochim. Acta,* **8,** 71 (1956).

9

Absorption Spectrometry and Filter Photometry

9-1. INTRODUCTION

The methods based on the absorption of radiation in the visible, ultraviolet, and infrared ranges are the most important of all the instrumental methods of analysis. These methods have been known for many years, but it is only since about 1940 that they have gained so much importance in chemical analysis, primarily because of major developments in instrumentation and of the availability of reliable commercial instruments.

The origin of absorption spectrophotometry can be traced to the work of Bouguer[1] and Lambert[2] in the eighteenth century, but it was not until one century later that a general law for the absorption of radiation was well established by Beer[3] and Bernard[4]. This law, which we shall discuss in Section 9–3, provided the basis for visual colorimetric analysis, a method well accepted as a useful adjunct to classical methods of analysis by the end of the last century. Errors of 5 to 20 per cent are not uncommon in visual colorimetry because of the relative inability of the human eye to detect differences in light intensities; and a major improvement resulted from the application of photoelectric cells to colorimetric measurements in the 1930's.

[1]P. Bouguer, *Essais d'Optique sur la Gradation de la Lumière*, 1729.
[2]Lambert, *Photometria Sive de Mensura et Gradibus Luminis, Colorum et Umbrae*, 1760. References 1 and 2 are from I. M. Kolthoff and E. B. Sandell, *Textbook of Quantitative Analysis*, 3rd ed., Macmillan, New York, 1952, p. 614.
[3]A. Beer, *Ann Physik Chem.*, (2) **86,** 78 (1852).
[4]F. Bernard, *Ann. chim. phys.*, (3) **35,** 385 (1852).

As we shall see in Section 9–3d, measurements in colorimetric analysis should be made with *monochromatic* radiation (i.e., radiation of a single wave length), but radiation in a narrow band of wave lengths is used in practice; as, for example, in *filter photometers*. Filter photometers equipped with photoelectric cells have progressively replaced visual colorimeters since the 1940's. In many applications the band transmitted through filters is much too wide, and a *monochromator* is then utilized. A monochromator is essentially a spectograph whose photographic plate is replaced by a metal piece with a narrow slit. The wave length of the beam emerging from the slit is adjusted by rotation of the prism or grating of the spectrograph. Monochromators are the heart of *spectrophotometers* (also called *spectrometers*, particularly for instruments in the infrared range) in which the entrance or exit beam of the monochromator is passed through a layer of material whose absorption is being studied, and the intensity of the radiation is measured with a suitable detector (phototube, etc.).

Until about 1940, the photographic method was applied in absorption spectroscopy in the visible and ultraviolet ranges. Thus, the absorption spectrum is photographed, and the absorption bands appear as transparent areas on the plate. This method is still applied in some physicochemical studies (kinetics, etc.), but spectrophotometers with photoelectric cells are universally utilized in chemical analysis.

Filter photometers and spectrophotometers have become essential tools in the analytical laboratory, and several hundred papers dealing with their application appear each year in the literature. Many have contributed to the application of filter photometry and spectrophotometry in the visible range to chemical analysis in the last two decades, but only a few names can be mentioned here: Kortüm, Lange, Mellon, F. Müller, Sandell, and Yoe. The relationship between light absorption and chemical structure also received much attention, thanks to the efforts of Brode, Hantzsch, V. Henri, von Halban, and many others.

Ultraviolet methods also greatly benefitted from the rapid development in instrumentation since about 1940. Instrumentation between 4000 and 2000 A is basically the same as in the visible range. Absorption in the range 30 to 2000 A did not receive much attention from chemists because most materials are opaque in that range.[5] However, there is a renewed interest in this field.

The impact of instrumentation is perhaps even more striking in infrared absorption spectrometry than in the visible and ultraviolet ranges. The existence of infrared radiation was known since 1800,[6] but quantitative

---

[5]See the pioneering work of V. Schumann, *Akad. Wiss. Wien.*, **102**, 2A, 625 (1893). The range 30 to 2000 A is sometimes called the *Schumann ultraviolet* or *vacuum ultraviolet*, since measurements must be made in vacuum because of absorption by air.

[6]W. Herschel, *Phil. Mag.*, **8**, 16, 126, 253 (1800).

measurements became possible only toward the latter part of the last century.[7] In 1892 Julius[8] showed for the first time that infrared spectrometry could be applied to qualitative analysis. Further work in this direction was done in the early 1900's by Coblentz,[9] who determined the infrared absorption spectra of numerous substances. A major advance in theory was made by Bjerrum[10] who showed that absorption spectra could be interpreted by mechanical models of the absorbing molecules.[11] This idea was fully exploited in the 1920's by Eucken, Lecomte, Randall, Sutherland, and many others. However, up to about 1935–1940 infrared spectrometry was mainly a subject for research of academic interest—not a tool in the analytical laboratory. Industrial applications then became more common, particularly in the United States, thanks to the efforts of Barnes, Gore, Van Zandt Williams, and many others. Commercial instruments having excellent characteristics were put on the market, and there resulted a more widespread application of infrared spectrometry. Several hundred papers are published each year in this field at the present.

9-2. ABSORPTION OF RADIATION: MOLECULAR INTERPRETATION

a. Changes in Electronic Levels. A detailed molecular interpretation of radiation absorption is beyond the scope of this text, and only a qualitative discussion will be given. For details, see physical chemistry texts, the books listed in Section 9–8, and the excellent treatments given by Bowen,[12] Bowen and Wokes,[13] and Ferguson.[14]

Activation of atoms by absorption of radiation corresponds to changes in the *electronic levels* of the atoms. Such changes are also observed for molecules which, in addition, can undergo changes in *vibrational and rotational levels*. These energy changes are quantized, i.e., they involve energy increments which can only have certain definite values. As was pointed out in Section 8–1, the frequency ν for a transition involving an energy change ΔE is

$$\nu = \frac{\Delta E}{h} , \qquad (9-1)$$

[7] S. P. Langley, *Proc. Am. Acad. Arts Sci.*, **16**, 342 (1881).

[8] W. II. Julius, *Verhandl. Akad. Wetenschappen Amsterdam*, **1**, 1 (1892).

[9] W. W. Coblentz, *Carnegie Inst. Technol. Bull.*, **35**, 1905; **65**, 1906; **97**, 1908. See detailed list of Coblentz' papers in the book by Barnes, *et al.* (see Section 9–8), pp. 136–139.

[10] N. Bjerrum, *Verhandl. deut. physik. Ges.*, **16**, 737 (1916).

[11] This mode of approach was made even more fruitful by the application of the group theory to the interpretation of infrared spectra. See the fundamental papers of E. Wigner [*Nachr. Ges. Wiss. Göttingen*, 133 (1930)] and E. B. Wilson, Jr., *Phys. Rev.*, **45**, 706 (1934).

[12] E. J. Bowen, *The Chemical Aspects of Light*, 2nd ed., Oxford University Press, London, 1946. This is an excellent example of exposition of a theoretical subject in nonmathematical language, and the reader should make it a point to examine this book.

[13] E. J. Bowen and F. Wokes, *Fluorescence of Solutions*, Longmans, Green and Co., New York, 1953.

[14] L. N. Ferguson, *Electron Structure of Organic Molecules*, Prentice-Hall, New York, New York, 1952.

where h is Planck's constant (6.624×10^{-27} erg sec). The correspondence between wave length and energy changes is given in Table X for several wave-length ranges. Shifts in electron orbitals which are the closest to the

TABLE X

Energies Involved in Transitions at Various Wave Lengths

WAVE LENGTH RANGE	WAVE LENGTH[a]	ENERGY, KCAL MOL^{-1}
X-rays................................ {	1 A	2.86×10^5
Vacuum ultraviolet.................. {	30 A	9.54×10^3
Ultraviolet.......................... {	2000 A	143
Visible.............................. {	4000 A	72
Very near infrared.................. {	8000 A	36
Near infrared....................... {	3μ	9.5
	25μ	1.1
Microwave range.....................	1 cm.	2.86×10^{-3}

[a] Approximate limits.

nucleus correspond to large energy changes (100 kcal mol^{-1} or more) and absorption in the X-ray and/or ultraviolet ranges. Shifts in the outer orbitals correspond to absorption in the ultraviolet, visible, and *very* near infrared ranges. Such shifts will now be considered in some detail for the particular case of a diatomic molecule. More complicated molecules will not be treated for the sake of simplicity, since the essential ideas can be presented in the discussion of the simplest possible case.

If energy is supplied to a molecule XY, vibration results, and the distance X and Y varies periodically with time. Actually, there is always some vibration because of the *zero-point energy*, but this matter will not be discussed here. As the energy increases, the amplitude of vibration becomes larger. The relationship between energy and its effect on the molecule can be represented by the *potential-energy curve*

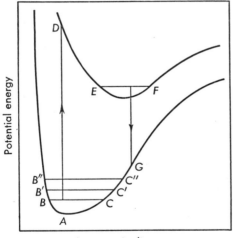

Interatomic distance

Fig. 79. Variations of potential energy with interatomic distance for a diatomic molecule.

of Fig. 79. The interatomic distance for the two atoms at rest is marked
by point A. The amplitude BC corresponds to the zero-point energy, and
the segments $B'C'$, $B''C''$ represent the amplitudes of vibration for successive (quantized) increments in the energy supplied to the molecule. The
branch $CC'C''$ . . . represents the maximum interatomic distance during
stretching of the molecule, and the branch $BB'B''$ . . . represents the minimum interatomic distance during compression. The compression branch
is very steep, and the stretching branch is asymptotic to the horizontal
line whose intercept with the ordinate axis corresponds to the energy required for dissociation of the molecule XY.

A shift in electronic level results in the formation of an *activated or excited
molecule* whose potential energy curve is above curve $B''AC''$ by perhaps
100 kcal mol^{-1} (see Table X). The interatomic distance practically does not
vary during the absorption of a quantum because the frequency of vibration of the atoms is appreciably lower than that of radiation causing activation. The latter is in the ultraviolet or visible range at frequencies of
approximately 10^{15} sec^{-1}, while vibration frequencies are perhaps 10^{14}
sec^{-1} or lower (infrared range), as we shall see. Hence, the electronic transition can be represented approximately by the vertical line AD in Fig. 79.
The potential-energy curve for the activated molecule is shifted toward
longer interatomic distances with respect to the molecule XY because
activation causes a weakening of the bond XY, i.e., an increase in interatomic distance. The activated molecule, therefore, is compressed in D,
and vibration results. Since changes in vibrational and rotational levels
accompany electronic transitions, the resulting absorption spectrum is
composed of a multitude of lines. This is especially the case for complicated
molecules in which numerous transitions are possible. The resulting lines
generally cannot be resolved, and only a *band spectrum* is observed.

If the activated molecule does not lose some of its energy by collision
with other inactivated molecules, radiation is re-emitted because of the
inverse transition from D to A. This re-emission of radiation can be observed with gases at low pressure, but collisions in liquids, which occur
with a frequency of about 10^{12} sec^{-1}, are highly probable during the average
life of 10^{-8} sec for the activated molecule. The activated molecules of most
substances then lose their energy in the form of heat, but in some cases
radiation is re-emitted by *fluorescence* because of transition from EF to G.
The energy change involved in the latter transition is smaller than the
energy required for activation, and consequently the wave length for
fluorescence is longer than for excitation. More will be said about fluorescence in Chapter 10.

The position of absorption bands in the scale of wave lengths depends
on the energies involved in the corresponding transitions. Inorganic ions,
except some colored ions of the transition elements and rare earths, have

absorption bands in the ultraviolet or the far ultraviolet ranges. Organic compounds exhibit absorption bands in the ultraviolet range, and for some substances such as dyes, in the visible. Electronic transitions for the latter substances are made easier by resonance as a result of the presence of *chromophore groups*: C=C, C=N, N=O,C=S, etc. The necessity of having such groups in molecules of colored substances was recognized many years ago by organic chemists. Conjugation between chromophore groups further decreases the energy required for electronic transitions and shifts absorption bands toward longer wave lengths (*bathochromic shift*).

Since electronic excitation disturbs the electron distribution in the molecule, the position of an absorption band depends somewhat on the structure of the whole molecule. However, absorption bands corresponding to various groups are observed in relatively constant wave-length intervals for a large number of substances (Table XI). The correlation between the

TABLE XI

Wave Lengths for Absorption for Some Chromophore Groups[a]

GROUP	WAVE LENGTH, Mμ
=CO	280
—OH	186
—SH	227
—NO₂	366
—O—NO₂	302
=C=C=	180

[a]From W. R. Brode, *Chemical Spectroscopy*, 2nd ed., Wiley, New York, 1943, p. 217.

structure of molecules or ions and their absorption spectra is a very interesting topic in spectroscopy and physical organic chemistry, but it is not within the province of this book. The reader can find ample material on this subject in the books of Bowen, Brode (see references in Section 9–8) and Ferguson.[14]

b. Changes in Vibrational Levels.   Changes in vibrational levels require smaller energies (1 to 20 kcal mol⁻¹) than electronic transitions and correspond to absorption bands mainly in the near infrared (up to 25μ). Energies, however, are larger than for rotational level changes, and vibrational spectra are complicated by transitions between rotational levels.

Numerous modes of vibration are observed for complicated molecules. Ranges of vibration frequencies can be assigned, but the over-all structure of the molecule affects the vibrational spectrum. Spectra, therefore, are characteristic of the absorbing molecule. This circumstance has been fully exploited in qualitative analysis and structure determinations.

The order of magnitude of vibrational frequencies can be determined by considering the simple case of a diatomic molecule, which can be treated as a harmonic oscillator. The force between the two atoms as they move from their equilibrium positions is proportional to the displacement. It can be shown (see problem 1 in Section 9–9) that the wave number for a harmonic oscillator is

$$\sigma = 1307\sqrt{\frac{k}{\mu}} \text{ cm}^{-1}, \qquad (9\text{-}2)$$

where μ is the reduced mass of the atoms as defined by the relationship

$$\frac{1}{\mu} = \frac{1}{M_1} + \frac{1}{M_2}, \qquad (9\text{-}3)$$

M_1 and M_2 being expressed in atomic mass units. The *force constant* k in equation (9–2) is characteristic of the oscillator and is such that

$$V = \frac{kx^2}{2}, \qquad (9\text{-}4)$$

where x is the displacement from the equilibrium position and V is the potential energy of the oscillator.

Force constants for a given bond vary somewhat from one compound to another, but at any rate the agreement between calculated and experimental wave numbers is quite good. For example, one has for the C=O bond in methyl alcohol:[15] $k = 5 \times 10^5$ dynes cm^{-1}, $\mu = 6.85$, and $\sigma = 1110$ cm^{-1}. A strong band for methyl alcohol is observed at the wave number 1034 cm^{-1}, which is, indeed, not too different from the calculated value 1110 cm^{-1}. Much more refined methods of calculation than the above very simple treatment have been developed, but this material is not within the scope of this book.

TABLE XII
Wave Number Assignment for Infrared Absorption

GROUP	TYPE OF VIBRATION	WAVE NUMBER, CM^{-1}
OH	stretching	3700–3000
NH	stretching	3700–3000
CH	stretching	3300–2700
C≡X	stretching	2400–2100
C=O	stretching	1850–1640
C=N	stretching	1700–1580
C=C	stretching	1700–1580
NH	bending	1650–1490
CH	bending	1475–1290
OH	bending	1450–1200
C—O	stretching	1300– 900
C—N	stretching	1300– 900
C—C	stretching	1200– 800
CH	rocking	900– 600
NH	rocking	900– 700

From the numerous infrared absorption spectra which have been studied, it is possible to assign limits of wave numbers to various groups. Such

[15]See p. 17 of the monograph of Barnes *et al.* listed in Section 9–8.

results have been presented by Colthup[16] in the form of a widely used chart. Some data taken from this chart are listed in Table XII.

c. Changes in Rotational Levels. Changes in rotational levels involve very low energies (less than 1 to 2 kcal mol^{-1}), and such changes accompany electronic and vibrational transitions. Absorption spectra corresponding only to rotational level changes are observed in the far infrared and the microwave ranges. Rotational spectra have been studied extensively since the end of World War II. Important information on the chemical bond has been gathered by microwave methods, but application to chemical analysis, although feasible, has been very scanty. Rotational spectra will not be discussed here, and the reader is referred to reviews and books.[17-20]

9-3. THE BEER-LAMBERT LAW

a. General Form for Absorption by a Single Substance. Consider the experiment in which a parallel beam of monochromatic radiation impinges on a detector M (Fig. 80). The energy measured by M per unit of

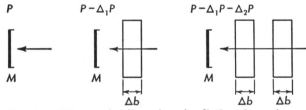

Fig. 80.   Diagram for discussion of radiation absorption.

time and per unit area is P. If a slab of absorbing substance of uniform thickness Δb is placed in front of M perpendicular to the direction of the beam, the detector reads $P - \Delta_1 P$, and the relative change of P in absolute value is $\Delta_1 P / P$. If a second slab is placed before the detector, M now reads $P - \Delta_1 P - \Delta_2 P$, and the relative change in P with respect to $P - \Delta_1 P$ is $\Delta_2 P / (P - \Delta_1 P)$. It is observed that

$$\frac{\Delta_1 P}{P} = \frac{\Delta_2 P}{P - \Delta_1 P}.$$ (9-5)

Thus, the relative change in the reading of detector M, resulting from

[16]N. B. Colthup, *J. Optical Soc. Am.*, **40**, 397 (1950). See also Bellamy's monograph listed in Section 9–8.

[17]B. P. Dailey, article in *Physical Methods of Organic Chemistry*, A. Weissberger, Ed., Vol. I, Part III, Interscience, New York, 1955, pp. 2321–2359.

[18]W. Gordy, W. V. Smith, and R. Tramburalo, *Microwave Spectroscopy*, Wiley, New York, 1953.

[19]M. W. P. Strandberg, *Microwave Spectroscopy*, Wiley, New York, 1954.

[20]C. H. Townes and A. L. Schawlow, *Microwave Spectroscopy*, McGraw-Hill, New York, 1956.

the introduction of the second slab of absorbing substance, is the same as the relative change caused by the first slab, both slabs having the same thickness. The same observation is also made for absorption by more than two slabs.

If the slab thickness is sufficiently small, $\Delta_1 P$ is *very* small in comparison with P, and one has $P - \Delta_1 P \approx P$, or in view of equation (9–5), $\Delta_1 P \approx \Delta_2 P$. This equality holds for each slab of thickness Δb, and consequently [see, equation (9–5)] the relative change in P is proportional to the total number of slabs of absorbing material. If ΔN is the number of absorbing centers (atoms, molecules) in all the slabs, the foregoing conclusion is expressed by

$$-\frac{\Delta P}{P} \approx q \, \Delta N, \qquad (9\text{–}6)$$

where q is a proportionality constant. The left-hand member in equation (9–6) is preceded by a minus sign because P decreases as ΔN increases. If infinitesimals are used, equation (9–6) can be written rigorously in the form

$$-\frac{dP}{P} = q \, dN, \qquad (9\text{–}7)$$

which yields upon integration

$$-\ln P = qN + \text{constant}. \qquad (9\text{–}8)$$

The quantity N in equation (9–8) represents the number of absorbing centers per unit area of the slab of uniform thickness b. The integration constant in equation (9–8) is evaluated by noting that P has a certain value P_0 when no absorbing layer is placed in front of M, i.e., when $N = 0$. Thus,

$$\ln \frac{P_0}{P} = qN, \qquad (9\text{–}9)$$

Equation (9–9), which expresses a general law for absorption of radiation, is of paramount importance. It holds as well in the X-ray range as in the ultraviolet, visible, infrared, and microwave ranges. It is worth pointing out that *we did not derive equation (9–9) from fundamental principles,*[21] but deduced it from relationship (9–5), based on experimental observations.

Equation (9–9) will be applied in Chapter 12, but in this chapter we need a modified form of this equation in which N is expressed for solutions of absorbing substances. We shall first extend equation (9–9) to absorption by several substances.

b. Absorption by Several Substances. It is observed that each substance in a mixture absorbs independently of the others, provided that

[21]For such a derivation, see F. C. Strong, *Anal. Chem.*, **24**, 338 (1952).

interaction between the different species can be neglected. Equation (9–7) thus becomes

$$-\frac{dP}{P} = q_1 \, dN_1 + q_2 \, dN_2 \cdots + q_j \, dN_j, \tag{9–10}$$

where the coefficients q are different for each substance. Upon integration one has

$$\ln \frac{P_o}{P} = q_1 N_1 + q_2 N_2 \cdots + q_j N_j. \tag{9–11}$$

c. Absorption by a Solution Containing a Single Solute. We consider the case of dilute solutions for which absorption by the solvent is practically independent of the concentration of solute.

The general equation (9–11) is applicable, but it is convenient to express N in terms of the molar concentration C_m of solute and the thickness of the absorption layer b. The number N of absorbing centers (molecules or ions) per unit area of a layer of solution of thickness b is

$$N_1 = N_a b C_m, \tag{9–12}$$

where N_a is Avogadro's number, and $b \times 1$ is the volume of solution corresponding to 1 sq cm of the face of the layer of solution placed perpendicularly to the incident beam. We could also calculate N for the solvent, but it suffices here to note that the detector in Fig. 80 reads P_s when a layer of thickness b of the solvent alone is examined. On the basis of this observation and in view of equation (9–12), we deduce from equation (9–11) after changing from natural to decimal logarithms ($\log x = 0.433 \ln x$)

$$\log \frac{P_0}{P} = \log \frac{P_0}{P_s} + \epsilon b C_m, \tag{9–13}$$

where $\epsilon = 0.434 \, q N_a$. Equation (9–13) can be written in the form

$$\log \frac{P_s}{P} = \epsilon b C_m. \tag{9–14}$$

There, $\log (P_s/P)$ is the *absorbancy* A; the ratio P/P_s, the *transmittancy* T; and ϵ, the *molar absorptivity*. The use of these terms is now recommended,[22] but other terms have been utilized for absorbancy (*optical density, density, extinction*) and for molar absorptivity (*molar extinction coefficient, molar extinction*). Symbols for the absorbancy and molar absorptivity greatly vary, and standardization could be desirable, but it is a simple matter to establish the correspondence between the different notations found in the literature.

[22]*Letter Circ. LC-857*, National Bureau of Standards, 1947. See report of the colorimetry committee of the Optical Society of America: L. A. Jones *et al.*, *J. Optical Soc. Am.*, **33**, 544 (1943); **34**, 183, 245, 633 (1944); **35**, 1 (1945). Consult also H. K. Hughes *et al.*, *Anal. Chem.*, **24**, 1349 (1952).

It is the practice in filter photometry to express concentrations in grams per liter, and equation (9–14) is thus written

$$\log \frac{P_s}{P} = abC \tag{9–15}$$

where a is the *absorptivity*. Note that $\epsilon = aM_w$, M_w being the gram molecular weight of the solute.

The dependence of the absorbancy on the thickness of the absorbing layer of solution was established experimentally by Bouguer[1] and Lambert,[2] and the dependence on concentration was established by Beer[3] and Bernard.[4] The relationship expressed by equations (9–14) or (9–15) is generally referred to as the "Beer-Lambert law."

Since the absorbancy is proportional to the concentration of solute, application of the Beer-Lambert law to chemical analysis is quite obvious. If the substance to be analyzed does not absorb in a suitable wave-length range, it can often be engaged in a reaction which yields a product having the proper absorption characteristics. Reagents yielding colored products which are studied in the visible range are frequently used, but the same idea can be applied in the ultraviolet and the near infrared ranges.

Several substances, such as a reagent or a complexing agent, may thus be present in solution, and it is useful to write the Beer-Lambert law in the form

$$\log \frac{P_b}{P} = abC, \tag{9–16}$$

where P_b is the detector reading for the "blank"; i.e., for the solution and reagents, but in the absence of the substance to be analyzed. The quantity $\log(P_b/P)$ is also called absorbancy, and P/P_b is also designated as transmittancy.

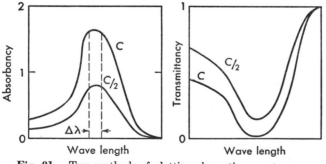

Fig. 81. Two methods of plotting absorption spectrograms.

Absorbancies vary with wave length, since substances do not absorb radiation uniformly over the whole range of wave lengths (see Section 9–2). As an example, the relationship between absorbancy and transmittancy is indicated in Fig. 81 for the concentrations C and $C/2$ of solute. The extreme values of A and T are as follows:

For a perfectly transparent solution: $A = 0$, $T = 1$
For a perfectly opaque solution: $A \to \infty$, $T = 0$.

Spectrograms such as the one in Fig. 81 can be plotted in a variety of ways. Analytical chemists prefer to plot wave lengths along abscissa axis, at least in the visible and ultraviolet ranges, while spectroscopists use wave numbers or frequencies. The latter procedure is more rational than the use of wave lengths, since frequencies and wave numbers are proportional to the change of energy involved in transitions, whereas the wave length is inversely proportional to this energy change [see equation (9–1)]. Wave lengths are often expressed in millimicrons rather than angstroms in the ultraviolet and visible ranges. The micron is the unit of length used in the infrared range. Absorbancies, molar absorptivities, absorptivities, or transmittancies can be plotted as ordinate in spectrograms.

d. Necessity of Having Monochromatic Radiation. It was assumed in the foregoing discussion that the incident radiation is monochromatic. If this is not the case, the Beer-Lambert law is not strictly obeyed. This can be shown as follows:[23]
Assume that radiation includes two wave lengths λ_1 and λ_2, and that the corresponding absorptivities are a_1 and a_2. One has for measurements, made at each wave length separately:

$$\log \frac{(P_b)_1}{P_1} = a_1 b C \qquad (9\text{–}17)$$

$$\log \frac{(P_b)_2}{P_2} = a_2 b C . \qquad (9\text{–}18)$$

The absorbancy for radiation including both wave lengths,

$$\log \frac{(P_b)_1 + (P_b)_2}{P_1 + P_2},$$

is different from the absorbancies at λ_1 and λ_2 except when $a_1 = a_2$. Thus, it is only when the absorptivity is independent of wave length over the interval being considered that one has

$$\log \frac{(P_b)_1}{P_1} = \log \frac{(P_b)_2}{P_2} = \log \frac{(P_b)_1 + (P_b)_2}{P_1 + P_2}, \qquad (9\text{–}19)$$

and that the Beer-Lambert law is obeyed. The same reasoning is applicable when the incident beam contains more than two wave lengths, and in general, when radiation is not monochromatic.
In many cases the incident beam may cover a relatively wide wave-

[23]See pp. 9–10 of the Charlot and Gauguin book listed in Section 9–8.

length band $\Delta\lambda$ (Fig. 81) because condition (9–19) is essentially fulfilled, and the Beer-Lambert law is valid for all practical purposes when the absorption band of the substance being examined is appreciably wider than $\Delta\lambda$. This situation generally prevails in filter photometry.

e. Absorbancy and Transmittancy Range with Minimum Error. Experimentally it is advantageous to have as large a variation in transmittancy as possible for a given change in concentration. The optimum experimental conditions can be deduced by calculating the relative change in concentration with transmittancy $(1/C)(dC/dT)$, as was shown by Twyman and Lothian.[24] Thus, equation (9–16) can be written in the form

$$A = abC \qquad (9\text{–}20)$$

where $A = \log(1/T) = -\log T$, T being the transmittancy. Hence,

and
$$abC = -\log T, \qquad (9\text{–}21)$$

$$ab\frac{dC}{dT} = -\frac{0.434}{T}, \qquad (9\text{–}22)$$

or, since $ab = A/C$,

$$\frac{1}{C}\frac{dC}{dT} = -\frac{0.434}{AT}, \qquad (9\text{–}23)$$

i.e.,

$$\frac{1}{C}\frac{dC}{dT} = \frac{0.434}{T\log T}. \qquad (9\text{–}24)$$

Variations of $(1/C)(dC/dT)$ with transmittancy are shown in Fig. 82. The value $T = 0.368$ at the minimum is obtained by setting to zero the derivative (with respect to T) of the second member of equation (9–24), and by solving for T. Errors made in measurements are minimized at the point $T = 0.368$ because the relative change in concentration with transmittancy is at a minimum at this point. In practice, errors are minimized when the transmittancy in the measurements is between 0.10 and 0.75, i.e., when the absorbancy is be-

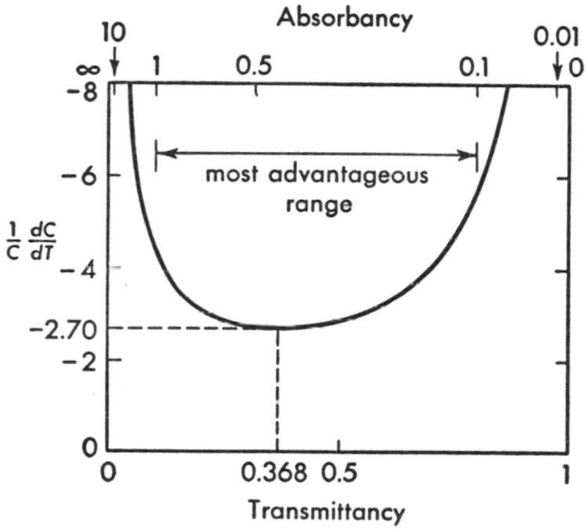

Fig. 82. Plot of the relative change of concentration with transmittancy versus transmittancy.

tween 1 and about 0.1. This corresponds to a tenfold concentration change.

For very dilute solutions (a few parts per million) the optimum range of

[24]F. Twyman and G. F. Lothian, *Proc. Phys. Soc. (London)*, **45**, 643 (1933).

absorbancies generally corresponds to the maximum of the plot of absorbency against wave length (Fig. 81). With more concentrated solutions, measurements can be made outside the range of maximum absorbancy to bring the absorbancy between 0.1 and 1. However, a serious error may result from minor deviations in wave length from one measurement to another with instruments in which the wave length is adjusted by means of a mechanical device (spectrophotometers).

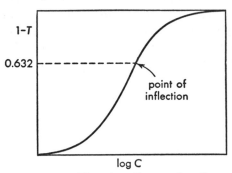

Fig. 83.   Plot of $1 - T$ versus $\log C$.

The most favorable range for experimental measurements can also be determined by making a plot of $1 - T$ against $\log C$, as was suggested by Ringbom[25],[26] (Fig. 83). The point of inflection corresponds to $1 - T = 0.632$, or to $T = 0.368$ (see problem 2 in Section 9–9). The experimental conditions are the most favorable in the vicinity of the point of inflection because the variation of T, for a given relative change in concentration, is then maximum. This is simply another way of expressing the result in formula (9–24) and Fig. 82.

The absorbancy for a relatively concentrated solution, which is above the upper limit, $A = 1$, of the range of minimum error, can be brought in a more favorable range by dilution. Another method of decreasing A is to substitute for the blank a standard solution of known concentration. This *differential method* was first applied by Kortüm[27] and was studied in detail by Hiskey and others.[28],[29]

The papers by Gridgeman,[30] Beckman and co-workers,[31] and Reilley[32] may be consulted for further details on errors in transmittancy and absorbancy measurements.

f. Deviations from the Beer-Lambert Law.   Reflection of radiation by the solution was neglected above, and a deviation from the Beer-

[25]A. Ringbom, *Z. Anal. Chem.*, **115**, 332 (1939); A. Ringbom and F. Sundman, *ibid.*, **115**, 402 (1939); **116**, 104 (1939).

[26]For applications of plots of $(1-T)$ *versus* $\log C$, see G. H. Ayres, *Anal. Chem.*, **21**, 652 (1949).

[27]G. Kortüm, *Angew. Chem.*, **50**, 193 (1937).

[28]C. F. Hiskey, *Anal. Chem.*, **21**, 1440 (1949); C. F. Hiskey, J. Rabinowitz, and I. G. Young, *ibid.*, **22**, 1464 (1950); C. F. Hiskey and I. G. Young, *ibid.*, **23**, 1196 (1951).

[29]R. Bastian, *Anal. Chem.*, **21**, 972 (1949).

[30]N. T. Gridgeman, *Anal. Chem.*, **24**, 445 (1952).

[31]L. S. Goldring, R. C. Hawes, G. H. Hare, A. O. Beckman, and M. E. Stickney, *ibid.*, **25**, 869 (1953).

[32]C. N. Reilley and C. M. Crawford, *ibid.*, **27**, 716 (1955).

Lambert law is observed when reflection is appreciably different for the blank and the solution being analyzed. On the basis of an equation established by Fresnel, one can write[33]

$$P = P_i \left[1 - \left(\frac{n_s - n_c}{n_s + n_c} \right)^2 \right],$$ (9–25)

where P is the reading on the meter M of Fig. 80, P_i would be the reading on M without reflection by the solution, n_s is the index of refraction of the solution, and n_c the index of refraction of the cuvette. In general, the index of refraction for the blank and the analyzed solution are practically the same, and the effect of reflection cancels. However, the difference between the n's for the blank and the analyzed solution increases as the concentration of analyzed solution increases, and an error results. When mixtures of water and an organic solvent are used, care should be taken to have the same proportions of organic solvent and water for the blank and the solution to be analyzed, since, otherwise, the error resulting from reflection might not be entirely negligible because of a difference in the indexes of refraction of the blank and the solution. Furthermore, the absorptivity generally depends on the ratio of water to organic solvent.

Deviations from the Beer-Lambert law, which result from the chemistry of the system being studied, are caused primarily by interionic actions and shifts in equilibria (dissociation of weak electrolytes, complex formation). Variations of absorptivity resulting from interionic actions are small, say, 1 per cent, even for large changes in ionic strength.[34] Shifts in equilibria, however, can cause a much more pronounced apparent departure from the Beer-Lambert law. Consider the case of a weak acid whose nonionized form absorbs radiation less strongly than its anion. The concentration of anion is approximately $\sqrt{K_a C^0}$, K_a being the dissociation constant of the acid, and C^0 its analytical concentration. This value of the anion concentration is derived in qualitative and quantitative analysis texts (see also Section 3–6b). The concentration of nonionized acid is $C^0 - \sqrt{K_a C^0}$. The total absorbancy is the sum of the absorbancies for the solvent, the nonionized acid, and the anion. Since the concentrations of the last two species depend on $\sqrt{C^0}$, the absorbancy of the solution is not proportional to C^0. The detailed calculation may be taken up as exercise (see problem 4 in Section 9–9). A similar calculation could be made for the dissociation of complex ions.

Association also causes an apparent departure from the Beer-Lambert law. For instance, the absorptivity of methylene blue, measured at pH 3.4 and 6565 A, drops by more than 50 per cent when its analytical concentra-

[33]See a book on physical optics; for instance, F. A. Jenkins and H. E. White, *Fundamentals of Optics*, 2nd ed., McGraw-Hill, New York, 1950, pp. 560–588.
[34]G. Kortüm and M. Seiler, *Angew. Chem.*, **52**, 687 (1939).

tion varies from 10^{-6} to 10^{-3} molar.[35] A quantitative interpretation of this effect can be given (see problem 5 in Section 9–9).

Absorptivities vary somewhat with temperature, and control of the temperature of the absorbing solution is advisable in very precise measurements. However, this control is, in general, not necessary in most analytical applications.

g. Absorption by a Solution Containing Several Solutes. The absorbancies are additive, provided that there is no reaction or interaction between the different solutes. In view of equation (9–16) one has

$$\log\left(\frac{P_b}{P}\right)_{\lambda_1} = a_{11}bC_1 + a_{12}bC_2, \tag{9–26}$$

$$\log\left(\frac{P_b}{P}\right)_{\lambda_2} = a_{21}bC_1 + a_{22}bC_2, \tag{9–27}$$

for a solution containing two solutes. There, b is the thickness of the layer of solution; the C's are the concentrations; a_{11} and a_{12} are the absorptivities of substances 1 and 2 at wave length λ_1; and a_{21} and a_{22} are the absorptivities at λ_2. This system of two linear equations in C_1 and C_2 can be solved, provided that the absorptivities are known. The latter are determined at wave lengths λ_1 and λ_2 in separate experiments in which only one substance is present at a known concentration.

The absorptivities of each substance must vary sufficiently with wave length because equations (9–26) and (9–27) are identical if $a_{11} = a_{21}$ and $a_{12} = a_{22}$. It is advantageous that coefficients a_{12} and a_{21} be as small as possible, since, under these conditions, substance 2 does not absorb appreciably at λ_1 and substance 1 does not strongly absorb at λ_2. These conditions are fulfilled, provided that the absorption spectrograms for substances 1 and 2 are sufficiently different and that wave lengths λ_1 and λ_2 are properly chosen[36] (Fig. 84).

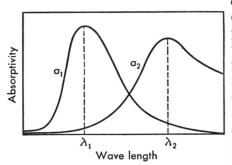

Fig. 84. Selection of the wave lengths λ_1 and λ_2 in the analysis of a two-component system.

The foregoing considerations can be extended to solutions containing j substances. The absorbancy of the solutions must then be measured at j different wave lengths, and a system of j linear equations with j unknown concentrations must be solved.

[35] E. Rabinovitch and L. F. Epstein, *J. Am. Chem. Soc.*, **63**, 69 (1941).

[36] For a modification of this method, see J. A. Perry, R. G. Sutherland, and N. Hadden, *Anal. Chem.*, **22**, 1122 (1950).

The numerical calculations are laborious when j exceeds 3, but time-saving calculators for solving simultaneous linear equations are available.[37] When the number of simultaneous equations increases, errors on each concentration are amplified and the accuracy may be quite poor. This is why it is difficult to analyze more than three components simultaneously[38] in the narrow wave-length interval of the visible range. Up to six compounds can be determined simultaneously in the near infrared range, which covers a much wider wave-length interval than the visible range.

The method can be applied also to cases in which the Beer-Lambert law is not obeyed but the absorbancies are additive. The absorptivities, then, are functions of the concentrations, and the latter are calculated by successive approximations. Cases in which the absorbancies are not additive have also been treated.[39]

9-4. FILTER PHOTOMETERS

A few comments about colorimeters will be made before the discussion of filter photometers. In colorimeters the thickness b of the absorbing layer is adjusted for two solutions—one with a known concentration of the substance being analyzed, the other with this substance at the unknown concentration. The thicknesses are adjusted to obtain equality of the light intensities. In view of equation (9–16), one then has

$$b_s C_s = b_x C_x, \qquad (9\text{–}28)$$

where the subscript s refers to the standard solution and x to the unknown. Errors of 5 to 20 per cent are not uncommon because of the relative inability of the eye to compare light intensities. Colorimeters are seldom used nowadays, but they were standard pieces of equipment in the analytical laboratory before 1940. Numerous instruments are described in the literature (Duboscq, Pulfrich, etc.).

We now turn to instruments in which radiation intensities are measured directly. As was pointed out in Section 9–3d, measurements must be made in a narrow wave-length band. This is achieved either by filtering the radiation of the source or by using a monochromator. The first method is applied in filter photometry and is used mainly in the visible range. The second method, namely, the use of a monochromator, is applied in spectrometry in the visible, ultraviolet, and infrared ranges. Filter photometers

---

[37]See for instance the description of such a calculator for computation in mass spectrometry; C. E. Berry, D. E. Wilcox, S. M. Rock, and H. W. Washburn, *J. Applied Phys.*, **17**, 262 (1946).

[38]For a discussion of errors, see C. F. Hiskey and D. Firestone, *Anal. Chem.*, **24**, 342 (1952).

[39]For details, see Mellon's monograph listed in Section 9–8.

are discussed in this section, and spectrophotometers (spectrometers) are treated in subsequent sections.

A filter photometer is composed of the following basic elements (Fig. 85): a source of light S, a filter F, an absorption cell C, and a detector D for measuring light intensities. These elements will be briefly described.

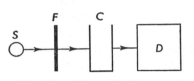

Fig. 85. Schematic diagram of one-cell filter photometer.

The source in filter photometry is simply a light bulb with a condenser lens (parallel beam). The absorption cell is a cuvette with parallel walls, or more simply, a test tube. The cuvette reproduces the geometric conditions assumed in the discussion of the Beer-Lambert law. However, a test tube can also be utilized when absorptivities need not be calculated and results are deduced from calibration curves showing the variations of absorbancy with concentration.[40] The same test tube or identical tubes must, of course, be used in the calibration and analysis. Cuvettes with parallel walls are generally calibrated, and the distance between the walls perpendicular to the beam of light is known. A correction should be made if cuvettes having different thicknesses are utilized [see formula (9–15) or 9–16)].

Filters are made of colored glass or a thin layer of dyed gelatin between two glass plates. The former type of filter is preferable because it is less easily damaged by heat. The color of filters and the wave length of the

TABLE XIII
Color of Filters and Absorption Band[a]

COLOR	WAVE LENGTH FOR ABSORPTION BAND,[b] mμ
Yellow	<450
Orange	<500
Red	<575
Purple	$450–650$
Blue	>480
Green	$\begin{cases} 400–475 \\ 575–700 \end{cases}$

[a]Data from W. R. Brode, *Chemical Spectroscopy*, 2nd ed., Wiley, New York, 1943, p. 285.
[b]Approximate limits.

transmitted band are indicated approximately in Table XIII for orientation purposes. Since the filtered radiation is far from being monochromatic, it is useful to characterize the quality of a filter by the wave-length interval $\Delta\lambda$ between the maximum transmittance[41] and one-half of this value (Fig.

[40]Absorptivities could be calculated from data obtained with a perfectly cylindrical test tube, but such calculations are not necessary.

[41]Transmittancy is defined as the ratio P/P_s [see equation (9–14)], where P is measured with the solution containing the substance to be analyzed and P_s is measured with the solvent. Transmittance is defined as the ratio P/P_0, where P is measured in vacuum (air, in practice) with a layer of the absorbing material and P_0 is measured without this layer.

86, left). This interval covers approximately 30 to 100 mμ for most commercial fibers. More narrow transmittance bands are obtained by the simultaneous use of two filters of proper characteristics (Fig. 86, right). The transmitted band for the resulting combination can be readily deduced from

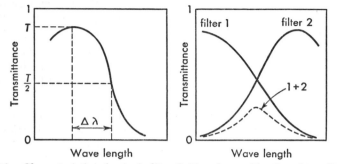

Fig. 86. Characteristics of a single filter (left) and a combination of two filters (right).

the characteristics of each filter. Filters having transmitted bands over the whole visible and near ultraviolet ranges are available commercially (Bausch and Lomb, Corning, and Eastman Kodak in the United States.)

Interference filters have somewhat narrower transmitted bands than colored filters. Interference filters are essentially composed of two transparent parallel films of silver which are so close as to produce interference effects. The wave-length range is modified by varying[42] the distance between the films. A wide selection of interference filters is now commercially available (Baird Associates, Bausch and Lomb, Farrand Optical Co.).

Detectors in filter photometry and spectrophotometry are phototubes or barrier layer cells with a suitable measuring or recording instrument. To the writer's knowledge, photocells were first used[43] in spectrophotometry in the 1920's. Under proper conditions the current through photocells is proportional to the energy absorbed per unit of time, and these detectors therefore are ideally suited to analytical determinations. Phototubes coupled with an amplifier are very sensitive (Section 8-7), but they are not often utilized[44] in filter photometry because barrier layer cells require simpler circuitry.

A barrier layer cell is essentially composed of a steel or copper plate coated with a thin layer of selenium or cuprous oxide. The selenium layer is coated with a transparent film of gold, platinum, or some other metal, which is protected by a transparent plate. A metal ring, which is one of the

[42]For a filter with continuously variable distance between films, see A. F. Turner and O. A. Ullrich (abstract only), *J. Optical Soc. Am.*, **38**, 662 (1948).

[43]R. H. Muller and H. M. Partridge, *Ind. Eng. Chem.*, **20**, 423 (1928); F. P. Zscheile, Jr., T. R. Hogness, and T. F. Young, *J. Phys. Chem.*, **38**, 1 (1934); T. R. Hogness, F.P. Zscheile, Jr., and A. E. Sidwell, Jr., *ibid.*, **41**, 379 (1937).

[44]Except in instruments which can be used either as a filter photometer or a fluorophotometer (Fisher). Fluorophotometers are described in Chapter 10.

terminals of the cell, is pressed on this metallic film. The other terminal is the iron or copper plate coated with selenium. When the two terminals are connected to a galvanometer, the layer at the junction of selenium and the outer metallic film offers a high resistance to the flow of electrons from selenium to the metallic film. Electrons acquire sufficient energy to overcome this barrier upon irradiation of the cell, and a current flows through the galvanometer. It is observed that the current is proportional to the intensity of incident light, provided that the resistance of the galvanometer is low, say, 100 ohms. If the resistance of the external circuit is too high, the current increases less rapidly with light intensity than at low resistance. This can be explained as follows:

At high light intensities, the electron density in selenium is relatively large, and the probability for an electron to overcome the barrier at the interface selenium metal decreases as the resistance of the circuit increases.

The current output is quite high, perhaps 100 μa per lumen, and measurements can be readily made with a galvanometer. Electronic amplification is not too practical because the output voltage of the cell is low and several stages of amplification are necessary. Amplifiers could, of course, be utilized to increase the sensitivity, but phototubes, which have a large voltage response, are more advantageous when an electronic amplifier is used. The current through barrier cells, for given illumination conditions, varies with temperature by, perhaps, 1 per cent per degree. This dependence of current on temperature is not a cause of error in filter photometry because the unknown concentration is determined from the ratio of the intensities for the blank and the analyzed solution, and the effect of temperature thus cancels.

Barrier layer cells age very slowly because of transformation of the selenium layer, and the current output for a given illumination slowly decreases over a period of years. Filter photometers with barrier layer cells must be calibrated periodically. A fatigue effect may also be observed, and the current for certain cells reaches a practically steady value only after a few minutes.

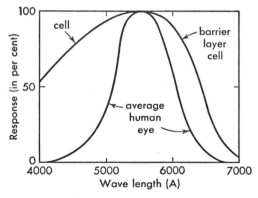

Fig. 87. Response of a barrier layer cell and the human eye (average) as a function of wave length. (Data from E. J. Bowen and F. Wokes, *Fluorescence of Solutions*, Longmans, Green, New York, 1953, p. 50.)

Barrier layer cells are sensitive over the whole visible range. This can be seen in Fig. 87, which also shows an average sensitivity characteristic for the human eye (compare with Fig. 76).

There are two types of filter photometers, namely, one-cell and two-cell instruments. The former type of instrument will be discussed first.

Measurements are made in two steps with one-cell instruments (Fig. 85). The intensity P_b for the blank is first read on detector D, and the intensity P is then determined for the analyzed solution. The scale of the detector is often calibrated directly in transmittancies and absorbancies. The needle of detector D must then be adjusted to the value $T = 1(A = 0)$ for the blank. This can be done either by varying the intensity of the incident beam by means of a diaphragm of variable aperture or by changing the sensitivity of detector D by means of a shunt until the reading $T = 1$ is obtained for the blank.

The source of radiation in one-cell instruments must be stable, since, otherwise, an error results. Light bulbs, which are always used as sources in filter photometry in the visible and near ultraviolet ranges, have a stable output, provided that the voltage at which they operate is constant. A 6-volt light bulb, connected to a storage battery which operates in the flat segment of its discharge characteristic (voltage-time curve), is entirely satisfactory. Constant voltage transformers, which are commercially available, are more convenient than batteries and are generally used in commercial photometers.

One-cell filter photometers have the advantages and disadvantages of direct-reading instruments: simplicity of construction and operation, but lower accuracy than two-cell instruments. The readings, which are made on a rather short dial (perhaps 4 in), are not very precise, and mechanical imperfections of the meter are also reflected in the results. Errors of 1 to 3 per cent, and possibly higher errors, are not uncommon, but are nevertheless acceptable in many control analyses.

In two-cell instruments the photocells are connected to two potentiometers P_1 and P_2, as shown in Fig. 88. One of these potentiometers P_1, whose dial is graduated in transmittancies and absorbancies, is set at $T = 1(A = 0)$ with the blank, and P_2 is varied until galvanometer G reads a current equal to zero. The solution to be analyzed is then substituted for the blank, and P_1 is adjusted until the current through G is equal to zero, the setting of P_2 remaining unchanged. The absorbancy or transmittancy is then read directly on the scale of potentiometer P_1.

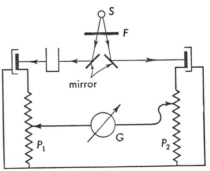

Fig. 88. Schematic diagram of a two-cell filter photometer.

The two main sources of errors of one-cell instruments are practically eliminated in two-cell filter photometers: (1) the galvanometer is utilized as zero-current indicator, and its mechanical imperfections do not affect the accuracy, provided that the sensitivity of the instrument is sufficient; (2) the scale of potentiometer P_1, on which readings are made, is much longer than the scale of the meter of one-cell instruments.[45] Furthermore, errors resulting from fluctuations in the intensity of the source are minimized, but this is not a great advantage in the visible range because stable sources (light bulb connected to voltage regulator) are available. Errors with good technique can be low as 0.2 per cent. In fact the error results mainly from chemical factors rather than instrumental ones.

Several different circuits and optical systems for two-cell instruments have been described. Details can be found in the chapter by Müller in Mellon's monograph listed in Section 9–8.

Commercial one-cell and two-cell filter photometers are available from several manufacturers in the United States and abroad (Beckman, Cenco, Evelyn, Fisher, Klett-Summerson, Leitz, Photovolt, etc.).

9–5. SPECTROPHOTOMETERS FOR THE VISIBLE, ULTRAVIOLET, AND VERY NEAR INFRARED RANGES

Curves showing the variations of transmittancy or absorbancy with wave length (*spectrograms*) are determined with spectrophotometers. The heart of these instruments is the *monochromator*, which is essentially a spectrograph whose photographic plate is replaced by a metallic plate with a narrow slit. The wave length of the beam emerging from the slit is

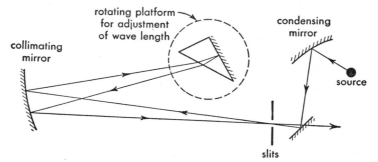

Fig. 89. Schematic diagram of a single-beam spectrophotometer with monochromator equipped with Littrow prism.

adjusted by rotation of the prism or the grating of the instrument. Monochromators need not have the high resolving power of emission spectrographs, and prism instruments are entirely satisfactory. However, grating instruments, especially with inexpensive replica gratings, are also used. The Littrow mounting (see Fig. 60 in Chapter 8) is preferred, but Féry

---

[45]Compact potentiometers in which the wire is wound in a helix (Beckman's Helipot potentiometers) can be utilized.

prisms are sometimes utilized because of the compactness of the mounting. As an example, a schematic diagram is shown in Fig. 89 of a monochromator with Littrow mounting, which is used in the Beckman spectrophotometers of the "D" series (compare with Fig. 60).

Optical parts are made of glass (visible, near ultraviolet) or quartz (visible and ultraviolet down to 200 mμ). Because of strong absorption of radiation, the optical parts are kept to a minimum in the vacuum ultraviolet, and concave gratings which need no focusing system are most advantageous.[46]

The source of radiation is a light bulb in the visible and near ultraviolet ranges or a gas discharge tube (hydrogen) in the ultraviolet range.

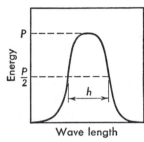 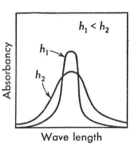

Fig. 90. Energy distribution in the beam emerging from a monochromator.

Fig 91. Influence of half-intensity width on absorption spectrogram.

The emerging beam of a monochromator covers a narrow band whose width largely determines the quality of the instrument. The *half-intensity width h*, which is determined from a plot of detector response versus wave length (Fig. 90), is generally quoted to characterize a monochromator. The

TABLE XIV
Half-Intensity Width h for Beckman DU Spectrophotometer[a,b]

Wave Length, mμ	h, mμ
200	0.78
300	3.7
400	10
600	35
800	64
1000	88
1200	96

[a]For 1-mm slit width.
[b]From data supplied by Beckman Instruments, Inc., Fullerton, California.

width h depends, of course, on the width of the exit slit. It varies with wave length in prism instruments (Table XIV) because the reciprocal linear

[46]For references on recent work in the vacuum ultraviolet range, see the periodic reviews in *Analytical Chemistry* listed in Section 9–8.

dispersion of a prism spectrograph depends on wave length (see Section 8–2). Conversely, the half-intensity width does not vary much with wave length in grating instruments because the reciprocal linear dispersion of grating instruments is essentially independent of wave length (see Section 8–3).

An increase in the half-intensity width causes a broadening of absorption bands and a decrease in absorption maxima (Fig. 91), and it is therefore advisable to adjust the width of the exit slit to a minimum. The resulting distortion of spectrograms has been interpreted theoretically by several authors.[47-49] The minimum width for a given instrument at which measurements can be made with a given solution depends on the energy output of the source, the sensitivity of the detector, and the absorbancy of the solution. Since these factors are affected by wave length, the minimum width of the exit slit depends on the wave length at which the absorbancy of a solution is measured.

The half-intensity width can be decreased by utilizing the emerging beam of a monochromator as the source for a second monochromator.[50] Such *double monochromators*, which are available commercially (Kipp and Zonen in the Netherlands), are generally not necessary in spectrophotometers for chemical analysis except when the scattered light must be kept to a minimum in the optical system. This is the case in the analysis of media of high absorbancy, such as films or solutions which cannot be diluted. A commercial unit with double monochromator is available in the United States (Cary recording spectrophotometer).

In addition to the source of radiation and monochromator, the spectrophotometer also includes an absorption cell and a detector. Photographic plates[51] were generally utilized as detectors until about 1940, but spectrophotometers with phototubes are universally preferred in the analytical laboratory nowadays. The first of these instruments was described[43] in the 1930's, and the first commercial spectrophotometer, the Beckman DU spectrophotometer, was put on the market about 1941. This spectrophotometer, which was described by Cary and Beckman,[52] has contributed much to the development of spectrophotometry as a practical analytical tool.

The width of the beam emerging from a monochromator is perhaps 0.01 to 1 mm, while the beam in a filter photometer may have a cross-sectional area of several square centimeters. Radiation intensities to be determined in spectrophotometry, therefore, are much lower than in filter photometry.

[47]A. C. Hardy and F. M. Young, *J. Optical Soc. Am.*, **39**, 265 (1949).
[48]W. H. Eberhardt, *ibid.*, **40**, 172 (1950).
[49]A. R. Philpots, W. Thain, and P. G. Smith, *Anal. Chem.*, **23**, 268 (1951).
[50]P. H. van Cittert, *Physica*, **3**, 181 (1923); *Rev. d'Optique*, **5**, 393 (1926).
[51]For a detailed discussion of photographic spectrophotometry, see Chapter 6 by E. R. Holiday in Mellon's monograph (see Section 9–8).
[52]H. H. Cary and A. O. Beckman, *J. Optical Soc. Am.*, **31**, 682 (1941).

Since amplification of the signal of a barrier layer cell is not so simple as for a phototube (see Section 9–4), the latter type of cell is generally preferred. However, barrier layer cells with lead sulfide as semiconductor are utilized in the near infrared up to 3 μ because phototubes have a very poor sensitivity above approximately 1 μ.

Direct- or indirect-reading instruments have been designed. In the direct-reading instruments (Beckman "B" spectrophotometer, for instance) the output meter is calibrated in absorbancies and transmittancies. The meter is set at the reading $T = 1$ ($A = 0$) with the blank, generally, by adjustment of the width of the exit slit. The analyzed solution is substituted for the blank and the value T or A is read directly. In indirect-reading instruments the ohmic drop in a resistance in series with the phototube is balanced, for instance, against a potentiometer P, whose dial is calibrated in values of T and A (Fig. 92). The voltage across P is adjusted by means

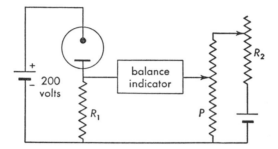

Fig. 92. Schematic diagram of circuit for measuring phototube current by the potentiometric method.

of R_2 according to the radiation intensity to be measured. Potentiometer P is set at $T = 1$ ($A = 0$) with the blank and the width of the exit slit of the monochromator is adjusted until amplifier A indicates balance between the voltage across R_1 and potentiometer P. The blank is then replaced by the solution to be analyzed and P is adjusted to obtain balance. The absorbancy and transmittancy are read on the scale of the potentiometer P. This indirect method yields more accurate results than the reading method for two reasons: (1) results are not affected by changes in the gain of amplifier A; and (2) readings are made on a potentiometer with a much greater accuracy than on the rather small scale of the output meter of a direct-reading spectrophotometer. Many variations in the design of the potentiometric circuit and its balance indicator are possible.

The above description covers *single-beam spectrophotometers,* which are the equivalent of one-cell filter photometers. *Double-beam instruments,* in which the beam emerging from the monochromator is split into two beams whose intensities are measured with two detectors, have also been designed. The absorption cell in double-beam instruments is placed in the path of one of the beams while the other beam impinges directly on the second detector. As in two-cell filter photometers, variations in the output of the source are essentially compensated for in double-beam spectrophotometers. These instruments are particularly advantageous when a rather unstable source must be used. The fluctuations in the source intensity can also be compensated in single-beam instruments by rapid commutation of the incident beam between a detector without absorption cell and a detector with cell (Beckman recording spectrophotometer "DK").

Excellent spectrophotometers are now available in the United States and abroad: Bausch and Lomb, Beckman, Central Scientific Co., Coleman, Unicam, etc.

The determination of absorption spectrograms with "manual" spectrophotometers becomes quite tedious when a large number of samples must be handled, and recording instruments are then preferable. The prism or grating in recording spectrophotometers is rotated continuously and the spectrogram is recorded with a pen-and-ink recorder. Absorbancies can be recorded directly if an element converting transmittancies to the logarithm of the reciprocal of transmittancies is inserted before the input of the recorder. Since the linear reciprocal dispersion of prism monochromators varies with wave length (see Section 8–2), the scale of wave lengths is not linear if the prism of the monochromator is rotated at a uniform speed. This disadvantage is eliminated when the prism is rotated with a cam mechanism which automatically varies the speed of rotation of the prism according to wave length. The design of recording spectrophotometers raised many problems which were solved in different ways by several manufacturers (Applied Physics Corporation, Beckman, Fisher, General Electric Co.).

A cathode-ray oscilloscope can be substituted for the pen-and-ink recorder, and the spectrogram is then displayed on the screen of the oscilloscope. A wide range of wave lengths—the visible range for instance—can be covered in a short time (1/60 sec) by rapidly rotating the prism or the grating of the monochromator, and a complete spectrogram is thus recorded. Such fast-recording instruments are of no particular value in chemical analysis, but they are useful in kinetic studies and in the monitoring of streams. A commercial unit is available (American Optical Co.).

An innovation is the use of the orthicon, a tube for television cameras, as detector and the transmission of the spectrum to a cathode-ray tube.[53]

9–6. INFRARED SPECTROMETERS

Spectrometers for the infrared range are composed of the same basic elements as instruments in the visible and ultraviolet ranges, but the de-

[53]J. T. Agnew, R. G. Franklin, R. E. Bann, and A. Bazarian, *J. Optical Soc. Am.*, **39**, 409 (1949).

tector and the materials used in the construction of the optical parts are different.

The discussion will be limited to instruments operating below 25 to 40 μ, since it is in this range of wave lengths that vibrational-rotational spectra (see Section 9–2b) are generally observed. Instruments in this range have prism monochromators, whereas reflection gratings are utilized above 40 μ because transparent materials are not available in that range.

Materials used in the construction of prisms are listed in Table XV with

TABLE XV
Materials for Optical System in Infrared Spectrometers

MATERIAL	UPPER WAVE LENGTH,[a] μ	LOWER WAVE NUMBER,[a] cm^{-1}
Glass	2	5000
Quartz	4	2500
Lithium fluoride	6	1600
Fluorite (calcium fluoride)	8	1200
Rock salt (sodium chloride)	15	650
Potassium bromide	25	400
Thallium bromoiodide	40	250

[a]Only *approximate* values.

the approximate upper wave length and the lower wave number at which they can be utilized. Some of these materials are very hygroscopic, and good control of the humidity in the room in which an infrared monochromator is installed is essential. It might be thought that the most suitable material for a prism is the one whose upper limit of wave length for transparency is maximum, but this is definitely not the case for the following reason.

The half-intensity width, which should be as low as possible (see Section 9–5), decreases with increasing reciprocal linear dispersion. The latter quantity for a prism spectrograph is proportional to the derivative $dn/d\lambda$ where n is the index of refraction and λ the wave length. Since the curve of n versus λ becomes steeper (i.e., $dn/d\lambda$ increases) as λ approaches the range in which the material is opaque,[54] the half-intensity width is smaller in the neighborhood of the range of absorption by the prism material than at longer wave lengths. For instance, resolution is higher in the range of wave lengths AB in Fig. 93 than along CD.

The source of radiation in infrared spectrometers is essentially a blackbody radiator. The energy emitted by a black-body radiator varies with wave length and with temperature, as indicated schematically[55] in Fig. 94. The energy emitted per unit area and unit of time increases with temperature, and the maximum of the plot of energy against wave-length curve is

[54]See discussion of dispersion in a text on physical optics; for instance, F. A. Jenkins and H. E. White, *Fundamentals of Optics*, 2nd ed., McGraw-Hill, New York, 1950, pp. 462–485.
[55]Review this material in a physics text.

shifted toward lower wave lengths as the temperature is increased. The emission characteristics of solids depart somewhat from the ideal behavior of the black-body radiator and vary with the nature of the radiating sub-

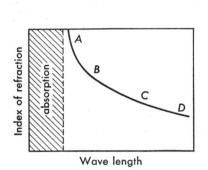

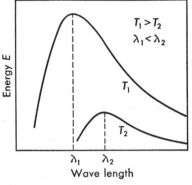

Fig. 93. Variations of index or refraction with wave length.

Fig. 94. Radiation of black-body.

stance. Materials such as silicon carbide and rare earth oxides, which have advantageous emission characteristics as infrared sources, are generally preferred to metals and other substances. Filaments made of these materials are heated to temperatures between 1200 and 1800°C by means of a power supply with proper current regulation (*Globar* and *Nernst* glowers).

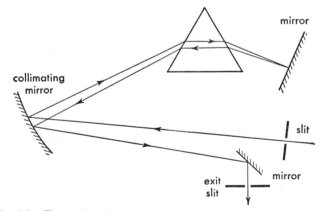

Fig. 95. Example of Littrow mounting for infrared monochromator.

Optical systems of varied design have been proposed for infrared monochromators. The dispersing element is generally a prism (Fig. 95) in the range below 40 μ, but diffraction gratings have also been utilized.[56] Spherical mirrors made by coating a glass surface with aluminum are used

[56]J. D. S. Goulden, *J. Sci. Instr.*, **29**, 215 (1952).

for focusing purposes, rather than lenses which would not be perfectly transparent and which are more difficult to manufacture than mirrors. A major problem in the design of the optical system is the necessity of reducing stray radiation because, otherwise, the beam emerging from the exit slit of the monochromator has some radiation at much shorter wave lengths than that indicated on the scale of the instrument. The sensitivity of the detectors utilized in the infrared range (see below) generally increases with decreasing wave length, and consequently stray light may cause a serious error on transmittancy readings.

The necessity of having very thin (0.01 to 0.3 mm) absorption layers of liquid is a source of difficulties in the design of absorption cells. Such small cell thicknesses are very difficult to reproduce from one cell to another, and the same cell is generally utilized in comparative measurements. The windows of the cell are made of one of the materials listed in Table XV. Silver chloride can also be utilized up to about 25 μ, i.e., down to 400 cm^{-1}. Polytrifluorochloroethylene[57] has proved most advantageous in cell design because of its resistance to many chemicals. Because of the small thickness of the cell, liquids are introduced by means of a small hypodermic syringe or by capillarity. Cells for gases have a thickness about 1000 times (the order of magnitude of the ratio, density of liquid/density of gas) that for liquids, i.e., 5 to 100 cm.

The transmittancy of small samples as encountered, for instance, in biochemical studies can be determined by the microscopic infrared technique of Burch.[58]

Bolometers and thermocouples are the classical detectors in the infrared range, but photoconductive cells (lead sulfide, lead telluride) and pneumatic detectors developed in the late 1940's have proven most valuable. The great progress made in the improvement of detectors since about 1940 was a decisive factor in the widespread application of infrared spectrometry.[59] While the recording of a spectrogram in the range from 3 to 15 μ was rather laborious in the 1920's or before, this operation is now completed in a few minutes with commercial instruments, or even in a much shorter time with special spectrometers (cathode-ray oscilloscope). The availability of fast detectors has had three consequences:[60] absorption bands of weak intensity have become easier to study; the resolution of spectrometers has improved; and faster recording instruments have been developed. The different infrared detectors will now be discussed in some detail.

A *bolometer* is essentially a thin platinum strip in an evacuated glass vessel with a window transparent in the infrared range. Losses by reflection are

[57]J. S. Kirby-Smith and E. A. Jones, *J. Optical Soc. Am.*, **39**, 780 (1949).

[58]C. R. Burch, *Proc. Phys. Soc. (London)*, **59**, 41 (1947).

[59]See the interesting review by V. Z. Williams on the evolution of infrared instrumentation, *Rev. Sci. Instruments*, **19**, 135 (1948).

[60]See the review of B. L. Crawford and D. E. Mann, *Ann. Rev. Phys. Chem.*, **1**, 151 (1950).

decreased by a black coating on the platinum strip, and losses due to convection are greatly minimized because of the low pressure of the gas in the vessel. The metal strip is made very thin to decrease the inertia of the bolometer, i.e., to decrease the time lag between signal and response. Irradiation by the infrared beam causes an increase in resistance of the metal strip, which is measured with a Wheatstone bridge. Since variations of resistance can be measured within 10^{-5} per cent and the temperature coefficient for the resistivity of platinum is 0.38 per cent per degree at room temperature, variations of the order of 10^{-5} degree in the temperature of the platinum strip can be determined. Two identical elements are generally placed in the opposite arms of a bridge; one of the elements is in the path of the infrared beam and the other compensates the variations in the ambient temperature.

Thermocouples are made by welding together two wires of metals 1 and 2 in such a manner that a segment of wire of metal 1 is connected to two terminal wires of metal 2. One junction between metals 1 and 2 is heated by the infrared beam, and the other junction is kept at constant temperature. Because of variations of the work function of metals (see Section 2–1) with temperature, a small voltage (less than 1 mv) is developed across the thermocouple. The output voltage is increased when several thermocouples are connected in series (*thermopile*). To avoid losses of energy by convection, the couples are enclosed in an evacuated vessel with a window transparent to infrared radiation. The metallic junctions are also covered with a black deposit to decrease reflection of the incident beam. Thermocouples which respond within 15 millisec are now available, whereas the response interval for thermocouples manufactured before 1940 was of the order of a few seconds.

Lead sulfide[61] and lead telluride[62] *photocells* are useful as detectors because of their sensitivity and rapidity of response. These detectors are sensitive up to 3.5 and 6 μ for the lead sulfide and lead tellurite cell, respectively. Other barrier layer cells respond only at wave lengths below 1 μ (Fig. 87).

In the *pneumatic detector* invented by Golay[63] the intensity of infrared radiation is measured by following the expansion of a gas upon heating. The delay in response can be as short as 1 millisec.

The signal of detectors is amplified by rather conventional methods and applied to a pen-and-ink recorder. Fast recording methods have been devised in which a range of 5 μ is scanned in 10 sec and the spectrogram is displayed on a cathode-ray oscilloscope.[64,65] Such fast recording methods

[61]Invented by R. J. Cashman, *U.S. Pat. No.* 2,448,516 (1948).
[62]O. Simpson, *Proc. Phys. Soc. (London)*, **61**, 486 (1948).
[63]M. J. E. Golay, *Rev. Sci. Instruments*, **18**, 347 (1947); **20**, 816 (1949).
[64]E. F. Daly and G. B. B. M. Sutherland, *Proc. Phys. Soc. (London)*, **59**, 77 (1947).
[65]E. F. Daly, *J. Sci. Instruments*, **28**, 308 (1951).

are of interest in the analysis of systems of varying composition (streams, kinetic studies, etc.).

Excellent spectrometers are commercially available (Baird, Beckman, and Perkin-Elmer in the United States; Grubb-Parsons, Hilger, and Unicam in England; Leitz in Germany, etc.).

A complete spectrogram is necessary in most applications of infrared spectrometry, but measurements without a monochromator are useful in some instances, particularly in the monitoring of gas streams. The operational principle[66] is as follows:

The gas mixture being monitored flows in an absorption cell C_1 (Fig. 96)

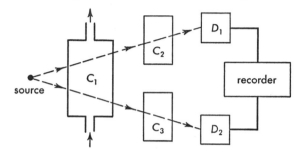

Fig. 96. Infrared photometer for continuous gas analysis.

which is irradiated with a double-beam infrared source. One of the beams falls on an absorption cell C_2, which contains the gas to be analyzed, say, carbon dioxide. The pressure of carbon dioxide and the thickness of cell C_2 are such that the transmittance of cell C_2 in the range of absorption by carbon dioxide is practically zero. Conversely, the transmittance of C_2 for the constituents of the mixture other than carbon dioxide is practically unity. In this manner, variations in the composition of the mixture for gases other than carbon dioxide are compensated for. The empty cell C_3 serves only to render the optical system symmetrical. The difference between the outputs of detectors D_1 and D_2 is proportional to the transmittance of cell C_1 for carbon dioxide and gives a measurement (continuous recording) of the concentration of this gas. The sensitivity of the method is excellent; for instance, 1 per cent of carbon dioxide, or even smaller concentrations, for full-range deflection of the recorder. This method is very valuable in industrial plants and several commercial units are available (Baird Associates, Beckman, Cary, Leeds and Northrup, Liston Becker, Perkin Elmer, etc.).

9–7. APPLICATIONS

a. Filter Photometry and Spectrophotometry in the Visible Range. The number of analytical applications of filter photometry and

[66]W. G. Fastie and A. H. Pfund, *J. Optical Soc. Am.*, **37**, 762 (1947).

spectrophotometry is truly amazing. An idea of the scope of the method can be gained by consulting the books of Sandell and the Snells and the periodical reviews in *Analytical Chemistry* (see references in Section 9–8). An article by Mellon[67] (1954) is a most valuable guide to source books and reviews. The bibliographies of Odeen[68] and Stillman and Dunlop[69] may also be consulted.

The emphasis in the past was on the photometric determination of inorganic compounds, but numerous procedures have now been developed for organic compounds. The colorimetric or photometric determination of *p*H's was of great practical value in the past, but *p*H meters with glass electrodes are often preferred nowadays.

Most inorganic substances do not absorb in the visible range, and a color must be developed by the addition of a reagent. Many reagents have been proposed, and the reader can find ample information on this subject in Welcher's treatise on organic reagents.[70] Only a few reagents can be mentioned here: dithizone, 8-hydroxyquinoline, α-nitroso-βnaphthol, diphenylcarbazide, *p*-dimethylaminobenzylidenerhodamine, etc. New reagents are continuously being discovered, and new applications of well-known reagents to filter photometry often appear in the current literature. Many of these reagents or the reactions in which they are involved are not specific, and separation of the elements to be determined is often necessary. The standard methods of separation, such as precipitation, extraction, and distillation, are often applied, but there is a tendency toward increased use of chromatography, ion-exchange methods, and electrolytic separations. Interfering reactions can in some cases be avoided by the judicious use of complexing agents.

A few parts per million of many substances, or even smaller amounts, can be determined by filter photometry; thus the sensitivity of this method is very good. The selectivity varies greatly from one determination to another. In general, absorption bands in the visible range are rather broad, and the simultaneous determination of several substances by the procedure described in Section 9–3g is limited to two, or possibly three, substances. The accuracy of determinations by filter photometry can be high, and errors can be as low as 0.2 to 0.5 per cent. The main difficulty is not of instrumental nature but rather a result of variations in the *chemical* conditions in consecutive determinations. The formation of colored substances often proceeds by rather complicated reactions, and variations in *p*H,

[67]M. G. Mellon, *Anal. Chem.*, **26**, 181 (1954).

[68]M. H. Odeen, *Bibliography of Applications for Beckman Model B and DU Spectrophotometers*, Bull. 222B, Beckman Instruments, South Pasadena, Calif., 1952.

[69]J. W. Stillman and E. C. Dunlop. *ASTM Spec. Tech. Publ.*, No. **125,** 25 pp. (1952).

[70]F. J. Welcher, *Organic Analytical Reagents*, 4 vols., Van Nostrand, New York, 1947–1948. For references to many other books, see p. 87 of Sandell's book (reference in Section 9–8).

temperature, ionic strength, etc., may cause serious errors. Many of the reactions used in filter photometry are not very rapid, and consequently the measurements must be properly timed.

Filter photometry and spectrophotometry can be applied to the determination of the equivalence point of titrations. The absorbancy is plotted against volume of titrant, and the equivalence point is obtained by graphic extrapolation. Such *photometric titrations* were discussed, perhaps for the first time,[71,72] as early as 1926, but applications for purely analytical purposes have been relatively scanty[73,74] because direct photometry is generally as simple and as accurate (at least in very careful work) as photometric titrations. The method may nevertheless be useful in certain cases; for instance, when the substance to be analyzed and the reagent do not absorb in the proper wave length. Photometric titration still is possible under such conditions, provided that a colored indicator can be found. Photometric titrations also may be preferable to direct photometry in the analysis of solutions containing several colored substances having similar absorption spectra. Only the variations in absorbancy during titration need be determined in the titration method. Photometric titrations often yield more precise results than potentiometric titrations at very low concentrations or for incomplete reactions at the equivalence point. Under these conditions potentiometry yields drawn-out curves which do not lend themselves to precise analysis, whereas photometric titration curves may have a much more favorable shape.

Titration curves of varied shape can be obtained as indicated in Fig. 97. Curve *A* corresponds to the titration of a colorless solution with a colored titrant, and curve *B* is obtained in the opposite case. The production of a colored substance yields curve *C* when both titrant and analyzed solution are colorless. Curve *D* corresponds to the production of a colorless substance from colored reagents. Curve *E* is obtained in stepwise titrations when the absorptivities of the products formed in the two steps are different. Curve *F* corresponds to a stepwise titration in which a color is developed in the first step and destroyed in the second step.

The curves of Fig. 97 are traced on the following assumptions:

Dilution by the titrant is negligible, the reactions are quantitative, and the Beer-Lambert law is obeyed. A correction can easily be made for the effect of dilution (see Section 5-2c), or dilution can be made negligible by

[71]J. Field and L. G. M. Baas-Becking, *J. Gen. Physiol.*, **9**, 445 (1926).

[72]An instrument for automatic termination at the equivalence point of photometric titrations was described in 1928 by R. H. Müller and H. M. Partridge, *Ind. Eng. Chem.*, **20**, 423 (1928).

[73]For a brief review of early work, see R. H. Osburn, J. H. Elliott, and A. F. Martin, *Ind. Eng. Chem., Anal. Ed.*, **15**, 642 (1943).

[74]R. F. Goddu and D. N. Hume [*Anal Chem.*, **26**, 1740 (1954)] give a good discussion of principles and a survey of applications.

the use of a sufficiently concentrated titrant. If the reactions are appreciably not quantitative, the absorbancy varies progressively in the vicinity of the equivalence point just as in amperometric titrations (see Fig. 41 in Chapter 5), but the determination of the equivalence point by extrapola-

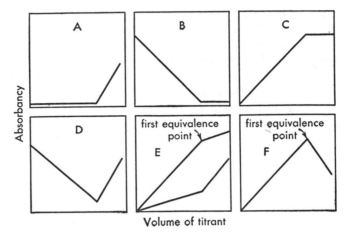

Fig. 97.   Types of photometric titration curves.

tion is still possible. Departure from the Beer-Lambert law is reflected by a curvature in the plots of absorbancy versus volume of titrant. Equivalence points can nevertheless be determined in most instances even when the Beer-Lambert law fails.

Photometric titrations involving colorless substances are possible in presence of a suitable colored indicator. The absorbancy, which is essentially constant before and after the equivalence point, varies rapidly with the volume of titrant in the vicinity of this point. Curves similar to potentiometric titration curves are obtained when the logarithm of the absorbancy is plotted against volume of titrant.

Photometric titrations have been applied to neutralizations, complexation reactions, and oxidation-reductions. Applications have also been made to precipitation reactions, but these are turbidimetric or nephelometric titrations (see Section 10–5). Detailed references to applications can be found in the review of Goddu and Hume[74] (see problems 21 to 24 in Section 9–9).

Of greater significance than purely analytical applications is the study of equilibria by photometric titrations, and the determination of equilibrium constants from titration curves. Detailed mathematical analyses can be found in the monograph of Charlot and Gauguin[75] and in books on

[75]G. Charlot and R. Gauguin, *Les Méthodes d'Analyse des Réactions en Solution,* Masson, Paris, 1951.

complex ions.[76],[77] Many applications of this method have been reported in the study of equilibria involving complex ions and weak acids or bases. Applications to oxidation-reduction reactions are rather scanty because electrochemical methods are generally preferred. An example of photometric study of the latter type of reaction is the determination of the degrees of oxidation of neptunium.[78]

A modified form of photometric titrations (the *method of continuous variations*) was described by Job[79] in fundamental papers even before these titrations were well known. The principle of Job's method is as follows:

Consider the reaction

$$X + mY = XY_m, \tag{9–29}$$

and assume that solutions containing varied amounts of X and Y are prepared in such a manner that the sum of the concentrations C_X and C_Y, which would be obtained if reaction (9–29) did not occur, is kept constant. The absorbancy of the resulting mixture is measured for different values of the ratio C_X/C_Y, and a plot of absorbancy versus C_X/C_Y is made. The maximum of the resulting curve has the abscissa $C_X/C_Y = 1/m$ if the species X and Y do not absorb and XY_m does (Fig. 98). Thus, the value of m can be readily determined. This result can be established as follows for the simple case in which reaction (9–29) is quantitative.

If 1 mole of X and m moles of Y are dissolved in a given volume of solution, 1 mole of XY_m is formed because reaction (9–29) is supposed to be quantitative. If p moles of X are mixed with $(1 + m - p)$ moles of Y, the total number of moles of X and Y still is $1 + m$, but less than 1 mole of XY_m is formed. Thus, for $p < 1$, species X is

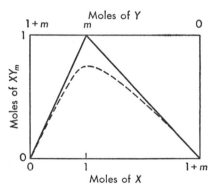

Fig. 98. Method of continuous variations.

completely consumed, but an excess of Y is left. The number of moles of XY_m is proportional to p for $p < 1$, and conversely, the number of moles of XY_m decreases linearly with p when p varies from 1 to $1 + m$ (Fig. 98).

[76]For instance, the excellent monograph of A. E. Martell and M. Calvin, *Chemistry of the Metal Chelate Compounds*, Prentice-Hall, New York, 1952.

[77]See the treatment of titration curves for reactions involving complexones (ethylenediaminetetraacetic acid, for example) in J. M. H. Fortuin, P. Karsten, and H. L. Kies, *Anal. Chim. Acta*, **10**, 356 (1954).

[78]J. C. Hindman, L. B. Magnusson, and T. J. LaChapelle, *J. Am. Chem. Soc.*, **71**, 687 (1949).

[79]P. Job, *Ann. Chim.*, (10) **9**, 113 (1928); (11) **6**, 97 (1936).

If only substance XY_m absorbs radiation at the wave length at which measurements are made, the absorbancy of the solution is proportional to the concentration of XY_m, it being assumed that the Beer-Lambert law is obeyed. The maximum of absorption then is observed for the mixture, for which the ratio C_x/C_y is equal to $1/m$. Actually, reactions are not rigorously quantitative and the dashed curve of Fig. 98 is observed. The maximum of this curve, however, still occurs for $C_x/C_y = 1/m$. No proof of this statement will be given here because the calculations are rather tedious, but the matter can be taken up as exercise (see problem 8 in Section 9–9). The method can still be applied when absorption by X and Y cannot be neglected, but a correction for the absorption by X and Y must be made. Application has also been made to reactions involving the formation of two and three substances[80] (see problem 9 in Section 9–9).

The method of continuous variations is of considerable importance in the study of complex ions, and the reader may consult references in footnotes 75 and 76 for further details. Applications are treated as a literature survey problem (see problem 28 in Section 9–9).

b. Spectrophotometry in the Ultraviolet Range.

Analytical applications of spectrophotometry in the ultraviolet range deal mainly with the determination of organic compounds, and especially aromatic and heterocyclic substances, or compounds with conjugated bonds. Applications to inorganic substances are rather limited, but there is a trend toward a greater use of ultraviolet spectrophotometry in the determination of these substances.

Some attention must be paid to the selection of a suitable solvent. Water is transparent in the whole spectral range in which quartz cells can be utilized, i.e., down to about 200 mμ; but unfortunately water is a poor solvent for many organic substances, and organic solvents are often required. Brode,[81] among others, determined the lowest wave lengths at which many organic solvents can be utilized, and this author's results are useful in the selection of a solvent. Ethyl alcohol and aliphatic saturated hydrocarbons, particularly isooctane, are often utilized. *Very pure* solvents are needed because traces of impurities may decrease the useful range toward the shorter wave lengths. Finally, it should be remembered that polar solvents may profoundly modify the absorption spectrogram of a substance.

Absorption spectrograms in the ultraviolet range are far from being as characteristic as those in the infrared range, and applications to qualitative analysis are rather limited. Quantitative determinations, however, are numerous, as the reader can readily see by consulting Rosenbaum's periodic

[80]W. C. Vosburgh and G. R. Cooper, *J. Am. Chem. Soc.*, **63**, 437 (1941); R. K. Gould and W. C. Vosburgh, *ibid.*, **64**, 1630 (1942).
[81]W. R. Brode, *J. Phys. Chem.*, **30**, 56 (1926).

reviews (see Section 9–8). Absorption bands in the ultraviolet range are relatively narrow, and application to the simultaneous determination of several substances by the method of Section 9–3g is more often possible than in the visible range. For instance, the determination of toluene in presence of benzene at 2700 A is possible because the former substance absorbs more strongly than the latter (Fig. 99). This rather extreme case in

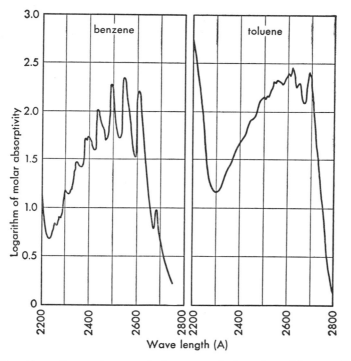

Fig. 99. Absorption spectrograms for benzene and toluene in cyclohexane. (Reprinted with permission from R. A. Friedel and M. Orchin, *Ultraviolet Spectra of Aromatic Compounds*, Wiley, New York, 1951.)

which the two substances to be determined, benzene and toluene, are quite similar is indicative of the potentialities of the method.

Further appreciation of potential applications of spectrophotometry in the ultraviolet range can be gained by consulting the atlas of spectra of Friedel and Orchin (see Section 9–8 for reference) and the compilation prepared by the American Petroleum Institute.[82]

The usefulness of correlating absorption spectrograms with molecular structure was already pointed out in Section 9–2. For further details, consult the books of Brode and Gillam and Stern (references in Section 9–8).

[82]*Catalog of Ultraviolet Spectrograms*, American Petroleum Institute, Research Project 44 at the National Bureau of Standards.

c. Spectrophotometry in the Infrared Range. The number of applications of infrared spectrometry has increased at a very rapid pace since the late 1930's when this method began to be applied in routine chemical analysis. Infrared spectrometry is ideally suited to the qualitative analysis of organic substances, but applications to inorganic compounds are limited because of the strong absorption of infrared radiation by water. Water exhibits strong absorption bands, particularly at about 3500 cm^{-1} for the stretching of the O—H bond, and at 1450 cm^{-1} for the bending of this bond. Because of the absorption of infrared radiation by water, inorganic materials are generally studied in the solid state, and this constitutes a very serious limitation in practical applications. A detailed investigation of the absorption by numerous inorganic compounds was made by Miller and Wilkins.[83]

Nonpolar solvents such as carbon tetrachloride are generally preferred in infrared spectrometry because interactions between solvent and solute are then minimized. Several solvents whose absorption bands are observed at markedly different wave lengths may have to be utilized when a rather broad range of wave lengths is to be explored. Solid substances are transformed into a paste by mixing them with mineral oil or a perfluorohydrocarbon. The *potassium bromide pellet technique* is very advantageous in the analysis of solid substances.[84] The substance being analyzed is mixed with a large excess of pure potassium bromide, and the mixture is pressed under high pressure. The transmittancy of the transparent pellet obtained in this manner is then measured with a spectrometer in the usual fashion.

It is not possible here to give a review of the applications of infrared spectrometry to analytical chemistry, and the reader is referred to some of the books and review articles listed in Section 9–8. The book of Bellamy and the chart prepared by Colthup[16] are particularly recommended for frequency assignments. The number of available spectra has increased so rapidly that the use of punched cards in the classification and sorting of spectrograms has become advantageous.[85,86] Automatic methods of sorting cards (International Business Machines) have been applied.

The main difficulty in the application of infrared spectrometry to quantitative analysis is the necessity of using a cell having a narrow thickness (0.3 mm or less), as was indicated in Section 9–6. Errors can be as low as 1 per cent in careful work, but the accuracy is often somewhat poor (errors of 5 per cent or even higher). The sensitivity of infrared spectrometry is good because of the strong absorption by numerous substances in the infrared range, and a sample of a few milligrams may suffice. The selectivity

[83]F. A. Miller and C. H. Wilkins, *Anal. Chem.*, **24**, 1253 (1952).
[84]M. M. Stimson and M. J. O'Donnell, *J. Am. Chem. Soc.*, **74**, 1805 (1952).
[85]H. C. Tingey and R. R. Hampton (abstract only), *J. Optical Soc. Am.*, **37**, 984 (1947).
[86]J. D. Stroupe, A. G. Knox, and J. F. Woodman (abstract only), *Anal. Chem.*, **20**, 1126 (1948).

is excellent because infrared spectrograms are characteristic of the absorbing substance. This is apparent in Fig. 100, which gives as an example the spectrograms of five isomers of the insecticide, hexachlorocyclohexane, and the spectrogram of heptachlorocyclohexane.[87] The simultaneous deter-

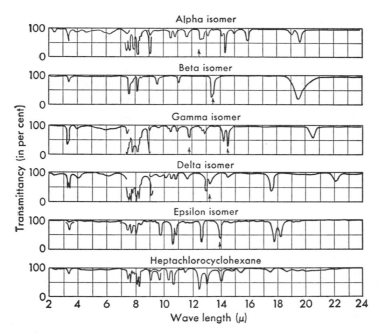

Fig. 100. Absorption spectrograms of five isomers of hexachlorocyclohexane and spectrogram of heptachlorocyclohexane. (From L. W. Daasch, *Anal. Chem.*, **19**, 779 (1947).)

mination of the five isomers by the method outlined in Section 9–3g is possible and quite simple, whereas the application of ordinary chemical methods would involve insurmountable difficulties.

The potentialities of the method are further increased when the spectra are recorded at liquid air temperature because absorption bands are then narrower than at room temperature.[88,89]

Application to continuous gas analysis in industrial plants by measurement of the absorbancy of the gas at a given wave length is an important application which was discussed in some detail in Section 9–6.

Summarizing, infrared spectrometry is a marvelous analytical tool with excellent selectivity, good sensitivity, and a relatively good accuracy.

[87]L. W. Daasch, *Anal. Chem.*, **19**, 779 (1947). This example is also quoted by Ferguson (see reference in footnote 14).
[88]W. H. Avery and C. F. Ellis, *J. Chem. Phys.*, **10**, 10 (1942).
[89]A. Walsh and J. B. Willis, *ibid.*, **18**, 552 (1950).

d. Applications to Physiochemical Studies.   Applications of absorption spectrometry in physical chemistry, and particularly the determination of thermodynamic data and the study of the chemical bond, are very important, but this material is not within the scope of this text.[90]

9-8. BIBLIOGRAPHY

a. Books and Articles

R. B. Barnes, R. C. Gore, U. Liddel, and V. Z. Williams, *Infrared Spectroscopy*, Reinhold, New York, 1944. The first book on applied infrared spectroscopy.

L. J. Bellamy, *Infrared Spectra of Complex Molecules*, Wiley, New York, 1953. Most recent critical survey; very valuable for frequency assignment.

E. J. Bowen, *The Chemical Aspects of Light*, 2nd ed., Oxford University Press, London, 1946. Excellent nonmathematical treatment.

W. R. Brode, *Chemical Spectroscopy*, 2nd ed., Wiley, New York, 1943. Classical textbook with detailed bibliography.

W. R. Brode, article in *Physical Methods in Chemical Analysis*, W. B. Berl, Ed., Vol. I, Academic Press, New York, 1950. An introductory treatment.

W. Brugel, *Einfuhrung in die Ultrarotspektroskopie*, Steinkopff, Darmstadt, 1954. A good text, well balanced between theory and experimental methods.

C. Candler, *Practical Spectroscopy*, Hilger and Watts, London, 1949. See particularly chapter on infrared spectroscopy.

G. Charlot and R. Gauguin, *Dosages Colorimétriques*, Masson, Paris, 1952. Good survey of theory and brief discussion of instrumentation; review of applications.

R. A. Friedel and M. Orchin, *Ultraviolet Spectra of Aromatic Compounds*, Wiley, New York, 1951. Carefully prepared compilation with 579 absorption spectrograms.

T. R. P. Gibb, *Optical Methods of Chemical Analysis*, McGraw-Hill, New York, 1942. Introductory treatment.

A. Gillam and E. S. Stern, *An Introduction to Electronic Absorption Spectroscopy in Organic Chemistry*, Arnold, London, 1954. Correlation of structure and absorption bands in the range 200 to 1000 mμ.

G. R. Harrison, R. C. Lord, and J. R. Loofbourow, *Practical Spectroscopy*, Prentice-Hall, New York, 1948. See sections on instrumentation for the various wavelength ranges.

H. M. Hershenson, *Ultraviolet and Visible Absorption Spectra—Index for 1930-1954*, Academic Press, New York, 1956.

G. Herzberg, *Infrared and Raman Spectra of Polyatomic Molecules*, Van Nostrand, New York, 1945. A classical work on theory.

G. Herzberg, *Molecular Spectra and Molecular Structure—Spectra of Diatomic Molecules*, Van Nostrand, New York, 1950. Classical work on theory.

G. Kortüm, *Kolorimetrie, Photometrie und Spektrometrie*, 3rd ed., Springer, Berlin, 1955.

[90]See, for instance, the detail of some calculations of this type in E. A. Guggenheim and J. E. Prue, *Physicochemical Calculations*, Interscience, New York, 1955.

B. Lange, *Kolorimetrische Analyse*, Verlag Chem., Weinheim, 1952. Numerous applications in the visible range.

J. Lecomte, *Spectrométrie Infrarouge et ses Applications Physicochimiques*, Presses Universitaires, Paris, 1949. Work by one of the pioneers in the field.

G. F. Lothian, *Absorption Spectrophotometry*, Hilger and Watts, London, 1949. Emphasis on instrumentation.

J. P. Mathieu, *Spectres de Vibration et Symétrie des Molécules et des Cristaux*, Hermann, Paris, 1945. Of interest for theoretical studies.

F. X. Mayer and A. Luszczak, *Absorptions-Spektranalyse*, de Gruyter, Berlin, 1951.

M. G. Mellon, Ed., *Analytical Absorption Spectroscopy*, Wiley, New York, 1950. Good treatment of fundamentals and extensive bibliography on applications, particularly in the visible range.

F. Müller, article in *Physikalische Methoden der Analytischen Chemie*, W. Böttger, Ed., Vol. III, Akademische Verlagsgesellschaft, Leipzig, 1939. Contains a detailed bibliography.

H. H. Nielsen and R. A. Oetjen, article in *Physical Methods in Chemical Analysis*, W. B. Berl, Ed., Vol. I, Academic Press, New York, 1950. Treatment of infrared methods.

H. M. Randall, R. C. Fowler, N. Fuson, and J. R. Dangl, *Infrared Determination of Organic Structures*, Van Nostrand, New York, 1949. Covers the subject from a practical point of view; many spectrograms.

E. B. Sandell, *Colorimetric Determination of Traces of Metals*, 2nd ed., Interscience, New York, 1950. Classical work with critical survey of many applications.

G. Scheibe, article in *Physikalische Methoden der Analytischen Chemie*, W. Böttger, Ed., Vol. I, Akademische Verlagsgesellschaft, Leipzig, 1933.

F. D. Snell and C. T. Snell, *Colorimetric Methods of Analysis*, 3rd ed., 3 vols., Van Nostrand, New York, 1948–1953. A treatise on applications in inorganic and organic chemistry.

G. B. B. M. Sutherland, *Infrared and Raman Spectroscopy*, Methuen, London, 1935. A classic by a pioneer in the field.

F. Twyman and C. B. Allsopp, *The Practice of Absorption Spectrophotometry*, 2nd ed., Hilger, London, 1934. Still valuable although instrumentation has greatly changed since the publication of this work.

J. W. T. Walsh, *Photometry*, 2nd ed., Constable and Co., London, 1953. Covers the physics of photometry.

W. West, two articles in *Physical Methods of Organic Chemistry*, A. Weissberger, Ed., Vol. I, Part 2, Interscience, New York, 1949. An introductory treatment.

W. West, Ed., *Chemical Applications of Spectroscopy*, Interscience, New York, 1956.

E. B. Wilson, Jr., J. C. Decius, and P. C. Cross, *Molecular Vibrations*, McGraw-Hill, New York, 1955. Authoritative theoretical treatment.

J. H. Yoe, *Photometric Chemical Analysis*, 2 vols., Wiley, New York, 1928–1929. A classical work.

b. Reviews

R. B. Barnes and R. C. Gore, *Anal. Chem.*, **21,** 7 (1949). Review of progress in infrared spectrometry.

R. C. Gore, *Anal. Chem.*, **22**, 7 (1950); **23**, 7 (1951); **24**, 8 (1952); **26**, 11 (1954); **28**, 577 (1956). Review of progress in infrared methods.

R. C. Hirt, *Anal. Chem.*, **28**, 579 (1956). Review of ultraviolet absorption spectrometry.

M. G. Mellon, *Anal. Chem.*, **21**, 3 (1949); **22**, 2 (1950); **23**, 2 (1951); **24**, 2 (1952); **26**, 2 (1954); M. G. Mellon and D. F. Boltz, *ibid.*, **28**, 559 (1956). Review of filter photometry and spectrophotometry in the visible and near ultraviolet ranges.

E. J. Rosenbaum, *Anal. Chem.*, **21**, 16 (1949); **22**, 14 (1950); **23**, 12 (1951); **23**, 14 (1952); **26**, 20 (1954). Review of absorption spectrometry in the ultraviolet range.

The following reviews in which physical chemistry is emphasized may also be consulted: B. L. Crawford, Jr., and D. E. Mann, *Ann. Rev. Phys. Chem.*, **1**, 151 (1950); L. G. S. Brooker and W. T. Simpson, *ibid.*, **2**, 121 (1951); N. S. Bayliss, *ibid.*, **3**, 229 (1952); G. B. B. M. Sutherland, *ibid.*, **4**, 189 (1953); A. B. F. Duncan, *ibid.*, **5**, 185 (1954); H. Sponer, *ibid.*, **6**, 193 (1955); R. M. Badger, **6**, 217 (1955); M. Kasha and S. P. McGlynn, *ibid.*, **7**, 403 (1956); R. S. Halford and I. Ichishima, *ibid.*, **7**, 425 (1956); S. Mizushima and T. Shimanouchi, *ibid.*, **7**, 445 (1956).

Volume 9 of the *Discussions of the Faraday Society* (1950) contains an important collection of papers on spectroscopy and molecular structure.

9–9. PROBLEMS

a. Extension of Theory

1. Show that the wave number for a harmonic oscillator is

$$\nu = 1307 \sqrt{k/\mu} \text{ cm}^{-1}$$

where k is the force constant of the oscillator, and μ is the reduced mass defined by

$$\frac{1}{\mu} = \frac{1}{M_1} + \frac{1}{M_2}.$$

M_1 and M_2 are the masses of the atoms of the oscillator expressed in atomic mass units. See physical chemistry text for a discussion of the harmonic oscillator.

2. Show that the point having the abscissa $T = 0.368$ is the point of inflection of the plot of $1-T$ versus log C (Ringbom plot).

3. Evaluate the accuracy of differential photometric measurements. See C. F. Hiskey, *Anal. Chem.*, **21**, 1440 (1949); C. F. Hiskey, J. Rabinowitz, and I. G. Young, *ibid.*, **22**, 1464 (1950); C. F. Hiskey and I. G. Young, *ibid.*, **23**, 1196 (1951); R. Bastian, *ibid.*, **21**, 972 (1949).

4. Make a plot of absorbancy against concentration in the range $10^{-2} - 10^{-4} M$ for a weak acid having a dissociation constant of $10^{-6.12}$. The absorbancy of the $10^{-2} M$ solution is 1.10 (assume $a = 0$ for the acid form). It can be assumed for the sake of simplicity that the dissociation constant is independent of the acid concentration.

5. The equilibrium constant for the transformation $X_2 \rightleftharpoons 2 X$ of a substance X existing as a monomer and a dimer in solution is K. Calculate the absorbancy of a

solution of this substance as a function of the total analytical concentration. Call ϵ_m and ϵ_d the molar absorptivities of the monomer and dimer, respectively. Apply your treatment to the data reported by E. Rabinovitch and L. F. Epstein [*J. Am. Chem. Soc.*, **63**, 69 (1941)] for methylene blue.

6. Discuss the method of J. A. Perry, R. G. Sutherland, and N. Hadden [*Anal. Chem.*, **22**, 1122 (1950)] for the analysis of multicomponent systems by spectrophotometry.

7. Discuss errors in the spectrophotometric analysis of multicomponent systems. See C. F. Hiskey and D. Firestone, *Anal. Chem.*, **24**, 342 (1952).

8. Show that the maximum in the plot of Fig. 98 for the method of continuous variations has the abscissa $C_X/C_Y = 1/m$.

9. Discuss the application of the method of continuous variations to reactions involving the formation of several substances. See W. C. Vosburgh and G. R. Cooper, *J. Am. Chem. Soc.*, **63**, 437 (1941); R. K. Gould and W. C. Vosburgh, *ibid.*, **64**, 1630 (1942).

b. Application of Theory and Literature Survey

10. Dithizone (diphenylthiocarbazone) is a weak acid ($K_d = 1.5 \times 10^{-5}$) and an excellent reagent for the photometric determination of many metals. The metal derivative is generally extracted with a solvent (chloroform, carbon tetrachloride) immiscible with water. Study the influence of pH on the efficiency of separation of metal dithizonates from the aqueous phase. See E. B. Sandell, *Colorimetric Determination of Traces of Metals*, 2nd ed., Interscience, New York, pp. 91–96.

11. Discuss the photometric determination of traces of cadmium, copper, lead, mercury, and zinc by dithizone. See reference in problem 10.

12. Discuss the extraction of hydroxyquinolates by organic solvents. See S. Lacroix, *Anal. Chim. Acta*, **1**, 260 (1947); C. H. R. Gentry and L. G. Sherrington, *Analyst*, **75**, 17 (1950).

13. Discuss the application of 8-hydroxyquinoline to the photometric determination of traces of aluminum and magnesium. See references in problems 10 and 12.

14. Select a suitable organic reagent for the determination of traces of the following metals and discuss briefly the corresponding photometric procedures: antimony, beryllium, bismuth, cobalt, chromium, nickel, silver, and zirconium. Use Sandell's book (reference in problem 10) as a source.

15. Discuss the use of o-phenanthroline in the photometric determination of iron. See Sandell's book (reference in problem 10).

16. Discuss the photometric determination of the following substances: acetaldehyde, α-amino acids, ascorbic acid, ethylenediaminetetraacetic acid, and glucose. See references in M. G. Mellon and D. F. Boltz, *Anal. Chem.*, **28**, 559 (1956).

17. Review the applications of hydrogen peroxide as a reagent in the photometric determination of titanium and vanadium. See Sandell's book referred to in problem 10.

18. Discuss the direct spectrophotometric determination of nitrate by absorption in the ultraviolet range. See A. Dolance and P. W. Healy, *Ind. Eng. Chem., Anal. Ed.*, **17**, 718 (1945).

19. Discuss the photometric determination of nitrites with the Griess reagent. See B. F. Rider and M. G. Mellon, *Ind. Eng. Chem., Anal. Ed.*, **18**, 96 (1946).

20. Discuss the photometric determination of phosphate by reduction of the phosphomolybdic complex. See D. F. Boltz and M. G. Mellon, *Anal. Chem.*, 19, 873 (1947).

21. Discuss the use of ethylenediaminetetraacetic acid as a reagent in photometric titrations. See P. B. Sweetser and C. E. Bricker, *Anal. Chem.*, 25, 253 (1953); 26, 195 (1954).

22. Discuss the photometric titration of iron with permanganate and dichromate. See references in the review of R. F. Goddu and D. N. Hume, *Anal. Chem.*, 26, 1740 (1954).

23. Discuss the photometric titration of weak acids. See review of R. F. Goddu and D. N. Hume, *Anal. Chem.*, 26, 1679 (1954).

24. Discuss bromate photometric titrations in the ultraviolet range. See P. B. Sweetser and C. E. Bricker, *Anal. Chem.*, 24, 1107 (1952).

25. Prepare a seminar on titrations with chelating agents. See G. Schwarzenbach, *Die Komplexometrische Titration*, Enke, Stuttgart, 1955.

26. Discuss the method of Bjerrum's formation function in the study of complexes. See J. Bjerrum, *Metal Ammine Formation in Aqueous Solution*, Haase and Son, Copenhagen, 1941. See also application to the study of the complexes of copper (II) with salicylaldehyde-5-sulfonic acid [M. Calvin and N. C. Melchior, *J. Am. Chem. Soc.*, 70, 3270, 3273 (1948)].

27. Study the spectrophotometric determination of the ionization constants of 8-hydroxyquinoline from tne variation of absorbancy (in the ultraviolet range) with pH. See J. P. Philips and L. L. Merritt, Jr., *J. Am. Chem. Soc.*, 70, 410 (1948).

28. A typical application of the method of continuous variations is the study of the complex of iron (III) with sulfosalicylic acid. Discuss this application on the basis of the paper of R. T. Foley and R. C. Anderson, *J. Am. Chem. Soc.*, 70, 1195 (1948).

29. Discuss some typical applications of ultraviolet absorption spectrometry to the determination of inorganic substances. See the review of E. J. Rosenbaum, *Anal. Chem.*, 26, 20 (1954); R. C. Hirt, *ibid.*, 28, 579 (1956).

30. Discuss the use of punched cards in qualitative analysis by infrared spectrometry. See A. W. Baker, N. Wright, and A. Opler, *Anal. Chem.*, 25, 1457 (1953).

31. Give a general review of the qualitative analysis of hydrocarbons by infrared spectrometry.[91] See H. L. McMurry and V. Thornton, *Anal. Chem.*, 24, 318 (1952); A. Pozefsky and N. D. Coggeshall, *ibid.*, 23, 1611 (1951); N. Sheppard and D. M. Simpson, *Quart. Rev.*, 6, 1 (1952); 7, 19 (1953).

32. Discuss the technique of C. R. Burch [*Proc. Phys. Soc. (London)*, 59, 41 (1947)] for infrared microscopic examination.

33. Review the application of photoconductive cells in infrared spectrometry (see references in footnotes 61 to 65 of text).

34. Discuss the application of infrared spectrometry to the structure determination of penicillin. See H. W. Thompson, R. R. Brattain, H. M. Randall, and R. S. Rasmussen, *Chemistry of Penicillin*, Princeton University Press, Princeton, N.J., 1949, pp. 382–414.

35. Discuss the distortion of spectrograms that results from an increase in the half-intensity width of a spectrometer. See references in footnotes 47 to 49 in text.

[91]For a list of numerous applications in organic chemistry, see (for instance) R. C. Gore, *Anal. Chem.*, 26, 11 (1954).

10

Fluorometry, Turbidimetry, and Nephelometry

10-1. MOLECULAR INTERPRETATION OF FLUORESCENCE

The term *fluorescence* was coined in 1852 by Stokes,[1] who derived it from "fluor-spar," a fluorescent mineral (calcium fluoride). Several thousand papers have now been published on this phenomenon, but most of them deal with the physics and physical chemistry of fluorescence and phosphorescence. Applications to analytical chemistry have become quite common only since the development of *fluorophotometers*, i.e., instruments equipped with phototubes or barrier layer cells for the measurement of fluorescence intensities. The first of these instruments was described, to the writer's knowledge, by Cohen[2] in 1935. Applications of fluorometry to analysis first dealt with the determination of naturally fluorescent substances, especially those of biochemical importance (vitamins). Extension to inorganic and organic substances which do not exhibit any fluorescence was made possible by the discovery of reactions yielding fluorescent products. Many investigators have contributed to the development of fluorescence as an analytical tool, but only a few can be mentioned: Bowen, Grant, and Radley in England; Danckwortt and Kortüm in Germany; and White in the United States.

Fuorescence and phosphorescence can be interpreted by a diagram

[1] G. Stokes, *Phil. Trans.*, **142**, 463 (1852).
[2] F. H. Cohen, *Rec. trav. chim.*, **54**, 133 (1935).

showing the variations of the potential energy of a diatomic molecule XY with interatomic distance[3] (Fig. 101). This diagram was discussed in some detail in Section 9–2, where it was pointed out that electronic excitation of the molecule XY corresponds to a transition from the energy level BC to D. The excited molecule, which has an average life of the order of 10^{-8} sec, loses energy because of collisions with adjacent molecules (10^{-12} sec) and reaches the energy level EF. In most cases there is further degradation of energy in the form of heat, and the molecule returns to the level BC. For some substances having rather stable excited states the transition from the level EF to G is observed with emission of fluorescence or

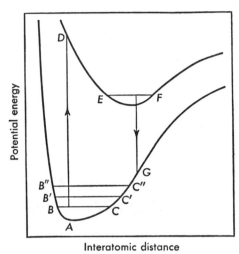

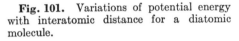

Fig. 101. Variations of potential energy with interatomic distance for a diatomic molecule.

phosphorescence. This transition, which occurs in a very short time in comparison with the period of vibration of the molecule XY, can thus be represented by a vertical line in Fig. 101. Emission of radiation by fluorescence practically stops about 10^{-8} sec—the average life of an excited molecule—after irradiation by the exciting radiation. However, certain substances remain in metastable excited states for much longer periods, perhaps up to several hours or even weeks, and radiation is then re-emitted by *phosphorescence*. The latter phenomenon is of great technological importance (screen of cathode-ray tubes, television tubes, etc.), but it is not within the scope of this discussion. For details, see, for instance,[4] Pringsheim's monograph listed in Section 10–6. Both fluorescence and phosphorescence are designated by the general term of *luminescence*.

Because of the large number of possible excited states, a band spectrum rather than a line spectrum is observed in the fluorescence of solids and liquids. *This band covers a range of wave lengths which are almost always longer than the wave length range of the exciting radiation (Stokes' law).*

---

[3]For a more detailed discussion see the monographs of Bowen and Wokes and Pringsheim listed in Section 10–6.

[4]See also, G. R. Fonda and F. Seitz, Eds., *Preparation and Characteristics of Solid Luminescent Materials*, Wiley, New York, 1948; G. F. J. Garlick, *Luminescent Materials*, Oxford University Press, London, 1949; F. A. Kröger, *Some Aspects of the Luminescence of Solids*, Elsevier, New York, 1948; H. W. Leverenz, *Introduction to Luminescence of Solids*, Wiley, New York, 1950.

This follows immediately from Fig. 101 and from the equation [see equations (8–2) and (8–4)]

$$\lambda = \frac{ch}{\Delta E},$$ (10–1)

correlating the energy change ΔE and the corresponding wave length λ involved in a transition. The symbol h represents Planck's constant, 6.62×10^{-27} erg sec, in equation (10–1), and c is the velocity of light in vacuum. Thus, the transition EF to G involves a smaller energy change than the transition BC to D, and consequently the fluorescence wave length is longer than for the exciting radiation. For a few rare substances, which do not obey Stokes' law, the excited molecule is first brought to a level above EF before returning to G. This very rare case need not be considered here.

The foregoing discussion dealt with the case of a diatomic molecule, but the results can be generalized to polyatomic molecules and to atoms.

10–2. INTENSITY OF FLUORESCENCE

It can be inferred from the preceding discussion that the intensity of fluorescence is proportional to the absorbed energy. Thus,

$$n_F = qn_A,$$ (10–2)

where n_F is the number of fluorescent quanta, n_A is the number of absorbed quanta, and q ($\leqslant 1$) is the *quantum yield* or *fluorescence efficiency*. The quantum yield is generally smaller than unity because of deactivation of the molecule under the form of heat. Some substances, iodide ion for instance, may also cause deactivation by *quenching* of fluorescence.[5]

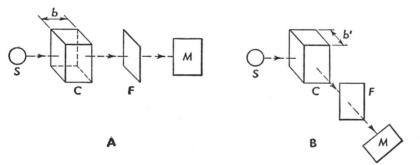

Fig. 102. (A) Measurement of fluorescence intensity. (B) Same as in (A), but with the detector M parallel to the direction of the incident beam of S.

The simple instrument schematically shown in Fig. 102A can be utilized for the measurement of fluorescence intensities in analytical

[5]See, for instance, Bowen and Wokes (reference in Section 10–6) for a simple discussion of possible mechanisms of quenching.

applications. S is a source of a parallel beam of monochromatic radiation; C is a cuvette containing the fluorescent solution; F filters out completely the radiation from source S, but transmits the fluorescence radiation; and M is an instrument measuring the intensity of fluorescence. The instrument of Fig. 102A does not enable one to obtain the quantum yield because the fluorescence intensity is not measured in all directions, but the intensity of fluorescence, as measured by instrument M, is nevertheless proportional to the intensity of absorbed radiation. A relationship for the fluorescence intensity obtained under such conditions can be readily derived as follows:

The intensity of absorbed radiation is calculated from the Beer-Lambert law and by application of equation (9–15), i.e.,

$$\log \frac{P_s}{P} = abC, \tag{10-3}$$

where a is the absorptivity of the fluorescent substance, b the thickness of the layer of solution in cuvette C, and C the concentration of fluorescent substance in grams per liter. P_s and P are proportional to the readings on instrument M for the solvent alone and the solution of fluorescent material, respectively, in an experiment in which F is replaced by a filter opaque to fluorescence but transparent to the incident radiation. It should be noted that the Beer-Lambert law cannot be applied in some cases (Chapter 9), and the following treatment is then approximate.

The radiation absorbed by the fluorescent substance is proportional to $P_s - P$, and the intensity of fluorescence F, as measured by instrument M, is

$$F = p(P_s - P) \tag{10-4}$$

where p (<1) is a proportionality constant. One deduces from equation (10–3)

$$\frac{P_s}{P} = \frac{1}{10^{-abC}}, \tag{10-5}$$

or

$$\frac{P_s - P}{P_s} = \frac{1 - 10^{-abC}}{1}. \tag{10-6}$$

Hence,

$$P_s - P = P_s(1 - 10^{-abC}), \tag{10-7}$$

and in view of equation (10–4),

$$F = pP_s(1 - 10^{-abC}). \tag{10-8}$$

Variations of F with the dimensionless group abC are shown in Fig. 103. If abC is sufficiently large, the term 10^{-abC} virtually vanishes and

$$F_m = pP_s \tag{10-9}$$

For $abC \leqslant 0.01$, one can write with a good approximation by expanding the exponential function,[6]

$$F \approx 2.303 p P_s abC. \tag{10-10}$$

Equation (10–8) is sometimes written in a different form by introduction of the intensity F_m defined by equation (10–9). Thus,

$$F = F_m(1 - 10^{-abC}), \tag{10-11}$$

or

$$\frac{F - F_m}{F_m} = -10^{-abC}. \tag{10-12}$$

Hence,

$$\log \frac{F_m}{F_m - F} = abC. \tag{10-13}$$

The fluorescence intensity is practically proportional to the concentration of fluorescent substance, *provided that $abC \leqslant 0.01$*. In practice, equation (10–10) holds for concentrations up to a few parts per million.

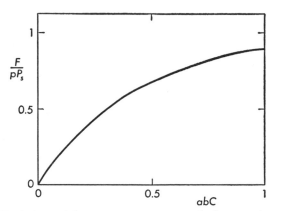

Fig. 103. Variations of fluorescence intensity with the quantity abC, according to equation (10-8).

Since F is proportional to P_s, i.e., to the energy output of source S, it would appear that one could determine extremely low concentrations by increasing sufficiently P_s. This would be a distinct advantage over filter photometry in which the lowest measurable concentration depends on the possibility of determining small differences between P and P_s [see equation (10–3)]. Actually, the fluorescence of the "blank" and possible quenching by impurities limit the application of fluorometry to very low concentrations. Nevertheless, the method can often be applied in the concentration range where filter photometry ceases to yield reasonably accurate results.

[6]Note that $10^{-abC} = e^{-2.303abC}$ and that $e^{-x} = 1 - x + x^2/2! \cdots$. Hence, $1 - 10^{-abC} \approx 2.303\, abC$ for $abC \leqslant 0.01$.

It was assumed above that the detector of instrument M in Fig. 102A is placed directly in the path of the parallel beam of source S. This detector is generally sensitive to the exciting radiation, which thus must be filtered out *completely*. This condition is quite stringent, and it is more advantageous to set the detector at 90 deg. with respect to the incident beam (Fig. 102B). Scattered incident light is absorbed by filter F in this layout. Equation (10–10) still holds under such conditions *but b must now be replaced by b', the depth of the cuvette in the direction perpendicular to the incident beam.* This is quite obvious: If the depth b' is doubled, all other conditions being the same, the number of fluorescent molecules per unit of time is doubled, and consequently the intensity of fluorescence read on instrument M is doubled.[7]

10–3. FLUOROPHOTOMETERS

The principle of fluorophotometers[8] was discussed in Section 10–2, and it was pointed out that the layout of Fig. 102B is often preferred to that of Fig. 102A.

The source of radiation is generally a mercury arc with a filter of Wood's glass (nickel silicate) to eliminate practically all the visible radiation except in the violet range. The strong mercury line at 3650 A is mainly transmitted in the ultraviolet range. Mercury arc lamps with a suitable phosphor (360 B-L), which converts the strong mercury line at 2537 A into radiation in the range 3000 to 4000 A, are also useful.[9]

Since the fluorescence intensity is proportional to the intensity of irradiation, the source must be very stable if fluctuations in its intensity are not compensated for. Such a stringent requirement is not imposed on the source in two-cell instruments.[10] The output of the mercury lamp S (Fig. 104) is filtered by F_1 (see above), and the resulting beam is split by a mirror into two beams which fall on the cuvette C_1, containing the analyzed solution, and a second cuvette C_2, respectively. Scattered incident radiation is absorbed by filters F_2 and F_3. Detectors T_1 and T_2 are placed in front of the faces of cuvettes C_1 and C_2 parallel to the incident beam (arrangement of Fig. 102B). Detector T_2 is not directly in the path of the incident beam for the following reason:

The response of a phototube or a barrier layer cell depends on wave length (see Figs. 76 and 87) and is therefore not the same for the incident beam and for the fluorescence radiation. Fluctuations of the source in-

---

[7] This is virtually correct, provided that the distance between cuvette and detector is very large in comparison with b'.

[8] "Visual" instruments somewhat similar to colorimeters were used for many years, but are seldom utilized nowadays.

[9] See *Eng. Bull.* 0–72 (1948) of Sylvania Electric Products, Boston.

[10] G. Kortüm, *Z. phys. Chem.*, **40B**, 431 (1938).

tensity are not compensated under such conditions unless the symmetrical arrangement of Fig. 104 with two cuvettes is adopted. Cuvette C_2 may contain the analyzed fluorescent solution at a known concentration or a solution of a substance such as quinine sulfate or fluorescein, whose fluorescence band coincides fairly well with that of the analyzed solution. A

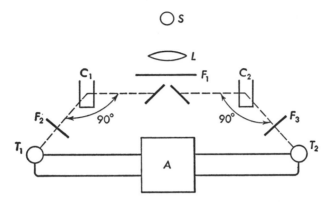

Fig. 104. Schematic diagram of two-cell fluorophotometer.

fluorescent glass can be substituted for cuvette C_2, provided that its fluorescence band is not too different from that of the solution in cuvette 1. The preparation of fluorescent glasses which fulfill this condition has been reported for various analyses (riboflavin, thiamine, beryllium, etc.).

Detectors T_1 and T_2 are connected to a balance circuit as in two-cell filter photometers (Fig. 88). Since weak fluorescence intensities generally must be measured, T_1 and T_2 are phototubes, or rather photomultiplier tubes, connected to amplifiers. Balance is achieved either by an electrical method similar to that applied in filter photometry or by an optical method in which the intensity of the beam impinging on one of the detectors, T_2 generally, is reduced by a diaphragm or a pair of polarizers. In either case, a calibration curve is constructed with standards prepared under exactly the same conditions as the analyzed solution (temperature, pH, ionic strength, time for development of fluorescence, etc.). Calibration with the blank is essential because of fluorescent impurities.

Very pure reagents must be utilized to avoid possible quenching by impurities. Since the quantum yield, and consequently the coefficient p in equation (10–8), does not vary rapidly with temperature,[11] (perhaps 1 to 2 per cent per degree), thermostatic control of the solutions is not required. However, variations in temperature exceeding more than 1 to 2° must be avoided.

[11]The quantum yield generally decreases as temperature increases.

The complete fluorescence spectrum is determined by replacing the detector M of Fig. 102B by a spectrograph or a spectrophotometer. The latter type of instrument is now preferred, and attachments for commercial spectrometers have been described by several authors[12] and have become commercially available (Beckman).

Commercial fluorophotometers are available from quite a few manufacturers (Cenco, Coleman, Farrand, Fisher, Hilger, Klett, Lumetron, Pfaltz and Bauer, Photovolt, etc.).

10-4. APPLICATIONS OF FLUOROMETRY

Fluorometry is generally applied when filter photometry is not satisfactory because either no suitable reagent is available (a rather rare case) or the concentration of analyzed substance is too low. The two methods complement one another very well.

The sensitivity of the method is generally excellent, as was pointed out in Section 10-2, and a few parts per million, or even less, can be determined in many instances. The accuracy is good, and results with an error as small as 1 to 3 per cent can be obtained on a routine basis with commercial instruments and without any elaborate technique. The selectivity varies greatly from one system to another. Reagents, as in filter photometry, are generally not specific, but reactions can be made specific by judicious choice of experimental conditions.

Numerous applications have been described, as the reader can ascertain by consulting the books of Danckwortt, Radley and Grant, and the periodic reviews of White referred to in Section 10-6. Procedures for the fluorometric determination of several elements are given by Sandell,[13] and in general, in books on filter photometry; many reactions yielding fluorescent products can be found in Feigl's book.[14]

The fluorometric determination of certain substances of biochemical interest, such as riboflavin, thiamine, vitamin A, and folic acid, have become classical. Applications to organic chemistry are relatively limited, but methods have been developed for substances such as glycerol and formaldehyde. Fluorometric methods for elements such as aluminum, beryllium, boron, uranium, and zinc have been investigated in detail. Some of these elements (boron, for instance) cannot be conveniently analyzed by filter photometry because of lack of a suitable reagent.

Many organic reagents have been useful in inorganic applications of

[12]See, for instance, F. B. Huke, R. H. Heidel, and R. H. Fassel, *J. Optical Soc. Am.*, **43**, 400 (1953).

[13]E. B. Sandell, *Colorimetric Determination of Traces of Metals*, 2nd ed., Interscience, New York, 1950.

[14]F. Feigl, *Spot Tests*, 4th ed., 2 vols., translation of R. E. Oesper, Elsevier, Houston, 1954.

fluorometry, but two of them, 8-hydroxyquinoline and morin,[15] have been particularly valuable and versatile. Molten salts may be useful solvents; as, for example, in the analysis of uranium in a solid flux of sodium fluoride or sodium fluoride-sodium carbonate mixture.[16]

The application of fluorescence to forensic chemistry can only be mentioned here, but the curious reader may find ample material on this subject in Danckwortt's book.

Specific applications are suggested as literature surveys in Section 10–7.

10–5. TURBIDIMETRY AND NEPHELOMETRY

Turbidimetry is based on the measurement of light transmitted by a suspension of particles. *Nephelometry* involves the measurement of the intensity of light scattered by a suspension. Techniques in analytical applications of these two methods resemble closely those of filter photometry and fluorometry, respectively. Turbidimetric and nephelometric methods are of minor importance as analytical tools, and no special chapter is devoted to their discussion in this text.

Two cases can be considered, depending on whether or not the particles in suspension are transparent in the wave length range of the incident beam. Only scattering of light must be considered for transparent particles, whereas both scattering and absorption must be taken into consideration for opaque particles.

Scattering of monochromatic radiation by a suspension of particles does not result in a change of wave length, but the intensity of scattered light does vary with wave length. If the average diameter of the particles is smaller than about one-tenth of the wave length of the incident beam, the intensity of scattered light is inversely proportional to the fourth power of wave length. Thus, blue light is scattered more strongly than red light. The intensity of scattered light depends on the number and size of particles in suspension, and analytical applications are thus possible, provided that the average size of particles is fairly reproducible. This requires that the concentration of reagents, the rate of mixing of reagents, the conditions of stirring, and the temperature be as identical as feasible in comparative experiments. A protective colloid (gelatin) is added to the solution to avoid the separation of a heavy precipitate, which would, of course, prevent any further measurements.

[15]This is 3, 5, 7, 2', 4'-flavone, or

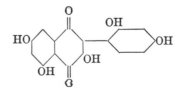

[16]C. J. Rodden, *Anal. Chem.*, **21**, 327 (1949).

Turbidimetric measurements can be carried out with a filter photometer. Monochromatic light is not required. A calibration curve is constructed, and a linear relationship between absorbancy and concentration of analyzed substance is generally obtained. Turbidimetric titrations similar to photometric titrations were first discussed by Ringbom.[17] Some applications have been made[18] (see problem 5, Section 10–7).

Nephelometric determinations can be made with a fluorophometer equipped with two cuvettes. The source is a light bulb rather than a mercury arc. A standard solution is placed in one cuvette, and the unknown in the other, both solutions being prepared *simultaneously* under identical conditions. The output meter of the instrument is balanced as in fluorophotometry, and a calibration curve of instrument reading against concentration is plotted.

The advantages of turbidimetry and nephelometry are simplicity of instrumentation and rapidity of measurement. Since there is the danger of obtaining erratic results, these methods are applied only when results need not be very accurate and when other instrumental or noninstrumental methods are too tedious. A classical application is the determination of sulfur as barium sulfate, which requires only a few minutes in routine work. The reader can find the description of numerous applications in the book of Yoe and Kleinmann.[19]

Of much greater inportance than the analytical applications of nephelometry is the determination of molecular weights for macromolecules by light scattering. The fundamental paper of Debye[20] and reviews by Oster[21,22] may be consulted for the details.

10–6. BIBLIOGRAPHY

a. Books

E. J. Bowen, *The Chemical Aspects of Light*, 2nd ed., Oxford University Press, London, 1946. Excellent nonmathematical presentation.

E. J. Bowen and F. Wokes, *Fluorescence of Solutions*, Longmans, Green and Co., New York, 1953. Excellent introduction.

M. Curie, *Fluorescence et Phosphorescence*, Hermann, Paris, 1946. See particularly the discussion of the relationship between fluorescence and constitution of organic substances.

P. W. Danckwortt, *Lumineszenz-Analyse in filtrierten ultra-violetten Licht*, 5th ed.,

[17]A. Ringbom, *Z. Anal. Chem.*, **122**, 263 (1941).
[18]For a review, see R. F. Goddu and D. N. Hume, *Anal. Chem.*, **26**, 1740 (1954).
[19]J. H. Yoe and H. Kleinmann, Vol. 2 of *Photometric Chemical Analysis*, Wiley, New York, 1929.
[20]P. Debye, *J. Phys. Colloid Chem.*, **51**, 18 (1947).
[21]G. Oster, *Chem. Revs.*, **43**, 319 (1948).
[22]G. Oster, chapter in *Progress in Biophysics*, J. A. V. Butler and J. T. Randall, Eds., Academic Press, New York, 1950.

Geest and Portig, Leipzig, 1949. Discusses applications with numerous references.

P. Pringsheim, *Fluorescence and Phosphorescence*, Interscience, New York, 1949. A classical work on fundamentals.

J. A. Radley and J. Grant, *Fluorescence Analysis in Ultraviolet Light*, 4th ed., Van Nostrand, New York, 1954. Good discussion of applications.

W. West, article in *Physical Methods of Organic Chemistry*, A. Weissberger, Ed., Vol. I, Part 2, Interscience, New York, 1949. An introductory treatment.

b. Reviews

C. E. White, *Anal. Chem.*, **21,** 104 (1949); **22,** 69 (1950); **24,** 85 (1952); **26,** 129 (1954); **28,** 621 (1956).

10-7. PROBLEMS

The books of Danckwortt, Randley and Grant, and Sandell, and White's reviews will be most valuable in answering problems 2 to 4.

1. The fluoride content of air can be determined continuously by the following method: A paper tape impregnated with magnesium-8-quinolinol passes slowly in the air sample and the intensity of the fluorescence resulting from traces of fluoride is recorded. Make a detailed study of this method by referring to the original article: S. W. Chaikin and T. D. Glassbrook, *Research for Industry*, **5,** 2 (1953).

Could a reagent yielding a colored product, not a fluorescent one, be used in this method? Discuss the matter by considering diffusion of reagents in the tape, etc.

2. Discuss the determination of uranium according to the method described in the reference of footnote 16.

3. Make a survey of the fluorometric determination of the following elements: (a) aluminum; (b) beryllium; (c) boron; (d) gallium; (e) uranium; (f) zinc.

4. Discuss some typical applications of fluorescence to the determination of chromatographic zones.

5. Discuss the turbidimetric titration of aluminum, magnesium, and copper with 8-hydroxyquinoline. See M. Bobtelsky and Y. Welwart, *Anal. Chim. Acta.*, **10,** 151, 156, 459, 464 (1954).

11

Raman Spectroscopy

11–1. MOLECULAR INTERPRETATION

Gases, liquids, and crystals scatter monochromatic radiation mainly without change in wave length (*Rayleigh scattering*) by a process which was accounted for more than fifty years ago on the basis of the classical electromagnetic theory.[1] Scattering with change in wave length (*Raman effect* or *Smekal-Raman effect*) was predicted by Smekal[2] in 1923 and first observed in 1928 by Landsberg and Mandelstam[3] in crystals and by Raman[4,5] in liquids. Investigations in Raman spectroscopy have proved most valuable in the interpretation of molecular structure and the calculation of thermodynamic data (Bhagavantam, Cabannes, Crawford, Goubeau, Herzberg, Hibben, Kohlrausch, Krishnan, Placzek, Sutherland, Wilson, etc.) for more than twenty-five years, but widespread analytical applications are far more recent—they had to await the development of direct-recording Raman spectrometers about 1945–1950 (Rank and others).

Light scattering by molecules can be readily explained by the classical electromagnetic theory. Atoms or molecules, which are polarized in an electrical field, re-emit radiation if the electrical field varies periodically, as is the case for the electrical component of light. Incident and scattered radiation have the same frequency if variations in the distances between atoms in the scattering molecules are neglected, as in Rayleigh scattering.

---

[1] J. W. S. Rayleigh, *Phil. Mag.*, **47**, 375 (1899).
[2] A. Smekal, *Naturwissenschaften.*, **11**, 873 (1923).
[3] G. Landsberg and L. Mandelstam, *ibid.*, **16**, 557 (1928).
[4] C. V. Raman, *Indian J. Phys.*, **2**, 387 (1928); *Nature*, **121**, 619 (1928).
[5] C. V. Raman and R. S. Krishnan, *Nature*, **121**, 501 (1928).

The intensity of scattering, however, depends on frequency and is proportional to the fourth power of frequency.[6] Actually, interatomic distances in molecules vary, and vibrational frequencies of the scattering molecules are superimposed on the fundamental frequency of the incident beam[7] (Raman spectrum). The resulting shift in wave number $\Delta\sigma$ can be quite pronounced as can be seen from the data for carbon tetrachloride in Table XVI. The Raman lines are symmetrical in the frequency scale (not in the

TABLE XVI

Raman Lines for Carbon Tetrachloride Irradiated with the 4358 A Line of the Mercury Arc[a]

WAVE LENGTH, A	WAVE NUMBER SHIFT $\Delta\sigma$, cm^{-1}	
4273	459	Anti-Stokes
4300	314	lines
4317	218	
4358	0	Incident radiation
4400	218	
4419	314	
4447	459	Stokes lines
4508	762	
4514	791	

[a]Data from J. H. Hibben, *The Raman Effect and its Chemical Applications*, Reinhold, New York, 1939, p. 138.

wave length scale) with respect to the frequency of the incident radiation. *Anti-Stokes lines* have shorter wave lengths than the exciting radiation, whereas the opposite holds for *Stokes lines* according to a nomenclature derived from Stokes' law for fluorescence (see Section 10–1). Anti-Stokes lines are much weaker than Stokes lines and are difficult to observe with most substances.

Since Raman lines are caused by the superposition of the vibrational frequencies of the scattering molecules upon the frequency of the exciting radiation, *shifts in wave number must be independent of the frequency of the incident radiation*. Experiment confirms this deduction. This property of Raman lines contrasts with fluorescence bands which have a well-defined position in the wave-length scale.

The intensity of Raman lines varies with the wave length of the incident radiation and is proportional to the fourth power of frequency, as for Rayleigh scattering. Thus, weak lines are easier to observe in the lowest

[6]This holds for particles whose "diameter" is small (less than one-tenth) in comparison with the wave length of the incident beam. This is the case for the scattering of light by molecules but is not so for macromolecules. This dependence of intensity on wave length accounts for the blue color of the sky; blue light is scattered by air several times more intensely than red light.

[7]For a simple mathematical treatment, see for instance R. C. Johnson, *An Introduction to Molecular Spectra*, Pitman, New York, 1949, pp. 254–257.

possible range of wave lengths at which observation is not prevented by absorption of the incident radiation.

Raman shifts result from molecular vibrations and correspond to the vibrational frequencies of the infrared spectrogram of the scattering

TABLE XVII
Comparison between Raman Wave Number Shifts and Infrared Wave Numbers[a]

GROUP	RAMAN SHIFT, cm^{-1}	INFRARED WAVE NUMBER,[b] cm^{-1}
OH	3400	3000–3700
CH	2800–3100	2700–3300
C$=$O	1700–1800	1640–1850
C$=$N	1650	1580–1700
C$=$C	1600–1650	1580–1700

[a]Raman shift from W. R. Brode, *Chemical Spectroscopy*, 2nd ed., Wiley, New York, 1943, p. 277.
[b]Infrared wave number for stretching; data from Table XII in Chapter 9.

molecules (Table XVII). Raman spectroscopy, therefore, finds application in frequency assignment, especially when the infrared spectrometry cannot be applied. It should be emphasized that certain vibration frequencies are observed in infrared spectrometry but not in the Raman method and *vice versa*. This difference in behavior will not be discussed here, and reference will be made to Hibben's monograph (p. 62–68), for instance, listed in Section 11–4.

It is useful in the assignment of frequencies to determine the *depolarization factor* of Raman lines. This factor can be defined as follows:

The substance being studied is irradiated with polarized light and the intensity of a given Raman line is measured in two separate experiments in which the plane of vibration of the polarized light is either parallel $(I_{\parallel})$ or perpendicular $(I_{\perp})$ to the axis of the Raman tube of Fig. 105. The depolarization factor then is

$$\rho = \frac{I_{\parallel}}{I_{\perp}}. \qquad (1\text{--}11)$$

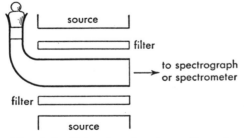

Fig. 105. Tube for the observation of Raman spectrum.

Since the depolarization factor depends on the degree of symmetry of the scattering molecule, its determination is valuable in the assignment of modes of vibration. It can be shown that ρ varies from 0 to 6/7 for Raman lines and from 0 to 1/2 for Rayleigh scattering. In the latter case, ρ is generally close to zero and there is little depolarization of incident radiation. It was customary to state only that a given Raman line was completely or partially depolarized, but quantitative data on ρ are reported nowadays.

The foregoing qualitative interpretation is based on the classical electromagnetic theory. The modern treatment of Raman spectra requires the application of quantum mechanics.[8]

11-2. EXPERIMENTAL METHODS

The apparatus for Raman spectroscopy or spectrometry is fundamentally quite simple, but the weakness of Raman lines in comparison with the intensity of irradiation and even with Rayleigh scattering[9] is a major source of experimental difficulties. The main problem is to reduce to a minimum the continuous background radiation superimposed on the Raman spectrum. The general layout (Fig. 105) comprises a cell (Wood's cell) containing the substance being examined (at least for liquids and gases) and a powerful irradiating source. The scattered light is examined with a spectrograph or a spectrometer through an optically flat window. Cells for liquids generally have a volume of a few milliliters, but volumes as small as 0.02 to 0.05 ml are sufficient if only a small sample is available.

The sample is irradiated with monochromatic light, and one of the lines at 4047 A (violet), 4358 A (blue), 5461 A (green) in the mercury arc is most frequently selected. It is advantageous to utilize a wave length as low as possible since the intensity of scattering is inversely proportional to the fourth power of wave length, but one generally is limited by absorption by the sample in the range of lower wave lengths. Each line of the mercury arc produces its Raman spectrum, and it is therefore essential to filter out all but the line selected for irradiation. The continuous background of the mercury arc must also be eliminated. Two different solutions, which serve as filters, are generally needed for absorbing light at wave lengths below and above the selected mercury line. Detailed information on the preparation of filter solutions is available in the literature,[10] and absorption spectrograms can be found in a paper by Stamm[11] for several of the most commonly used solutions (copper sulfate, sodium chromate, sodium nitrite, iodine in carbon tetrachloride, praseodynium salts, rhodamine dyes, etc.). Glass filters are seldom utilized in Raman work. Interference filters might possibly be advantageous.

The irradiating source should be as powerful as feasible. Furthermore, the continuous background of the source should be as low as possible, and the operating conditions of the mercury arc, such as mercury pressure,

[8]For detailed accounts see the books of Herzberg and Wilson, Decius, and Cross referred to in Section 11-4.
[9]At least this is the case for liquids and gases. Raman and Rayleigh scatterings have intensities of the same order of magnitude for crystals although very weak at any rate.
[10]See Kohlrausch's book in particular (Section 11-4).
[11]R. F. Stamm, *Ind. Eng. Chem., Anal. Ed.*, **17**, 318 (1945).

current, temperature, cooling system, and regulation of the voltage applied to the lamp, should be controlled accordingly. The cell is generally surrounded by a set of four to eight tubular mercury lamps equipped with reflectors and a cooling system. The helicoidal mercury arc lamp developed at Toronto by Crawford and Welsh for Raman spectroscopy of gases is particularly powerful and is available commercially (Applied Research Laboratories).

Because of the weakness of the Raman effect, stray light in the spectrograph should be minimized, for example, by the use of multiprism systems (Fig. 106). The spectrograph should have a reasonably low linear reciprocal dispersion (see Section 8–2a); for instance, 5 to 10 A per millimeter in the wavelength range being used.

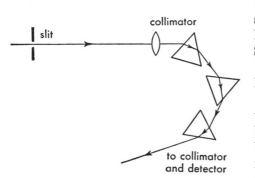

Fig. 106. Schematic diagram of multiprism spectrograph.

Prism spectrographs were universally utilized until 1945–1950 because too much light was lost by diffraction in grating instruments. This trend is now reversed, especially in the United States, because of the development of improved methods for the ruling of gratings, and grating spectrographs are increasingly adopted for Raman work.[12-14]

Photographic recording and photometric examination of the plate according to the usual techniques of emission spectroscopy was the universal practice until 1945–1950, at which time recording Raman spectrometers became quite common. The first of these instruments in the United States was, to the writer's knowledge, designed by Rank and Wiegand.[12] Other similar instruments have been reported, and the considerations entering in their design have been reviewed in some detail.[13,14] Raman spectrometers are similar, in principle at least, to recording spectrophotometers. The light scattered by the Raman tube falls on a dispersing element (prism, grating) which is rotated, and the exit beam passes through a slit and impinges on a photomultiplier tube whose response is amplified and recorded. The position of Raman lines is readily determined and their intensity is measured on the resulting spectrogram (Fig. 107). The detector is a photomultiplier tube, rather than an ordinary phototube, because of the weakness of the Raman effect. The noise level ("dark" current) of the photomultiplier tube,

[12]R. H. Rank and R. V. Wiegand, *J. Optical Soc. Am.*, **36**, 325 (1946).
[13]W. R. Busing, *ibid.*, **42**, 774 (1952).
[14]R. F. Stamm, C. F. Salzman, Jr., and T. Mariner, *ibid.*, **43**, 119, 126, 708 (1953).

which is too high at room temperature in Raman work, is decreased by the cooling of the tube at dry ice or liquid nitrogen temperature.[15] Variations in the intensity of irradiation can be corrected for by a two-cell system

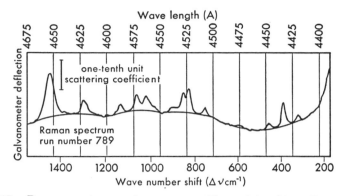

Fig. 107. Raman spectrogram for *n*-pentane. The undulated base line corresponds to the background radiation. [From M. R. Fenske *et al., Anal. Chem.*, **19**, 700 (1947).]

similar in principle to a two-cell filter photometer. Commercial recording Raman spectrometers are available from Applied Research Laboratories and Hilger.

A complete Raman spectrogram for liquids is obtained with a recording spectrometer in 15 to 60 min, depending on the rate of scanning and the details desired in the spectrogram. Exposures of several hours were not uncommon with the photographic method in the pioneering days of the prewar period.

Gases are studied by the photographic method because Raman lines are too weak for direct-recording instruments. Very long exposures, one day perhaps, are necessary with instruments which would require only a 5- to 30-min exposure with liquids.[16] Exposure times are shortened by increase of the gas pressure to a few atmospheres.[17]

Depolarization factors are measured either in one step or in two steps. In the first method the analyzed substance is irradiated by a narrow beam of parallel light in a plane, and the light scattered perpendicularly to the plane is analyzed with a birefringent prism. This method requires a precise geometry of the instrument, and the two-step method developed by Crawford and Horwitz[18] is easier to apply. The cell is surrounded by a Polaroid[19]

[15]For a review on the use of photomultiplier tubes in spectrometry, see P. O. Kinell and P. Traynard, *Acta Chem. Scand.*, **2**, 193 (1948).

[16]J. R. Nielsen and N. E. Ward, *J. Chem. Phys.*, **10**, 81 (1942).

[17]J. S. Kirby-Smith and L. G. Bonner, *J. Chem. Phys.*, **7**, 880 (1939).

[18]B. L. Crawford, Jr., and W. Horwitz, *J. Chem. Phys.*, **15**, 268 (1947); this paper contains references to previous work of Cabannes, Reitz, Wilson, etc.

[19]Sheet of material which polarizes light (Polaroid Corporation).

cylinder, which polarizes light in a plane parallel to the axis of the cell, and the spectrum is recorded. The operation is repeated with another Polaroid cylinder whose plane of polarization is perpendicular to the axis of the cell, and the depolarization factor is finally computed by formula 11–1. This method requires a stable source, since fluctuations in irradiation are reflected by errors on the depolarization factor. This factor can be determined in a similar fashion with a direct-recording spectrometer, as was done by Fenske and co-workers.[20]

It has been customary in physicochemical applications to compare line intensities of a Raman spectrum in a scale of 0 to 10, where 0 corresponds to the weakest line and 10 to the strongest one. This method, however, cannot be applied in the comparison of different spectrograms, which is precisely the operation required in analytical applications. Absolute measurements with a given instrument may be affected by a serious error if care is not taken to compensate for variations of the intensity of irradiation. Comparison between the intensities of lines (as measured by the height of the corresponding peaks on the spectrogram) for the unknown and an external standard (carbon tetrachloride) may be applied to quantitative determinations.[20] The spectrum of the external standard should, of course, be obtained under the same conditions of irradiation as the unknown. In another method developed by Rank, Scott, and Fenske,[21] an internal standard (10 per cent carbon tetrachloride by volume) is added to the sample. The originators[20,21] of this method define the *scattering coefficient* as the ratio of the line intensity for the unknown to the intensity of the 459-cm^{-1} line of carbon tetrachloride.

The internal standard method offers a sound basis for comparing intensities, but it may have two possible disadvantages: (1) there is contamination by the standard; (2) the spectrogram of the standard may overlap with that of the substance being analyzed. A rather inert substance such as carbon tetrachloride is selected as standard to minimize interaction with the analyzed species. Furthermore, carbon tetrachloride is a good solvent for organic substances.[22]

Analytical determinations are simplified when line intensities vary linearly with the concentration of analyzed substance, but this is only the case for nonpolar substances having similar structures. Otherwise, this linearity relationship is not followed, and the position of lines may even depend on concentration as a result of varying conditions for intermolecular interaction. Benzene-dioxane mixtures, for instance, exhibit the latter behavior, and so do aqueous solutions of electrolytes.[23]

[20]M. R. Fenske, W. G. Braun, R. V. Wiegand, D. Quiggle, R. H. McCormick, and D. H. Rank, *Anal. Chem.*, **19**, 700 (1947).

[21]D. H. Rank, R. W. Scott, and M. R. Fenske, *Ind. Eng. Chem., Anal. Ed.*, **14**, 816 (1942).

[22]See also the reference in footnote 11 for a discussion of various schemes of analysis.

[23]T. G. Kujumzelis, *Z. Physik*, **110**, 742 (1938).

11-3. APPLICATIONS AND COMPARISON WITH INFRARED SPECTROMETRY

Raman spectrometry is a qualitative and quantitative tool for the analysis of liquids. Application to gas analysis is not practical because very long exposure times are required, and infrared spectrometry is far more advantageous. The Raman method cannot be applied to the determination of solutions of one constituent in presence of a large excess of another substance, at least when the spectra overlap. The minimum measurable concentration is about 1 per cent, and perhaps 5 to 10 per cent for substances with weak Raman lines. The method is selective, since vibrational frequencies are characteristic of a given species. Accurate results are obtained, especially with direct-recording spectrometers, and errors as low as 1 to 2 per cent are not uncommon.

Since the Raman method supplies information similar, but not necessarily identical, to that obtained by infrared spectrometry, it is of interest to compare the two methods from the viewpoint of their application to chemical analysis. The sample in Raman spectrometry must be almost colorless to avoid absorption, clear to prevent an increase in background radiation by light scattered by particles, and nonfluorescent to minimize background radiation. In general, these conditions need not be fulfilled in infrared spectrometry. It is difficult or impossible to analyze dilute solutions by the Raman method, whereas this is not so for infrared spectrometry. Some substances undergo photochemical decomposition in the wave-length range utilized in the Raman method, whereas this difficulty is not experienced with infrared radiation. These various disadvantages are partially compensated by some other features of the Raman method. Thus, water, which has a simple Raman spectrum, can be utilized as solvent, whereas absorption above 3 μ precludes its use in infrared spectrometry. The wave-length range in *conventional* infrared spectrometry is limited up to 15 to 25 μ and possibly 40 μ. However, large molecules have vibrational frequencies which require spectrometric measurements up to perhaps 200 μ. Such difficult measurements have been made, but wave shifts of 50 cm^{-1}, which correspond to absorption at 200 μ, can be measured more readily by the Raman method with a spectrograph having a sufficiently low linear reciprocal dispersion.

Summarizing, Raman spectrometry is an accurate, specific, and relatively insensitive method of analysis. It cannot compete as an analytical tool on an equal basis with infrared spectrometry, but it has neverthless potentialities in organic analysis (hydrocarbons, etc.). The value of the method, especially as a qualitative tool, is enhanced by the availability of spectrograms recorded under well-controlled conditions with well-purified substances.[24] For specific applications, see literature sources (Section 11-4).

---

[24]Project 44 of the American Petroleum Institute, Bureau of Standards, Washington. See also the reference in footnote 20 for spectrograms of 172 different hydrocarbons.

11–4. BIBLIOGRAPHY

a. Books

S. Bhagavantam, *The Scattering of Light and the Raman Effect*, Brooklyn Chemical Publishing Co., Brooklyn, N.Y., 1942.

J. Goubeau, article in *Physikalische Methoden der Analytischen Chemie*, W. Böttger, Ed., Vol. III, Akademische Verlagsgesellschaft, Leipzig, 1939; reprinted by Edwards, Ann Arbor, Michigan, 1943.

J. Goubeau, *Die Ramanspektren von Olefinen*, Beiheft 56, *Deut. Chem. Z.*, Deutscher Chemiker Verlag Chemie, G. m. b. H., Berlin, 1948.

G. R. Harrison, R. C. Lord, and J. R. Loofbourow, *Practical Spectroscopy*, Prentice-Hall, New York, 1948. See chapter on experimental methods in Raman spectroscopy.

G. Herzberg, *Infrared and Raman Spectra of Polyatomic Molecules*, Van Nostrand, New York, 1945. Classical work on fundamentals.

J. H. Hibben, *Raman Effect and its Chemical Applications*, Reinhold, New York, 1939.

J. H. Hibben, article in *Physical Methods in Chemical Analysis*, W. B. Berl, Ed., Vol. I, Academic Press, New York, 1950.

K. W. F. Kohlrausch, *Ramanspektren*, Akademische Verlagsgesellschaft, Leipzig, 1943; reprinted by Edwards, Ann Arbor, Michigan, 1945.

W. Otting, *Der Raman-Effect und seine analytische Anwendung*, Springer, Berlin, 1952.

G. B. B. M. Sutherland, *Infrared and Raman Spectra*, Methuen, London, 1935.

E. B. Wilson, Jr., J. C. Decius, P. C. Cross, *Molecular Vibrations*, McGraw-Hill, New York, 1955. Detailed treatment of theory.

b. Reviews

W. G. Braun and M. R. Fenske, *Anal. Chem.*, **21**, 12 (1949); **22**, 11 (1950).

G. Glockler, *Rev. Mod. Phys.*, **15**, 111 (1943).

E. J. Rosenbaum, *Anal. Chem.*, **28**, 596 (1956).

R. F. Stamm, *Ind. Eng. Chem.*, *Anal. Ed.*, **17**, 318 (1945).

R. F. Stamm, *Anal. Chem.*, **26**, 49 (1954).

See also sections in the following reviews on spectroscopy in which physical chemistry or chemical physics is emphasized:

B. L. Crawford, Jr. and D. E. Mann, *Ann. Rev. Phys. Chem.*, **1**, 151 (1950); L. G. S. Brooker and W. T. Simpson, *ibid.*, **2**, 121 (1951); N. S. Bayliss, *ibid.*, **3**, 229 (1952); G. B. B. M. Sutherland, *ibid.*, **4**, 189 (1953); A. B. F. Duncan, *ibid.*, **5**, 185 (1954); R. M. Badger, *ibid.*, **6**, 217 (1955); R. S. Halford and I. Ichishima, *ibid.*, **7**, 425 (1956); S. Mizushima and T. Shimanouchi, *ibid.*, **7**, 445 (1956).

A *Raman Bibliography* by G. Andermann has been published by the Applied Research Laboratories, Glendale, California, 1952.

11-5. LITERATURE SURVEY PROBLEMS

1. Discuss in some detail the design of Raman direct-recording spectrometers; see references in footnotes 12–14.

2. Discuss the determination of *total* olefin and aromatic contents in hydrocarbon mixtures according to J. J. Heigl, J. F. Black, and B. F. Dudenbostel, *Anal. Chem.,* **21,** 554 (1949). This is a good example of application.

3. Discuss the application of the Raman effect to the determination of the ionization constant of nitric and perchloric acids. See O. Redlich and J. Bigeleisen, *J. Am. Chem. Soc.,* **65,** 1883 (1943); O. Redlich, E. K. Holt, and J. Bigeleisen, *ibid.,* **66,** 13 (1944).

4. Discuss the determination of the γ isomer of hexachlorocyclohexane in the technical product according to A. Simon and D. Jentzsch, *Z. Anorg. u. Allgem. Chem.,* **266,** 193 (1951) (in German).

5. Review the method proposed by H. Gerding and A. P. van der Vet, *Rec. trav. Chim.,* **64,** 257 (1945) for the analysis of binary and ternary mixtures of pentenes.

6. Prepare a discussion of Raman spectra of inorganic compounds. See L. A. Woodward, *Quart. Revs.,* **10,** 185 (1956).

12

X-Ray Methods

12-1. EMISSION AND ABSORPTION OF X-RAYS

a. Emission of X-rays. Every student of elementary physics is made aware of the formidable impetus the discovery of X-rays by Roentgen gave to the study of the structure of matter, thanks to pioneers such as J. J. Thomson, von Laue, H. Bragg and W. L. Bragg, Debye, and many others. These developments will not be recounted here, since this chapter primarily deals with applications to analytical chemistry based on X-ray absorption, diffraction, and fluorescence. Diffraction of X-rays has long been applied in chemical analysis, but absorption methods, and particularly, X-ray fluorescence, have become increasingly important analytical tools only since about 1945–1950. The discussion of these methods will be preceded by a simple treatment of X-ray emission and absorption.

X-rays are emitted in the bombardment of atoms by electrons. In an X-ray Coolidge tube, electrons emitted by a hot filament (cathode) in high vacuum are accelerated in a strong electrical field and stopped by a target (anode). In "gas" tubes, which are seldom utilized nowadays, electrons liberated in a gas at low pressure (0.01 mm mercury) by a high-voltage discharge are accelerated in the field between the two electrodes of the discharge tube and stopped by the anode. The latter tubes do not have a hot cathode.

X-ray spectra of elements are composed of a *characteristic radiation* of a few lines at well-defined wave lengths and a continuous background, often referred to as *white radiation* (Fig. 108). Plots of the intensity of the X-ray beam against wave length are characterized by a sharp cut-off wave length below which the intensity is equal to zero. This critical wave length, which depends on the voltage applied to the tube, can be calculated from equa-

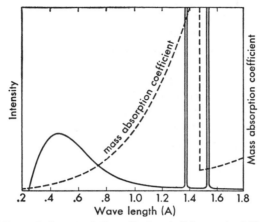

Fig. 108. White and characteristic radiation (solid curve) of X-ray beam from a copper target bombarded with electrons accelerated at 50,000 volts, and absorption coefficient of nickel filter (dashed curve). (From C. W. Bunn, *Chemical Crystallography*, Oxford University Press, London, 1945, p. 106.)

tions (8–2) and (8–4). Thus,

$$\Delta E = h\nu, \tag{12-1}$$

$$\nu = \frac{c}{\lambda}, \tag{12-2}$$

where ΔE is the energy involved in the transition resulting in the emission of an X-ray quantum; ν, the frequency; λ, the wave length of the X-ray; h, Planck's constant; and c, the velocity of light. The maximum energy of the incident electron is eV, where e is the charge of the electron and V the voltage applied between the cathode and anode of the tube. The transition for which $\Delta E = eV$ corresponds to the cut-off wave length, i.e.,

$$\lambda = \frac{hc}{eV}, \tag{12-3}$$

or after substitution of numerical data,[1]

$$\lambda = \frac{12,400}{V}, \tag{12-4}$$

where V is in volts, and λ in angstroms. It follows from equation (12–4) that voltages of the order of 10 to 30 kv are required for the production of X-rays at 0.5 to 1 A.

[1] $h = 6.624 \times 10^{-27}$ erg sec; $c = 2.998 \times 10^{10}$ cm sec^{-1}; $e = 4.802 \times 10^{-10}$ esu; 1 volt = 1/300 esu of difference of potential.

Most electrons of the beam impinging on the anode lose their energy
in more than one collision with atoms of the target, and the emitted quanta
are smaller than eV, i.e., radiation has a longer wave length than the
cut-off value of equation (12–4). Since the intensity falls off progressively
as the wave length increases and is equal to zero below the cut-off wave
length, the intensity wave-length curve passes through a maximum
(Fig. 108).

The emission of the characteristic radiation follows the transition of
electrons from their innermost orbital to another orbital as a result of the
impact of electrons on the target. An electron in the K orbital is dislodged
by excitation and is replaced by an electron from the L orbital, with the
resulting emission of the K line. Actually, the $K\alpha$ line is a doublet because
the energy of the electrons in the L orbital has two possible values. Likewise, the $K\beta$ line is emitted by the filling of the K orbital by an electron of
the M orbital. Wave lengths for the K lines of a few elements most commonly selected as targets are listed in Table XVIII. Note that the wave
lengths for the doublets $K\alpha_1$ and $K\alpha_2$ are indeed very close.

TABLE XVIII
Wave Lengths of $K\alpha$ and $K\beta$ Lines for Various Targets and Corresponding Filters for Removal of $K\beta$ Line[a]

TARGET			FILTER		
Element	Line	Wave length, kX units[b]	Element	Adsorption edge, kX units[b]	Thickness in mm to reduce $K\beta/K\alpha$ to 1/600
Mo	$K\alpha_1$	0.707831	Zr	0.6874	0.108
	$K\alpha_2$	0.712105			
	$K\beta_1$	0.630978			
Cu	$K\alpha_1$	1.537395	Ni	1.4839	0.021
	$K\alpha_2$	1.541232			
	$K\beta_1$	1.38935			
Ni	$K\alpha_1$	1.65450	Co	1.6040	0.018
	$K\alpha_2$	1.65835			
	$K\beta_1$	1.49705			
Co	$K\alpha_1$	1.78529	Fe	1.7394	0.018
	$K\alpha_2$	1.78919			
	$K\beta_2$	1.61744			
Fe	$K\alpha_1$	1.932076	Mn	1.8916	0.016
	$K\alpha_2$	1.936012			
	$K\beta_1$	1.753013			
Cr	$K\alpha_1$	2.28503	V	2.2630	0.106
	$K\alpha_2$	2.28891			
	$K\beta_1$	2.0806			

[a]Data from C. W. Bunn, *Chemical Crystallography*, Oxford University Press, London,
1945, p. 107.
[b]The kX unit is equal to 1.00203 A. It was set as being equal to 1 A on the basis of a value
of Avogadro's number, which has since been slightly corrected.

b. Absorption of X-rays. The Beer-Lambert law can be applied in its general form of equation (9-9). Thus,

$$\ln \frac{P_0}{P} = qN, \qquad (12\text{-}5)$$

where P_0 and P are the intensities of a *monochromatic* beam of X-rays as measured without and with the sample, respectively, in an experiment similar to the one schematically represented in Fig. 80; N is the number of absorbing atoms; and q is proportional to the mass m of the sample and inversely proportional to its cross-sectional area A. Thus,

$$\ln \frac{P_0}{P} = \frac{\mu_m m}{A}, \qquad (12\text{-}6)$$

or

$$\log \frac{P_0}{P} = \frac{\mu_m m}{2.303 A}, \qquad (12\text{-}7)$$

where μ_m is the *mass absorption coefficient*. The value of μ_m is independent of the physical and chemical state of an element and is characteristic of this element for a given wave length. Detailed tables of mass absorption coefficients of the elements at different wave lengths are available in the literature.[2]

The mass absorption coefficient of a sample containing several elements is simply related to the composition of the sample by

$$\mu_m = W_1 \mu_1 + W_2 \mu_2 \cdots + W_i \mu_i, \qquad (12\text{-}8)$$

where the W's are the weight fractions of each element in the sample. There may be deviations from equation (12-8) with polychromatic beam, but this need not be discussed here.[3] X-ray photometry and analytical application of X-ray absorption are based on equation (12-8).

EXAMPLE. Calculate the reduction in intensity of an X-ray monochromatic beam (copper target, $K\alpha$ line at 1.542 A) resulting from the interposition of 1 ml of a 1 per cent by weight solution of tetraethyllead in *n*-octane in a cell having a cross-sectional area of 11.21 cm². Express the result in per cent of the beam intensity which is obtained without the sample. One has at 1.54 A, $(\mu_m)_C = 5.50$ cm² g⁻¹; $(\mu_m)_{Pb} = 241$ cm²g⁻¹; and $(\mu_m)_H \approx 0$. Specific gravity of solution, 0.72. Atomic weights: 12.0 for C, 207.2 for Pb, and 1.00 for H.

---

[2]For instance, in the *Handbook of Chemistry*, N. A. Lange, Ed., Handbook Publishers, Inc., Sandusky, Ohio. See also the text (pp. 236–237) of Henry, Lipson, and Wooster listed in Section 12-8.

[3]See, for instance, P. D. Zemany, E. H. Winslow, G. S. Poellmitz, and H. A. Liebhafsky, *Anal. Chem.*, **21**, (1949).

One readily computes that the weight fractions of lead and carbon in tetraethyllead are

$$W_{\text{Pb}} = \frac{207.2}{323.2} = 0.641,$$

$$W_{\text{C}} = \frac{8 \times 12.0}{323.2} = 0.297;$$

and one deduces from equation (12–8) for tetraethyllead,

$$\mu_m = 0.641 \times 241 + 0.297 \times 5.50$$
$$= 156 \text{ cm}^2 \text{ g}^{-1}.$$

Likewise, one has for *n*-octane, C_8H_{18},

$$\mu_m = \frac{8 \times 12}{8 \times 12 + 18 \times 1} \times 5.51$$
$$= 4.64 \text{ cm}^2 \text{ g}^{-1}.$$

The mass absorption coefficient of the 1 per cent by weight solution is

$$\mu = \frac{1}{100} 156 + \frac{99}{100} 4.64$$
$$= 6.16.$$

Hence, in view of equation (12–7),

$$\log \frac{P_0}{P} = \frac{6.16 \times 1 \times 0.72}{2.303 \times 11.21}$$
$$= 0.172,$$

and $P_0/P = 1.49$, i.e., $P = 0.67 P_0$.

The layer of tetraethyllead solution causes a decrease of 33 per cent in intensity.

Since equation (12–7) is of the same general form as equation (9–16), it follows from the treatment of Section 9–3e that the relative change $(1/\mu_m)[d\mu_m/d(P/P_0)]$ at constant m and A is maximum when $P/P_0 = 0.368$. The consequences of experimental errors are minimized at this value of P/P_0, and the limits 0.1 to 1 for $\log P_0/P$ can be prescribed as the advantageous range in X-ray photometry.

Mass absorption coefficients increase with wave length up to an *absorption edge* at which there is a discontinuity. An absorption edge corresponds to the dislodging of an electron in the innermost orbitals of the absorbing element by the incident X-ray. Since such a transition is quantized, absorption edges are observed at well-defined wave lengths. Vacancies in the innermost orbitals are filled by electrons of the adjacent orbital and an X-ray fluorescence quantum at a longer wave length than the absorption edge is emitted (Table XVIII). One *K* absorption edge is observed, and there are three L edges, five M edges, etc. This phenomenon of X-ray fluorescence has been developed into a very elegant method of chemical analysis, as we shall see in Section 12–6.

The absorption edge effect is applied to the removal of $K\beta$ lines by the use of a thin metallic sheet as filter. If the $K\alpha$ and $K\beta$ lines bracket the absorption edge of the filter (Fig. 108), $K\beta$ is much more strongly absorbed than $K\alpha$, and the filtered radiation is more nearly monochromatic than the initial beam. The ratio of intensities $K\beta$ to $K\alpha$ can be reduced to perhaps 1/600 of its value without a filter (Table XVIII).

Mass absorption coefficients can be calculated by the *approximate* relationship

$$\mu_m = \frac{Z^4\lambda^3}{NCW_a},$$ (12–9)

where Z and W_a are the atomic number and atomic weight of the absorbing element, respectively; λ, the wave length; N, Avogadro's number; and C, a constant between consecutive absorption edges. The verification of equation (12–9) with experimental data may be taken up as a problem (Section 12–9). Since μ_m increases with λ, the longer wave lengths in a polychromatic beam are more strongly absorbed than the shorter ones. Hence, the mass absorption coefficient measured with a polychromatic beam and with a given sample decreases as the thickness of the sample increases.

As was first shown by Glocker and Frohnmayer,[4] absorption measurements at nearly identical wave lengths on each side of the absorption edge enable one to determine quantitatively an element in a sample containing other absorbing substances. After writing equation (12–7) in the condensed form

$$\log \frac{P_0}{P} = km,$$ (12–10)

we have

$$\log \frac{P_0}{P} = m[k_X f + k_s(1 - f)],$$ (12–11)

where f is the weight fraction of element X, k_X corresponds to X, and k_s corresponds to the sample without X. If $\log P_0/P$ is measured at two nearly identical wave lengths λ and λ' on each side of the absorption edge, k_s has practically the same value at λ and λ'. Likewise, P_0 is virtually the same at λ and λ'. Thus,

$$\log \frac{P_0}{P_\lambda} - \log \frac{P_0}{P_{\lambda'}} = mf[(k_X)_\lambda - (k_X)_{\lambda'}],$$ (12–12)

or

$$\log \frac{P_{\lambda'}}{P_\lambda} = mf[(k_X)_\lambda - (k_X)_{\lambda'}].$$ (12–13)

[4] R. Glocker and W. Frohnmayer, *Ann. Physik*, **76**, 369 (1925).

The value of f is readily computed from equation (12–13), provided that the quantity between brackets is known. The latter can be determined from a plot of μ_m against λ for element X, and by extrapolating the k's to the wave length of the absorption edge. Values of the k's in equation (12–13) are also available in the literature.[4]

The method fails when the absorption edge of the analyzed element nearly coincides with absorption edges for other elements in the sample.

12–2. DIFFRACTION OF X-RAYS

In the discussion of diffraction of light by gratings in Section 8–3a, it was pointed out that the distance between two adjacent lines of the grating should be of the order of magnitude of the wave length of the diffracted radiation. This condition, as was first pointed by von Laue in 1912, is fulfilled when a crystal is the diffracting system for X-rays.[5] This brilliant idea was soon confirmed by experiment.[6]

The condition for diffraction is most simply derived for diffraction of a monochromatic beam impinging on a row of atoms (ions) with an incident angle θ (Fig. 109). The beam is "reflected," i.e., diffracted in the direction θ if the difference in path for the wave trains for consecutive rows of atoms is a multiple of the wave length. Thus,

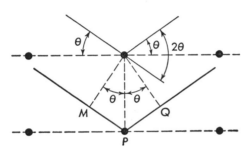

Fig. 109. Diffraction by a crystal.

$$MP + PQ = n\lambda, \quad (12–14)$$

or

$$2d \sin \theta = n\lambda, \quad (12–15)$$

where n is the order of the diffraction pattern. This very simple condition deduced by W. L. Bragg[7] is another form of the diffraction law expressed by equation (8–11), and it can be shown[8] that the latter formula yields condition (12–15) (see problem 1 in Section 12–9). Conditions for diffraction of polychromatic radiation were derived by von Laue, but details will not be given here since the interpretation of the resulting diffraction pattern is more involved than for monochromatic radiation.[7,9]

[5]The circumstances under which this momentous discovery was made and first put to an experimental test are related in some detail in K. Lonsdale, *Crystals and X-Rays*, Bell, London, 1948. Readers shoudl make it a point to study this very interesting account.
[6]W. Friedrich, P. Knipping, and M. von Laue, *Sitzb. math.-naturw. Kl. Bayer. Akad. Wiss. München*, 303 (1912).
[7]W. L. Bragg, *Nature*, **90**, 410 (1912); *Proc. Cambridge Phil. Soc.*, **17**, 43 (1913).
[8]See, for instance, J. M. Robertson, *Organic Crystals and Molecules*, Cornell, Ithaca, N.Y., 1953, pp. 55–56.
[9]W. H. Bragg, *Nature*, **90**, 219, 360 (1912).

The values of θ satisfying condition (12–15) can be determined experimentally by rotating the crystal and by measuring the values of θ in the direction 2θ with respect to the incident beam (Fig. 109) for which the intensity of the diffracted beam is maximum. This method developed by the Braggs[10] enabled them to determine the wave length of X-rays. The value of d needed in the computation of λ, was calculated from the density of the crystal (sodium and potassium chlorides) and Avogadro's number. Once λ had been obtained for sodium chloride it became possible to determine d for other crystals, and the path was open to X-ray crystallography. The emphasis was first on inorganic substances, but applications to the structural study of organic derivatives have become increasingly important since the 1930's (J. M. Robertson, and others). It is now possible to deduce from X-ray diffraction patterns maps which show electron densities in a molecule. The serious mathematical difficulties which may be encountered in the preparation of such maps are overcome by the use of electronic computers, and the electron density contour can even be displayed on the screen of a cathode-ray oscilloscope.[11] Application of X-rays to such structural investigations is not within the realm of analytical chemistry, and the reader is referred to Robertson's book[8] and the specialized literature (Section 12–8).

Diffraction by single crystals is of paramount importance in structural studies, but it is less useful as an analytical tool than the *powder diffraction method* devised independently by Debye and Scherrer[12] and by Hull.[13] A

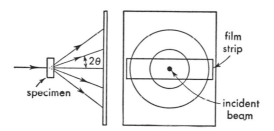

Fig. 110. Powder diffraction method.

narrow beam of filtered and essentially monochromatic X-rays impinges on the powder sample, and the diffraction pattern is recorded on a photographic film perpendicular to the incident beam (Fig. 110). The powder of a crystalline material contains crystals with all possible orientations,

[10]W. H. Bragg and W. L. Bragg, *Proc. Roy. Soc. (London)*, **A88**, 428 (1913).

[11]R. Pepinsky, *J. Applied Phys.*, **18**, 601 (1947); B. C. Frazer and R. Pepinsky (abstract only), *Phys. Rev.*, **80**, 124 (1950); P. F. Eiland and R. Pepinsky, *Acta Cryst.*, **3**, 160 (1950); see review by R. Pepinsky, *Rec. Chem. Progress*, **17**, 145 (1956).

[12]P. Debye and P. Scherrer, *Physik. Z.*, **17**, 277 (1916).

[13]A. W. Hull, *Phys. Rev.*, **10**, 661 (1917).

and therefore condition (12–15) is fulfilled. The reflecting planes which make the proper angle θ with the incident beam are otherwise oriented at random, and the diffracted beams are circular cones having the incident beam as axis. The intersections of these cones with a plane perpendicular to the axis (the photographic plate) are circles. There often is no point in obtaining the complete circular diffraction pattern, and thus photographs are made on a narrow film strip as shown in Fig. 110. Diffraction patterns consisting of vertical lines, rather than arcs of circle, can be produced by using a curved film. The spacing between lines in such patterns and the relative intensities of the lines are characteristic data which are extensively utilized for qualitative and even quantitative purposes in much the same way as emission spectra. Samples containing several compounds can be analyzed by this method, and the line intensities can be correlated to the mass absorption coefficients of the constituents. This quantitative treatment[14] can be taken up as an exercise (see problem 2 in Section 12–9).

12–3. FUNDAMENTAL INSTRUMENTAL UNITS

a. X-ray Tubes, Collimators, and Monochromators. Details about the construction of X-ray tubes can be found in the specialized literature (Section 12–8). Only a few general comments will be made here. The principle of operation of the Coolidge tube, which is almost exclusively utilized at the present, was already discussed in Section 12–1. This tube is either permanently sealed or demountable. Tubes of the latter type require a high-vacuum system and are utilized less frequently than permanently sealed tubes, although they offer the possibility of rapid change of target material. The target is water-cooled and (sometimes) rotated when a very intense X-ray beam is generated. Rotation greatly helps the cooling of the target because the impact area is continuously renewed. Tubes are provided with a transparent window made of a metal (aluminum, beryllium) having a low atomic number, i.e., with a low mass absorption coefficient (see equation 12–9; μ is proportional to Z^4).

The index of refraction of materials for X-ray is equal to unity for all practical purposes[15] and "lenses" cannot be devised. A long metallic (nickel) tube or a set of closely spaced parallel tubes serve as a collimating system. The emerging beam is essentially parallel when the collimating tubes are at least a few centimeters long and have a sufficiently small internal diameter (0.5 mm or less).

Monochromatic radiation is produced either by filtering a polychromatic beam or by "reflection" of the polychromatic beam on a crystal. The background radiation is not completely removed by a filter (see Section

[14]L. Alexander and H. P. Klug, *Anal. Chem.*, **20**, 886 (1948).
[15]The index of refraction of glass at 1.93 A, for instance, is 0.9999876.

12–2), but the emerging beam is sufficiently monochromatic for most diffraction work. Reflection by a crystal, according to Bragg's law [equation (12–15)] yields virtually monochromatic radiation. Crystals of mica, quartz, sodium chloride, pentaerythritol, and urea nitrate, [16],[17] which have particularly strong reflections, are most generally selected, but even so, the diffracted beam is far less intense (perhaps one-tenth or less) than the incident beam. A simple monochromator of a type found in some *X-ray spectrometers* is shown in Fig. 111A.

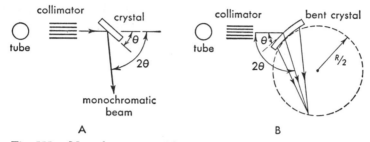

Fig. 111. Monochromators with (A) a flat and (B) a curved crystal.

The monochromatic beam can be focused by means of a bent crystal (mica, for instance), as was first shown by Guinier.[18] If R is the radius of curvature of the crystal, the diffracted beam converges on a point located on the circle of radius $R/2$, which is tangent to the crystal (Fig. 111B). The circle of radius $R/2$ is the equivalent of the Rowland circle for concave gratings (see Section 8–3b). Some focusing of the beam diffracted with an unbent crystal is achieved by grinding the surface of the crystal along a curved surface.[16]

b. Detectors. Photographic film has long been used in X-rays studies, but other detectors are now preferred when intensities have to be measured with accuracy. The reasons for this trend are the same as those discussed in Section 8–7 in connection with emission spectrography. Ionization chambers, Geiger-Müller counters, proportional counters, scintillation counters, and photoconducting crystals are utilized as detectors. Ionization chambers find few applications nowadays, although they played a major role in the pioneering work of the Braggs and others. The discussion of Geiger-Müller counters will be reserved for Chapter 14, and it will suffice to know here that the intensity of an X-ray beam is measured by the number of impulses in the current through the tube in a given time. The accuracy of the results is improved when the number of counts in-

[16] I. Fankuchen, *Nature*, **139**, 193 (1937).
[17] K. Londsdale, *Proc. Roy. Soc. (London)*, **A177**, 272 (1941).
[18] A. Guinier, *Compt. rend.*, **204**, 1115 (1937).

creases, and weak intensities require rather long counting times, perhaps 10 min. or longer periods. Very accurate results, i.e., with an error of 0.1 per cent, can be obtained. Geiger-Müller tubes are utilized as X-ray detectors mainly in X-ray spectrometry where intensities are low and a high accuracy may be required.

Proportional counters (see Chapter 14) have been applied[19] to X-ray measurements since the early 1950's, but they have not yet been widely used in this field.[20] They will probably find increased application, particularly in X-ray microscopy.

A scintillation counter is a photomultiplier tube (see Section 14–2e) whose window exposed to radiation is coated with a phosphor which emits light upon irradiation by X-rays.[21] The current through the tube is proportional to the intensity of the light, i.e., to the intensity of X-ray irradiation. Scintillation counters with visual observation (microscope) of the phosphor were used in early investigation on radioactivity, but these have been progressively replaced by Geiger-Müller counters. With the invention of photomultiplier tubes in 1939, scintillation counters again became important radiation detectors and the idea of applying them to the measurement of X-ray intensities was soon put forward by Morgan.[22] Since phosphors with fast response (10^{-5} sec) are available, rather rapid variations in intensity of an X-ray beam can be followed continuously. Scintillation counters yield quite accurate results (0.1 per cent error under the most favorable conditions[23]), but they are less sensitive than Geiger-Müller counters. This type of detector is particularly advantageous in X-ray photometers.

Crystals (zinc or cadmium sulfide) whose conductivity greatly increases upon irradiation by X-rays are utilized as X-ray detectors,[24] but their response is not sufficiently precise in most quantitative work. They have potentialities, however, as detectors in the nondestructive testing of materials.

12–4. EXPERIMENTAL METHODS FOR X-RAY ABSORPTION

The basic components of an X-ray photometer are the X-ray source and the detector. Measurements are made either with monochromatic or filtered radiation, or with a polychromatic beam. The latter method is the

[19]A. R. Lang, *Nature*, **168**, 907 (1951).

[20]For a comparison with Geiger-Müller counters, see U. W. Arndt and D. P. Riley, *Proc. Phys. Soc.*, **A65**, 74 (1952).

[21]See detailed discussion in J. Birks, *Scintillation Counters*, McGraw-Hill, New York, 1953.

[22]R. H. Morgan, *Am. J. Roentgenol. Radium Therapy*, **48**, 220 (1942).

[23]F. H. Marshall, J. W. Coltman, and L. P. Hunter, *Rev. Sci. Instruments*, **18**, 504 (1947).

[24]See, for instance, J. E. Jacobs (abstract only), *Phys. Rev.*, **80**, 124 (1950); R. Frerichs, *J. Applied Phys.*, **21**, 312 (1950).

simpler experimentally, but it supplies only very limited information about the composition of the sample. Single- or double-beam instruments[25,26] similar in principle to filter photometers have been devised. Stabilization of the X-ray beam intensity in single-beam instruments is essential, and this imposes very stringent requirements on the regulation of the tube voltage (fluctuations smaller than 0.05 to 0.01 per cent). Such requirements, however, need not be met in double-beam instruments. In the instrument developed by Rich and Michel[25] (General Electric), the incident beam is split into two beams which pass alternatively (30 cps) through the sample and the standard. The two exit beams impinge on a single scintillation counter, whose output current includes a periodic component when the sample and standard do not absorb identically. Balance is achieved by reducing the intensity of the exit beam for the standard by means of a calibrated aluminum wedge.

Application of the method of Glocker and Frohnmayer,[4] described in Section 12–1b, requires a monochromator and a stable source. Spectrometers for diffraction studies can be conveniently adapted to such absorption measurements. The absorption can be followed continuously by means of a recording instrument as the wave length is varied, or readings may be taken only in the immediate vicinity and on both sides of the absorption wedge. A differential method in which two identical samples are exposed to two beams of *slightly* different wave lengths has been devised.[27] Microtechniques for application of the method of Glocker and Frohnmayer have been developed and fully used, notably by Engström.[28] Experimental methods applied in nondestructive testing and thickness gaging may be studied as an exercise (see problem 15 in Section 12–9).

12–5. EXPERIMENTAL METHODS FOR X-RAY DIFFRACTION

Diffraction patterns for powder and single crystals are recorded either on photographic film or with an X-ray spectrometer. The photographic method (Fig. 110) will first be discussed.

The sample is not moved in the powder diffraction method, but more complicated arrangements in which the sample and even the film are moving are often necessary in structure studies. Only cameras for powder diffraction will be discussed here, and the reader is referred to Bunn's book and other monographs listed in Section 12–8 for a review of other types of cameras. Cylindric, flat cassette, and focusing cameras are employed in the

[25]T. C. Michel and T. A. Rich, *Gen. Elec. Rev.*, **50**, No. 2, 45 (1947).

[26]H. A. Liebhafsky, H. M. Smith, H. E. Tanis, and E. H. Winslow, *Ind. Eng. Chem., Anal. Ed.*, **19**, 861 (1947).

[27]J. Drahokoupil, *Czechoslov. J. Phys.*, **1**, 147 (1952); *Chem. Abstracts*, **47**, 7313 (1953).

[28]See summary in chapter by A. Engström in *Progress in Biophysics and Biophysical Chemistry*, J. A. V. Butler and J. T. Randall, Eds., Vol. 1, Academic Press, New York, 1950.

powder method. A collimated narrow (0.5 mm) beam impinges on a sample of small volume in cylindric and flat cassette cameras, whereas a diverging beam is diffracted by a large sample and is focused on the film in focusing cameras. The incident beam is stopped by a strongly absorbing metal to prevent fogging of the film by diffraction on various parts of the camera. The resolution increases with the radius of a cylindric camera and with the distance between sample and film for a flat cassette camera, but line intensities decrease as the camera becomes larger and exposure times are thus longer.[29] A compromise between these two design considerations generally results in diameters between 5 and 15 cm for cylindric cameras.

High resolution is achieved in *back-reflection cameras* in which θ is close to 90 degrees. This follows from the Bragg condition [equation (12–15)],

$$n\lambda = 2d_p \sin \theta, \tag{12–16}$$

where d_p is substituted for d to avoid confusion with the symbol for differentiation used below. By differentiation of equation (12–16), there follows,

$$2d(d_p) \sin \theta + 2d_p \cos \theta \, d\theta = 0, \tag{12–17}$$

or

$$\frac{d\theta}{d(d_p)} = -\frac{\tan \theta}{d_p}. \tag{12–18}$$

The resolution increases with $d\theta/d(d_p)$, and consequently with $\tan \theta$. Since $\tan \theta$ tends to infinity when θ approaches 90 degrees, high resolution is achieved with values of θ close to this critical angle.

Cameras are calibrated with a known sample (rock salt, for example) for which the parameter d is known very exactly. It is then a simple matter to correlate θ to the spacing between lines in diffraction patterns. The resolution increases with wave length [see equation (12–15)] but lines lose their sharpness because scattering of X-rays by air when λ is too large ($\lambda > 2$–$3A$). The $K\alpha$ doublet for copper at 1.54 A is often selected for diffraction, the $K\beta$ line being virtually removed by a nickel filter (Table XVIII and Fig. 108). Certain elements emit X-ray fluorescence upon irradiation by the $K\alpha$ copper line, with the resulting fogging of the film, and another target must then be selected.

Numerous cameras are described in the literature and excellent commercial units are available from X-ray equipment manufacturers. Special purpose cameras for studies at low temperatures[30] (gaseous or liquid compounds at room temperature) and high temperatures[31] (alloys, metal-

[29]For a review of design considerations see M. J. Buerger, *J. Applied Phys.*, **16**, 501 (1945).

[30]First described by A. H. Jay, *Proc. Phys. Soc.*, **45**, 635 (1933).

[31]First used by E. Pohland, *Z. phys. Chem.*, **B26**, 238 (1934).

lurgy) have also been described. A microcamera in which the incident beam has a diameter of only 25 μ was constructed by Chesley.[32]

The sample should be finely divided (200 to 300 mesh) and its volume should be so small as to avoid pronounced absorption of diffracted radiation. The optimum thickness of a sample of uniform thickness can be shown to be $1/\mu_m\rho$, ρ being the density of the sample. This result can be established as an exercise (problem 3, Section 12–9). Samples are generally prepared in the form of cylinders not exceeding 0.5 mm in diameter. Substances are best examined without containers to avoid interference by diffraction of the container material, but in many cases the sample has not the consistency to permit the preparation of an extruded cylinder. A small tube with a thin wall (0.01 mm) is then utilized. Such tubes are most frequently made of "Lindemann" glass (lithium borate) or plastics because these materials have low mass absorption coefficients. Samples are diluted with an amorphous substance, such as flour, when the quantity $1/\mu_m\rho$ for the undiluted powder is much smaller than the diameter of the tube.

The photographic method has proved invaluable in diffraction studies, but direct-recording spectrometers are often preferred nowadays. In the application of these instruments to powder diffraction, the detector is mounted on a goniometer and is slowly rotated about the sample while the intensity of diffracted radiation is recorded as a function of the angle of rotation. In application to single crystals, the crystal and the detector are rotated simultaneously, the detector being rotated at twice the speed of the crystal (Bragg relationship). Numerous instruments are described in the literature[33] and commercial X-ray spectrometers are available (Baird Associates, General Electric, Hayes Scientific Appliances, North American Philips Co., Ohio X-ray Co., and Picker X-ray Co. in the United States; and Hilger of London, among others abroad).

Diffraction patterns are identified by comparing the distance between lines (generally the three strongest lines) and the relative intensities of lines for the unknown with these data for known specimen. A systematic scheme for identification was first developed by Hanawalt, Rinn, and Frevel,[34] who reported spacings and relative intensities for 1000 compounds. This compilation has been enlarged by the American Society for the Testing of Materials (Philadelphia), and a card index covering more than 3000 compounds (mainly inorganic substances) has become available. Corrections and additions to this index have been reported,[35] and an even

[32]F. G. Chesley, *Rev. Sci. Instruments*, **18**, 422 (1947).

[33]See, for instance, R. A. Coyle, K. F. Hale, and C. Wainright, *J. Sci. Instruments*, **30**, 151 (1953).

[34]J. D. Hanawalt, H. W. Rinn, and L. K. Frevel, *Ind. Eng. Chem., Anal. Ed.*, **10**, 457 (1938).

[35]H. E. Swanson and E. Tatje, *J. Research Natl. Bur. Standards*, **46**, 318 (1951).

more extensive compilation is in preparation at the Bureau of Standards. W. C. McCrone and coworkers have contributed regularly to *Analytical Chemistry* crystallographic and X-ray data on organic substances for a number of years. The use of punched cards greatly simplifies identification procedures.[36,37]

Errors on the parameter d in index cards are within 0.001 A for $d \leqslant 1$ A, but larger possible errors (0.01 to 0.05 A) affect values of d up to 8 A. One should remember when using index cards that the relative intensities of the diffraction lines depend on the wave length of the incident beam. Thus, the angles 2θ for the diffracted beam, and consequently the absorption paths and lines intensities, vary with wave length.

The reader is referred to a paper of Frevel[38] for a discussion of the limitations of the method.

12-6. EXPERIMENTAL METHODS FOR X-RAY FLUORESCENCE

The X-ray emission spectrum of a sample can be excited either by electron impact or by irradiation by X-rays. The former method, which was applied to analytical chemistry long ago,[39] has seldom been utilized, mainly because of the inconvenience resulting from the use of the sample as a target (pumping, etc.). Irradiation of the sample by X-rays does not involve the difficulties associated with demountable tubes, and the technique is quite simple. The fluorescence radiation is studied with an X-ray spectrometer[40-45] whose monochromator is either a flat or a curved crystal (Fig. 111). The main problem in the design of spectrometers for X-ray fluorescence is the necessity of obtaining adequate resolution without undue decrease in the intensity of the diffracted beam. Several designs in which this goal is reached with varying success are discussed by Birks, Brooks, and Friedman.[40] Attachments for adapting commercial spectrometers to X-ray fluorescence are available (General Electric, North American Philips Co.).

Elements are identified by the angle 2θ of their fluorescence lines, i.e., by the corresponding wave lengths, and the amount of each element is determined from line intensities. Calibration with standards having a composition similar to that of the sample being analyzed is essential. The

[36]F. W. Matthews and A. D. McIntosh, *Can. Chem. Process Ind.*, **29**, 662 (1946).
[37]C. R. Hudgens and A. M. Ross, *Anal. Chem.*, **25**, 734 (1953).
[38]L. K. Frevel, *Ind. Eng. Chem.*, *Anal. Ed.*, **16**, 209 (1944).
[39]See, for instance, G. von Hevesy, *Chemical Analysis by X-rays and Its applications*, McGraw-Hill, New York, 1932, p. 86.
[40]L. S. Birks, E. J. Brooks, and H. Friedman, *Anal. Chem.*, **25**, 692 (1953).
[41]J. L. Abbott, *Iron Age*, **162**, No. 18, 58; No. 19, 121 (1948).
[42]M. A. Cordovi, *Steel*, **123**, No. 25, 88 (1948).
[43]H. Friedman and L. S. Birks, *Rev. Sci. Instruments*, **19**, 323 (1948).
[44]R. M. Brissey, *Anal. Chem.*, **24**, 1034 (1952).
[45]J. Despujols, *J. phys. radium*, **13**, 31A (1952).

percentage of an element in the sample is then readily computed from the ratio of the numbers of counts registered by the detector for a given time for the unknown and the standard. A correction for the background (see Fig. 112) must be made. A departure from linearity between response and

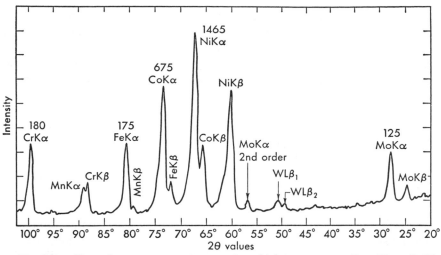

Fig. 112. X-ray fluorescence spectrogram for a high-temperature alloy. [From R. M. Brissey, *Anal. Chem.*, **25**, 190 (1953).]

composition is often observed, but methods for coping with this difficulty have been developed.[46-48] The result can be automatically computed,[49] as in the quantometer for emission spectrometry (Section 8–7).

12–7. APPLICATIONS

X-ray methods are, after spectroscopic methods, probably the most important of instrumental analysis. They have the unique feature of supplying information which often cannot be obtained by other methods. Intermetallic compounds can be identified in an alloy by X-ray diffraction, whereas only the percentage of each element can be obtained by other analytical methods; the amounts of certain elements in a sample can be determined without destruction of the sample, etc. X-ray diffraction finds more applications than absorption or fluorescence methods, but the latter method is beginning to compete with emission spectroscopy in some metallurgical analyses. The cost of an X-ray diffraction or fluorescence

[46]E. Gillam and H. T. Heal, *Brit. J. Appl. Phys.*, **3**, 353 (1952).
[47]P. K. Koh, B. Caugherty, and R. E. Burket, *J. Appl. Phys.*, **23**, 698 (1952).
[48]R. M. Brissey, *Anal. Chem.*, **25**, 190 (1953).
[49]M. F. Hasler and J. W. Kemp, paper presented at the 56th meeting of the ASTM, Atlantic City, 1953.

installation is comparable with that of a good emission spectrograph and its accessories, or of an infrared recording spectrometer. However, the saving in manpower, especially in industrial laboratories, generally more than compensates for the cost of equipment even over a short period. X-ray photometers are somewhat less expensive than diffraction units.

a. Absorption Methods. Absorption methods are very valuable in fairly specific cases and in the nondestructive testing of materials. However, there is a tendency to substitute γ-ray sources for X-ray tubes in the this application. The absorption method yields accurate results, and errors can be as small as 1 per cent, or even smaller in careful work. Absorption with polychromatic radiation is not selective, but the absorption edge method is. The sensitivity varies enormously with the composition of the sample. An element with a large mass absorption coefficient can be determined in presence of a large excess of poorly absorbing substances. An extreme example is the determination of calcium and phosphorus in quantities of the order of 10^{-10} gram in biological tissues.[50] Because of the rapidity and simplicity of measurements the method is ideally suited to routine work and continuous analysis. Typical applications are the determination of lead tetraethyl in gasoline, sulfur in petroleum, uranium in aqueous solutions, etc. References on these and other applications will be found in problems in Section 12–9 and in Liebhafsky's reviews listed in Section 12–8b. See also Clark's book (Section 12–8a).

b. Diffraction Methods. Diffraction methods are primarily utilized as a qualitative tool, although quantitative determinations can also be made. A most valuable feature of these methods is the possibility of obtaining information on the compounds present in a sample. Applications in the past dealt primarily with the identification and the structural study of inorganic substances, but numerous organic derivatives, high polymers, and biological materials have been investigated. Gaseous or liquid substances at room temperature can often be studied at liquid air temperatures, and the number of potential applications is thus increased.[51]

X-ray diffraction is an elegant method for the determination of the size of small particles having diameters of less than 500 A. The lines in the diffraction pattern become broader and more diffuse as the particle size decreases, and this enables the determination of particles sizes. The interpretation of this effect was first advanced by Scherrer,[52] and many papers have since been published on the subject.[53] The low-angle scattering method introduced by Guinier[54] is particularly valuable in such stud-

---

[50]A. Engström, *Nature*, **158**, 664 (1946); see also the reference in footnote 28.
[51]See review of B. Post and I. Fankuchen, *Anal. Chem.*, **25**, 736 (1953).
[52]P. Scherrer, *Nachr. Ges. Wiss. Göttingen*, 96 (1918).
[53]For instance, A. L. Patterson, *Phys. Rev.*, **56**, 972, 978 (1939).
[54]A. Guinier, *Ann. Phys.*, **12**, 161 (1939).

ies,[55] but this material is beyond the scope of this text (see problem 17 in Section 12–9).

The selectivity and sensitivity of diffraction methods greatly depend on the composition of the sample. The overlapping of diffraction patterns may limit the application to the determination of minor constituents. The accuracy in quantitative work is rather poor (5 to 10 per cent error) although progress could probably be made, especially by the application of an internal standard method.[56]

c. Fluorescence Method. The X-ray fluorescence method is particularly suited to routine analysis of samples whose composition varies within narrow limits. Application is limited to elements having an atomic number larger than 20 because the wave lengths in emission spectra of lighter elements are too long for analysis by the crystal spectrometers generally available.

The method is selective and quite sensitive. Elements whose weight fraction exceed 1 per cent can readily be determined, and the method can be applied to trace analysis under favorable condition (a few parts per million). The background correction is critical in trace work. Errors are small (1 to 2 per cent, or even smaller errors), and the accuracy can be improved by the use of an internal standard.[57] Some typical applications (high temperature alloys, uranium, zirconium, and hafnium, etc.) can be discussed in detail as an exercise (Section 12–9).

12-8. BIBLIOGRAPHY

a. Books

W. H. Bragg, Ed., *The Crystalline State*, 3 vols., Macmillan, New York, 1949–1954.

M. J. Buerger, *X-Ray Crystallography*, Wiley, New York, 1942.

C. W. Bunn, *Chemical Crystallography*, Oxford University Press, London, 1945.

G. L. Clark, *Applied X-Rays*, 4th ed., McGraw-Hill, New York, 1955.

G. L. Clark, article in *Physical Methods in Chemical Analysis*, W. G. Berl, Ed., Vol. I, Academic Press, New York, 1950. Review of X-ray absorption methods.

A. H. Compton and S. K. Allison, *X-Rays in Theory and Experiment*, 2nd ed., Van Nostrand, New York, 1943.

W. L. Davidson, article in *Physical Methods in Chemical Analysis*, W. G. Berl, Ed., Vol. I, Academic Press, New York, 1950. Review of X-ray diffraction as applied to powders and metals.

I. Fankuchen, article in *Physical Methods of Organic Chemistry*, 2nd ed., Vol. I, Part II, A. Weissberger, Ed., Interscience, New York, 1949.

[55]K. L. Yudowitch, *Anal. Chem.*, **25**, 721 (1953).
[56]First used by G. L. Clark and D. H. Reynolds, *Ind. Eng. Chem., Anal. Chem.*, **8**, 36 (1936); see also, S. T. Gross and D. E. Martin, *ibid.*, **16**, 95 (1944).
[57]G. T. Kokotailo and G. F. Damon, *Anal. Chem.*, **25**, 1185 (1953).

A. Guinier, *X-Ray Crystallographic Technology*, Translation by T. L. Tippell and K. Lonsdale, Hilger and Watts, London, 1952.

D. Harker, article in *Physical Methods of Organic Chemistry*, 2nd ed., Vol. I, Part III, A. Weissberger, Ed., Interscience, New York, 1954. Application of X-ray diffraction to the structure of organic compounds.

N. F. M. Henry, H. Lipson, and W. A. Wooster, *The Interpretation of X-Ray Diffraction Photographs*, Macmillan, New York, 1951.

H. Hirst, *X-Rays in Research and Industry*, Chapman and Hall, London, 1947.

J. A. Howsmon, article in *Physical Methods in Chemical Analysis*, W. G. Berl, Ed., Vol. I, Academic Press, New York, 1950. Review of X-ray diffraction as applied to fibers.

H. P. Klug and L. E. Alexander, *X-Ray Diffraction Procedures*, Wiley, New York, 1954. Very thorough treatment.

K. Lonsdale, *Crystals and X-Rays*, Bell, London, 1948. An introductory text.

H. Mark, article in *Physikalische Methoden der Analytischen Chemie*, W. Böttger, Ed., Vol. I, Akademische Verlagsgesellschaft, Leipzig, 1933; reprinted by Edwards, Ann Arbor, Michigan, 1943.

H. S. Peiser, H. K. Rooksby, and A. J. C. Wilson, *X-Ray Diffraction by Polycrystalline Materials*, Inst. of Physics, London, 1955.

M. H. Pirenne, *The Diffraction of X-Rays and Electrons by Free Molecules*, Cambridge University Press, London, 1946. Does not cover analytical applications.

W. T. Sproull, *X-Rays in Practice*, McGraw-Hill, New York, 1946.

J. M. Robertson, *Organic Crystals and Molecules*, Cornell University Press, Ithaca, New York, 1953.

R. W. G. Wycoff, *Crystal Structures*, 3 vols., Interscience, New York, 1948.

W. H. Zachariasen, *Theory of X-Ray Diffraction in Crystals*, Wiley, New York, 1945.

b. Reviews

H. S. Kaufman and I. Fankuchen, *Anal. Chem.*, **21**, 24 (1949); **22**, 16 (1950); **24**, 20 (1952); **26**, 31 (1954); B. Post and I. Fankuchen, *ibid.*, **28**, 591 (1956); Periodic reviews of diffraction methods, mainly the powder method.

H. A. Liebhafsky, *Anal. Chem.*, **21**, 17 (1949); **22**, 15 (1950); **23**, 14 (1951); **24**, 16 (1952); **26**, 26 (1954); H. A. Liebhafsky and E. H. Winslow, *ibid.*, **28**, 583 (1956). Reviews of analytical applications of X-ray absorption methods.

See also the proceedings of the "Symposium on X-Rays as an Analytical Tool" (American Chemical Society, Atlantic City, 1952) in *Anal. Chem.*, **,25** 688–751 (1953).

The following reviews emphasize the physicochemical aspects (structure): J. L. Hoard and S. Geller, *Ann. Rev. Phys. Chem.*, **1**, 215 (1950); R. E. Rundle, *ibid.*, **2**, 235 (1951); W. H. Zachariasen, *ibid.*, **3**, 359 (1952); W. N. Lipscomb, *ibid.*, **4**, 253 (1953); E. G. Cox, *ibid.*, **5**, 357 (1954).

12–9. PROBLEMS

a. Extension of Theory

1. Show that the general condition for diffraction expressed by equation (8–11) can be transformed into the Bragg condition [equation (12–15)]. See reference in footnote 8.

2. Correlate the intensity of lines in the diffraction pattern of powders to the mass absorption coefficients of the components of the powder. See reference in footnote 14.

3. Show that the optimum thickness for maximum intensity of diffraction lines in the powder method is $1/\mu_m\rho$, ρ being the density of the sample.

This result, which holds for a sample of uniform thickness, is established by noting (a) that the intensity I of a diffraction line increases with the thickness of the sample, and (b) that I decreases exponentially with thickness because of absorption.

b. Application of Theory

4. Calculate the thickness of sheets of beryllium, aluminum, iron, copper, platinum, lead, which are required to reduce the intensity of the $K\alpha$ molybdenum line (0.711 A) to 1/100 of its value. Neglect absorption by air. Densities: 1.80 (Be), 2.71 (Al), 7.86 (Fe), 8.50 (Cu), 21.61 (Pt), 11.34 (Pb). Mass absorption coefficients: 0.30 (Be), 5.30 (Al), 38.3 (Fe), 49.7 (Cu), 123 (Pt), 141 (Pb) cm² g⁻¹.

5. Calculate the relative decrease in intensity of an X-ray beam ($K\alpha$Mo, 0.711 A) which is caused by a 1-cm thick layer of 10^{-1} M aqueous solution of uranyl nitrate (assume that the density ≈ 1). What is the relative decrease for pure water? Repeat the calculations for the line $K\alpha$Cr at 2.29 A and deduce which wave length is more advantageous; explain why this is so. Mass absorption coefficients (cm² g⁻¹) at 0.711 A: H (0), N (1.10), O (1.50), U (153). At 2.29 A: H (0), N (27.7), O (40.1), U (805).

6. (a) The radius of a diffraction circle on the film of a flat cassette camera is 4.63 cm for diffraction of the $K\alpha$ copper line (1.54 A) by a crystal powder. Calculate the parameter d ($n = 1$) for this crystal, knowing that the distance sample-film is 7.31 cm.

(b) What would be the distance between the corresponding lines (symmetrical with respect to the point of impact of the undiffracted beam) on the diffraction pattern obtained under the same conditions with a cylindric camera having a diameter of 9.87 cm?

7. Verify equation (12–9) for mass absorption coefficients by plotting (a) μ_m against Z^4 at constant λ, and (b) μ_m against λ^3 for given values of Z. Find the necessary data in the literature (reference in footnote 2, for instance) and have at least 10 to 20 points for plot (a), and at least 6 elements for plot (b). Keep in mind the absorption edge.

c. Literature Surveys

8. Discuss the design of a typical X-ray photometer. See T. C. Michel and T. A. Rich, *Gen. Elec. Rev.*, **50**, No. 2, 45 (1947).

9. Discuss the conditions under which accurate X-ray photometric measurements can be made with scintillation counters. See F. H. Marshall, J. W. Coltman, and L. P. Hunter, *Rev. Sci. Instruments*, **18**, 504 (1947).

10. Review the application of X-ray absorption to the determination of tetraethyllead in gasoline. Consult H. A. Liebhafsky, *Anal. Chem.*, **24**, 16 (1952) as a guide to the abundant literature on this application.

11. Discuss the determination of sulfur in petroleum by X-ray photometry. See R. C. Vollmar, E. E. Petterson, and P. A. Petruzzelli, *Anal. Chem.*, **21**, 1491 (1949).

12. Prepare a review of some typical application of X-ray photometry in biology. See chapter by A. Engström in *Progress in Biophysics and Biophysical Chemistry*, J. A. V. Butler and J. T. Randall, Eds., Vol. I, Academic Press, New York, 1950; A. Engström, *Discussion Faraday Soc.*, **9**, 427 (1950); A. Engström, *Rev. Sci. Instruments*, **18**, 681 (1947); L. von Hamos and A. Engström, *Acta Radiol.*, **25**, 325 (1944).

13. Discuss the X-ray photometric determination of uranium. See T. W. Bartlett, *Anal. Chem.*, **23**, 705 (1951); C. J. Rodden, *Analytical Chemistry of the Manhattan Project*, McGraw-Hill, New York, 1950, p. 734.

14. Discuss the thickness gaging of steel strip in plant control. See C. W. Clapp and R. V. Pohl, *Elec. Eng.*, **67**, No. 5, 441 (1948).

15. Compare X-ray and γ-ray nondestructive testing methods. See selection of references in H. A. Liebhafsky, *Anal. Chem.*, **26**, 26 (1954).

16. Discuss the X-ray microscopic method developed by R. Castaing and A. Guinier [*Anal. Chem.*, **25**, 724 (1953)] and its application to the structural study of alloys.

17. Discuss the technique of low temperature X-ray diffraction. See S. C. Abrahams, R. L. Collin, W. N. Lipscomb, and T. B. Reed, *Rev. Sci. Instruments*, **21**, 396 (1950); D. F. Clifton, *ibid.*, **21**, 339 (1950); B. Post, R. S. Schwartz, and I. Fankuchen, *ibid.*, **22**, 218 (1951).

18. Discuss the application of small-angle scattering to particle size determination. See K. L. Yudowitch, *Anal. Chem.*, **25**, 721 (1953); K. L. Yudowitch, *Rev. Sci. Instruments*, **23**, 83 (1952); J. Riseman, *Acta Cryst.*, **5**, 193 (1952).

19. Review a few typical applications of X-ray diffraction in organic chemistry (to the exclusion of electron density mapping). Consult H. S. Kaufman and I. Fankuchen, *Anal. Chem.*, **24**, 20 (1952); *ibid.*, **26**, 31 (1954) as a guide to the literature.

20. Discuss a few typical applications of X-ray diffraction to high polymer studies. See references in problem 19.

21. Discuss the application of X-ray fluorescence to the analysis of high-temperature alloys. See R. M. Brissey, *Anal. Chem.*, **24**, 1034 (1952); **25**, 190 (1953).

22. Examine the potentialities of X-ray fluorescence in the determination of traces of tetraethyllead and sulfur in petroleum. See L. S. Birks, E. J. Brooks, and H. Friedman, *Anal. Chem.*, **25**, 692 (1953); G. T. Kokotailo and G. F. Damon, *ibid.*, **25**, 1185 (1953).

23. Discuss the application of X-ray fluorescence to the analysis of zirconium and hafnium. See D. M. Mortimore and P. A. Romans, *J. Optical Soc. Amer.*, **42**, 673 (1952).

24. Study the analysis of uranium in aqueous solution by X-ray fluorescence. See L. S. Birks and E. J. Brooks, *Anal. Chem.*, **23**, 707 (1951).

13

Mass Spectrometry

13-1. MASS SPECTOGRAPHS AND SPECTROMETERS

The origin of mass spectrometry can be traced to the classical work of J. J. Thomson[1] on the behavior of positive ions in gases under the combined effect of electric and magnetic fields. A collimated beam of positive ions, produced by ionization of a gas (neon) by high-voltage discharge, was subjected to the simultaneous action of parallel electric and magnetic fields. Ions were deflected in two perpendicular directions, and the resulting pattern for each ionic species was a parabola which could be recorded on a photographic plate. This method was of fundamental importance, but it lacked sensitivity because of the spreading of ions over a rather long segment of curve. Aston[2] used perpendicular electic and magnetic fields and succeeded in focusing the beam of ions of a given mass and charge in a narrow line on the photographic plate. There resulted a *mass spectrum*, and Aston's instrument thus was a *mass spectrograph*. In the hands of Aston and others (Bainbridge, Dempster, Jordan, Mattauch, etc.) the mass spectrograph became an extraordinarily precise (1 part in 10^5) tool for atomic mass measurements.

Mass spectrographs are not well suited to the determination of the relative abundance of isotopes because the photometric analysis of line intensities does not yield sufficiently accurate results. Abundance measurements became possible with the development of the *mass spectrometer*, which was

[1] J. J. Thomson, *Rays of Positive Electricity and their Application to Chemical Analysis*, Longmans, Green and Co., London, 1913.
[2] F. W. Aston, *Phil. Mag.*, **38**, 707 (1919).

invented by Dempster[3,4] at about the time Aston was constructing his mass spectrograph. Ions are collimated in a narrow beam in a mass spectrometer and are accelerated up to a certain velocity in the electric field between two electrodes e_1 and e_2 (Fig. 113). The ions are then deflected in a magnetic

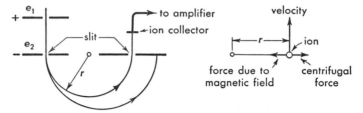

Fig. 113. Schematic diagram of Dempster's mass spectrometer.

field of constant intensity and perpendicular to the plane of the paper. Under these conditions the ions, which follow circular trajectories, can be sorted by means of a narrow slit placed in front of an ion collector connected to an electrometer or amplifier. The radii of the trajectories can be changed by varying either the ion velocities or the intensity of the magnetic field. The nature and abundance of the various ionic species are determined from the current in the collector circuit as the trajectory radii are varied.

Originally the mass spectrometer was developed for the determination of the relative abundance of isotopes. Utilization in isotopic-tracer work soon followed, but it was only in the early 1940's that application to routine analysis (particularly in the petroleum industry) became common. Many improvements in design were made, notably by Bleakney, Tate and Smith, Nier, and others. Further impetus toward increased application resulted from the development (Hipple,[5] Washburn[6]) of commercial instruments (Consolidated Engineering Corporation in the United States, Metropolitan-Vickers in England, etc.).

Mass spectrometers completely different in their principle from Dempster's instrument have also been devised and have proved useful in fairly specific applications (See section 13–5).

13–2. FUNDAMENTAL RELATIONSHIPS

The equation for ion trajectories can be simply derived by considering the ideal case in which ions having a uniform velocity v enter a magnetic

[3]A. J. Dempster, *Phys. Rev.*, **11**, 316 (1918).

[4]A similar arrangement had been utilized by J. Classen [*Physik. Z.*, **9**, 762 (1908)] in his determination of the ratio mass/charge of the electron.

[5]J. A. Hipple, *J. Applied Physics*, **13**, 551 (1942).

[6]H. W. Washburn, H. F. Wiley, and S. M. Rock, *Ind. Eng. Chem., Anal. Ed.*, **15**, 541 (1943).

field of constant intensity H that is perpendicular to the direction of the ion velocity vector.[7] Ions are submitted to a constant force perpendicular to the plane formed by the velocity vector and the lines of forces of the magnetic field. The trajectory, under these conditions, is a circle whose radius r can be calculated by noting that the magnetic and centrifugal forces must compensate one another (Fig. 113). Thus,

$$Hev = \frac{mv^2}{r} \tag{13-1}$$

or

$$r = \frac{mv}{eH}, \tag{13-2}$$

where H is the magnetic field intensity; e, the charge of the ion; v, the ion velocity; m, the ion mass; and r, the radius of the circular trajectory.

The velocity v is expressed in terms of the accelerating voltage by noting that the kinetic energy ($mv^2/2$) of the ion as it enters the magnetic field must be equal to the energy eV, V being the difference of potential between the accelerating electrodes e_1 and e_2 in Fig. 113. Thus,

$$\frac{1}{2} mv^2 = eV, \tag{13-3}$$

or

$$v = \left(\frac{2eV}{m}\right)^{1/2}, \tag{13-4}$$

and in view of equation (13-2),

$$r = \left(\frac{2V}{H} \frac{m}{e}\right)^{1/2}. \tag{13-5}$$

It follows from equation (13-5) that, for a given accelerating voltage V and intensity of magnetic field, all ions having the same ratio m/e travel along the same circular trajectory. The radius of this trajectory can be varied by changing the accelerating voltage V at constant magnetic field intensity H, or by varying H at constant V.

There are, in practice, many causes for the broadening of the exit beam, but only a brief analysis can be made here.[8]

1. The intensity of the magnetic field does not vary abruptly from zero outside the poles of the magnet to a constant value in the pole gap; ions thus travel in a field of progressively varying intensity and there results some line broadening.

2. Ion velocities are distributed around the value v, and this departure from a single velocity also causes line broadening.

3. Mechanical imperfections have the same effect.

---

[7]It is assumed that v is small in comparison with the speed of light and that—as is indeed the case—the relativity correction can be neglected.

[8]See the following fundamental papers: R. Herzog, *Z. Phys.*, **89**, 447, (1934); J. Mattauch and R. Herzog, *ibid.*, **89**, 786 (1934); N. F. Barber, *Proc. Leeds Phil. Lit. Soc. Sci. Sect.*, **2**, 427 (1933); W. E. Stephens, *Phys. Rev.*, **45**, 513 (1934).

4. Finally, ions do not leave the exit slit of the accelerating electrode (Fig. 113) with the same direction, and there results an error in focusing known as *spherical aberration*. This error, which is important, can be evaluated by considering two trajectories 1 and 2 having the same radius r, but diverging by an angle α (Fig. 114). Since $KM = 2r \cos \alpha$, the error in

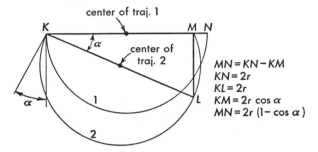

Fig. 114. Spherical aberration.

focusing, MN, is $2r\,(1 - \cos \alpha)$, or[9] approximately $r\alpha^2$. If, for instance, $\alpha = 0.05$ radian (about 3 deg) and $r = 100$ mm, $r\alpha^2 = 0.25$ mm, and the line broadening resulting from spherical aberration is comparable with the collector slit width (a few tenths of a millimeter).

Mass spectrometers are characterized by their resolution, which is defined as the ratio $m/\Delta m$, where Δm is the minimum increment in mass units between two peaks that still can be resolved. The distance between peaks corresponding to Δm must be equal or larger than the sum of the image spread and the width of the collector slit.

Dempster[3] showed that the resolution is $r/(w_1 + w_2)$, w_1 and w_2 being the widths of the entrance and collector slits, respectively. Line broadening was not taken into account in the derivation of this formula, which can be applied only to obtain the order of magnitude of r and the w's required for a certain resolution. Thus, with a relatively large magnet $r = 100$ mm, and the resolution should not exceed 250 with $w_1 = w_2 = 0.2$ mm. Actually, resolution would be much lower, perhaps 50 to 100, because of line broadening.

The resolution of commercial instruments can be as high as 400.

13-3. *EXPERIMENTAL METHODS*

The three essential components in a mass spectrometer, namely, the generator of the ion beam, the magnetic focusing system, and the ion collector, will be discussed in some detail.

[9]By retaining only the first two terms of the series $\cos \alpha = 1 - \dfrac{\alpha^2}{2!} + \dfrac{\alpha^4}{4!} - \dfrac{\alpha^6}{6!} \cdots$.

a. Generation of Ion Beam.   Ions in mass spectrometry are generally produced by electron impact on the analyzed substance in the gaseous form at low pressure ($10^{-4} - 10^{-7}$ mm mercury). This method of electron bombardment was applied by Dempster[3,10] and improved by Nier.[11] The principle is as follows:

Electrons emitted by a tungsten filament (Fig. 115) are attracted by

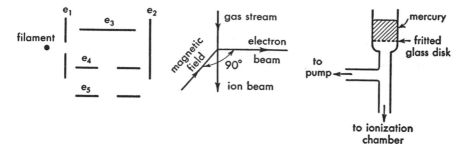

Fig. 115. Schematic diagram of electron gun and ionization chamber.

Fig. 116. Schematic diagram of an inlet system for liquids.

electrode e_1, which is positive with respect to the filament. Electrons passing through a narrow hole in e_1 (*electron gun*) ionize the gas between e_1 and e_2, and finally are collected on the anode e_2, which is positive with respect to e_1. Positive ions, which are separated from electrons by a weak electric field (a few volts per centimeter) applied between e_3 and e_4, are accelerated between electrodes e_4 and e_5 and acquire a kinetic energy of a few thousand electronvolts. Such a relatively high energy is imparted to the ions to produce an almost monoenergetic beam [see equation (13–5)]. The variable kinetic energy (perhaps 1 electronvolt) of the ions as they are produced is then negligible in comparison with the energy resulting from acceleration between e_4 and e_5.

Various designs of the electron gun and ionization chamber have been proposed (additional electrodes, collimating magnetic field, etc.), but we need not go into the details (see Nier's papers[11]).

Known quantities of gases are introduced into the mass spectrometer by conventional methods of gas manipulation. Liquids can be conveniently introduced by the ingenious device of Taylor and Young.[12] A cylinder closed by a fritted glass disk and a layer of mercury is connected to the ionization chamber, as indicated in Fig. 116. Mercury does not flow through the fritted glass disk because of surface tension. The tip of a micropipette containing the liquid to be analyzed is brought in contact

[10]A. J. Dempster, *Phys. Rev.*, **20**, 631 (1922).
[11]A. O. Nier, *Rev. Sci. Instruments*, **11**, 212 (1940); **18**, 398 (1947).
[12]R. C. Taylor and W. S. Young, *Ind. Eng. Chem., Anal. Ed.*, **17**, 811 (1945).

with the disk, and a small volume of liquid (0.001 ml) is allowed to enter the ionization chamber through the disk. Since the vapor of a mixture of several liquids generally has not the same composition as the liquid phase, it is important to let the liquid, rather than its vapor, enter the mass spectrometer.

Solids can be ionized by evaporation from a hot filament as suggested by Dempster.[3] This method of producing ions was seldom applied in the early work. It has been recently reinvestigated and used in the analysis of traces of material (less than 1-mg sample). In general, solids are evaporated in a furnace, and the vapor is ionized with an electron gun.[13] Difficulties arise because the rate of evaporation and condensation of solid substances depend on their molecular or atomic weights, and consequently rates are not the same for the various constituents of the sample.

Several ionic species are generally produced by ionization of a single compound under electron impact (*cracking*), and it is important to understand and to control the factors affecting ion production. The most important of these factors, namely, the accelerating voltage in the electron gun and the temperature of the gas, will be considered.

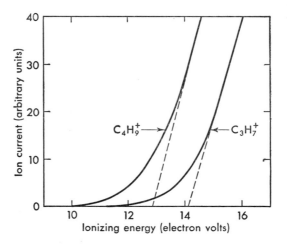

Fig. 117. Rate of ion production as a function of the energy of ionization for 2,2,3-trimethylbutane. The sensitivity for $C_4H_9^+$ is 0.45 times that for $C_3H_7^+$. [From data of D. P. Stevenson, *Discussions Faraday Soc.*, **10**, 35 (1951), reproduced by permission of the Faraday Society.]

The ion current increases progressively with accelerating voltage (Fig. 117), then levels off, and ultimately drops after reaching a plateau (not shown in Fig. 117). The existence of a plateau or maximum is questioned,

[13]See, for instance, the design of A. E. Shaw and W. Rall, *Rev. Sci. Instruments*, **18**, 278 (1947).

and only the initial rising segment of the current-voltage curve is generally considered.[14] Such curves are characterized by their *appearance potential,* i.e., by the accelerating voltage at which the current "begins to become noticeable." Appearance potentials depend, among other factors, on the ionization potential of the molecules producing the ions, i.e., on the energy that is required to remove the most weakly bound electron from the molecule. The definition of the appearance potential is not rigorous because of the difficulty of defining the potential at which the current "begins to increase." However, methods have been developed for correlating appearance and ionization potentials. Details can be found, for instance, in Robertson's monograph.

The ion current varies with temperature,[15,16] but no stringent requirement on temperature control need be imposed in analytical applications.

TABLE XIX

Relative Abundance of Some Products in the Cracking of Butane and Isobutane by Electron Impact[a]

$\dfrac{m}{e}$	RELATIVE ABUNDANCE[b]	
	Butane	Isobutane
15	4.83	5.55
26	5.36	1.95
27	37.9	27.9
28	33.3	2.51
29	44.8	6.37
39	13.0	16.6
41	28.4	37.7
42	12.4	33.9
43	100.0	100.0
58	12.6	2.75

[a]From American Petroleum Project 44, National Bureau of Standards, Washington, D. C.
[b]In per cent of abundance of $C_3H_7^+$ of specific mass 43 for ionization at 50 volts.

The cracking pattern of a substance (Table XIX) varies somewhat from one instrument to another, but it is quite stable for a given instrument. Random fluctuations of the order of 1 to 2 per cent are observed in the relative abundance of the fragments. The magnitude of these fluctuations varies from one fragment to another. A systematic change in the cracking pattern is also observed over long periods, mainly because of a change in the surface of the electrodes in the ion source. An abnormal behavior can readily be detected by frequent calibration with a gas having a known cracking pattern (butane).

[14]The theoretical analysis of current-voltage curves is difficult. See the first analysis by N. D. Coggeshall, *J. Chem. Phys.,* **12,** 19 (1944) and the more recent paper of D. Rittenberg, *Nucleonics,* **4,** No. 1, 41 (1949).
[15]R. E. Fox and J. A. Hipple, *J. Chem. Phys.,* **15,** 208 (1947).
[16]D. P. Stevenson, *ibid.,* **17,** 101 (1949).

b. Focusing System. Dempster's design, in which ions travel along a 180-deg trajectory, has been adopted for many years[17] and is still often selected, although a rather bulky magnet is required. This disadvantage prompted Nier[11] and Hipple[18,19] to develop *sector instruments* in which the angle of the sector is either 60 (Nier) or 90 (Hipple) deg. The relative merits of sector and 180-deg instruments have been argued at length, but sector instruments seem to be preferred nowadays.

The current through the magnet coil must be rigorously controlled [see equation 13–5)], and rather heavy equipment is required to achieve this result. This control equipment is eliminated and the instrument is simplified when permanent magnets (Alnico alloy) are utilized, as is increasingly the case at the present.[20]

The magnetic field is generally kept constant, and the scale of m/e values is scanned by varying the ion accelerating voltage. Stepwise selection of different ranges of masses is achieved with magnetic shunts.

c. Ion Collector and Recording of Mass Spectrograms. Ion currents are small (10^{-10}—10^{-14} amp) and must be amplified before their recording. Ions are collected in a cylinder (Faraday cylinder) which is connected to the grid of an electrometer tube (see Section 2–10a) whose output is in turn amplified. The amplified ion current is recorded as a function of the ratio m/e. A four-element recording oscillograph (sensitivity 1, 1/3, 1/10, 1/30) has the advantage of covering simultaneously a wide range of ion currents[21] (Fig. 118) and the disadvantage of requiring photographic processing. A pen-and-ink recorder can also be utilized, but it must be provided with an automatic sensitivity selector[22] (scale expander) to permit the recording of peaks of greatly varying intensity. The latter type of recorder is preferred in recent instruments.

Vibrating reed electrometers[23-25] have also been used in the recording of mass spectrograms.

Rapid recording of mass spectrograms by means of a cathode-ray

[17]W. Bleakney, *Phys. Rev.*, **40**, 496 (1932).

[18]J. A. Hipple, *J. Appl. Phys.*, **13**, 551 (1942).

[19]J. A. Hipple, D. J. Grove, and W. M. Hickam, *Rev. Sci. Instruments*, **16**, 69 (1945).

[20]For design considerations, see D. Hadfield and D. L. Mawson, *Brit. J. Appl. Phys.*, **3**, 199 (1952).

[21]H. W. Washburn, H. F. Wiley, and S. M. Rock, *Ind. Eng. Chem., Anal. Ed.*, **15**, 541 (1943).

[22]D. J. Grove and J. A. Hipple, *Rev. Sci. Instruments*, **18**, 837 (1947).

[23]H. Palevsky, R. K. Swank, and R. Grenchik, *Phys. Rev.*, **70**, 117A (1946); *Rev. Sci. Instruments*, **18**, 298 (1947).

[24]S. A. Scherbatskoy and R. E. Fearon, *Phys. Rev.*, **70**, 96 (1946); S. A. Scherbatskoy, T. H. Gilmartin, and G. Swift, *Rev. Sci. Instruments*, **18**, 415 (1947).

[25]In a vibrating reed electrometer the voltage to be measured is applied to a vibrating condenser. The resulting alternating signal is amplified, rectified, and finally fed back to the vibrating condenser in such a way as to compensate the voltage to be measured. The feedback voltage is measured or recorded.

oscilloscope is advantageous with systems of rapidly changing composition, as in kinetic studies. The recording time is as low as 1/30 or even 1/200 sec in instruments described in the literature.[26,27]

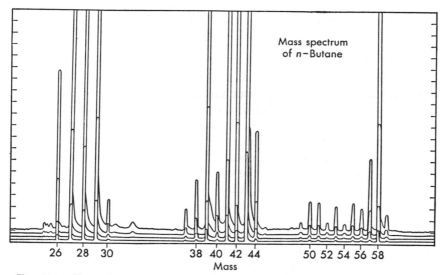

Fig. 118. Example of mass spectrogram. (Courtesy Consolidated Electrodynamics Corporation, Pasadena, California.)

d. Auxiliary Equipment. Auxiliary equipment such as a pumping system and voltage regulator need not be discussed. One point, however, which is of considerable practical importance should be mentioned; namely, the necessity of preventing stopcock grease from entering the vacuum system. Otherwise, grease vapor, which yields many different ions, increases the background ion current.

13-4. APPLICATIONS

a. Chemical Analysis. Three fundamental requirements should be satisfied in quantitative analysis by mass spectrometry: (1) the substance being analyzed should have a stable cracking pattern; (2) the ion currents of the components should be additive; and (3) the ion current of each component should be proportional to the partial pressure of this component. These conditions are never rigorously fulfilled, but quantitative results can nevertheless be obtained with a stable instrument. The method of calculation for a mixture of j components is as follows:

The partial pressures of the components are $p_1, p_2, \cdots p_j$, and the peak

[26] A. T. Forrester and W. B. Whalley, *Rev. Sci. Instruments*, **17**, 549 (1946).
[27] W. Siri, *ibid.*, **18**, 540 (1947).

heights corresponding to the masses $1, 2, \cdots m$ are $H_1, H_2, \cdots H_m$. Then,

$$\left.\begin{array}{l} h_{11}p_1 + h_{12}p_2 \cdots + h_{1j}p_j = H_1 \\ h_{21}p_1 + h_{22}p_2 \cdots + h_{2j}p_j = H_2 \\ \cdots\cdots\cdots\cdots\cdots\cdots\cdots\cdots\cdots \\ h_{m1}p_1 + h_{m2}p_2 \cdots + h_{mj}p_j = H_m \\ p_1 + p_2 \cdots + p_j = p \end{array}\right\}, \qquad (13\text{-}6)$$

where p is the pressure of the gas admitted in the ionization chamber. The coefficients h_{ij} can be determined in an analysis with a mixture of known composition. Since each component yields several fragments by cracking, the number of equations in (13-6) exceeds the number of unknowns, and some equations are not independent of others. Altogether the set of equations (13-6) involves j independent equations and j unknowns, and the solution is thus uniquely determined. The labor involved in numerical calculations is greatly reduced by the use of an electrical computer,[28] and the solution for eight unknowns, for instance, may then be obtained in perhaps 30 to 60 min. Some of the methods of matrix algebra are also useful in the handling of equations (13-6).[29]

The above method requires the measurement of the pressure p, and while this measurement is entirely feasible, it is sometimes practical to avoid presure determinations and to apply the following *peak ratio method*.[30] The method will be discussed for the case of two components, but the same reasoning can be extended to more complicated cases.

Let m_1 and m_2 be the masses of the components; H_1 and H_2, the peak heights in a mixture of known partial pressures p_1 and p_2; and H_1' and H_2', the peak heights for the mixture at the unknown partial pressures p_1' and p_2'. In view of equations (13-6), one has

$$\left.\begin{array}{l} h_{11}p_1 + h_{12}p_2 = H_1 \\ h_{21}p_1 + h_{22}p_2 = H_2 \end{array}\right\}, \qquad (13\text{-}7)$$

and a similar set of equations in p_1' and p_2' with H_1' and H_2' in the second members. These systems of equations can readily be solved for the ratio p_1'/p_2'. After some algebra, there results

$$\frac{p_1'}{p_2'} = \left[\frac{(h_{12}/h_{22}) - (H_1'/H_2')}{(H_1'/H_2') - (h_{11}/h_{21})}\right]\left[\frac{(H_1/H_2) - (h_{11}/h_{21})}{(h_{12}/h_{22}) - (H_1/H_2)}\right]\frac{p_1}{p_2}. \qquad (13\text{-}8)$$

Reliable results are obtained in mass spectrometry, as was shown by a comparison with conventional gas analysis methods.[31] Errors generally do

[28]C. E. Berry, D. E. Wilcox, S. M. Rock, and H. W. Washburn, *J. Appl. Phys.*, **17**, 262 (1946).

[29]See a brief treatment in A. J. B. Robertson, *Mass Spectrometry*, Wiley, New York, 1954, pp. 98–100.

[30]S. E. J. Johnsen, *Anal. Chem.*, **19**, 305 (1947).

[31]M. Shepherd, *J. Research Natl. Bur. Standards*, **38**, 19, (1947); *Ind. Eng. Chem. Anal. Ed.*, **19**, 635 (1947).

not exceed 1 to 2 mole per cent, and the accuracy can be further improved by blending the unknown with an internal standard, such as neon or argon for gases and benzene for liquids.[32-35] However, the accuracy of results greatly depends on the nature and composition of the analyzed gas, and the quotation of data may be misleading. The absorption of certain components of the sample and the retention of past samples are sources of difficulties, in particular with oxygenated compounds. These compounds may also react with the filament (removal of the carbide layer) of the ion source, with a possible resulting modification of the cracking pattern.

Mass spectrometry is commonly applied to the detection of leaks in vacuum systems. A mass spectrometer is connected to the vacuum system and a weak jet of helium is directed on the parts being tested. A leak results in the appearance of the helium peak. Direct-reading leak detectors of this type are available.

Even free radicals in chemical reactions can be determined by mass spectrometry at concentrations as low as 10^{-3} per cent, as was shown by Eltenton[36] in a pioneering investigation.

Summarizing, mass spectrometry is an accurate tool for qualitative and quantitative analysis. The method is eminently suited to routine work and results can be obtained at a rapid pace—less than 1 hr for a complete analysis, including calculations. The method is particularly adapted to the analysis of gases or liquids. Application to solids involves serious difficulties which are progressively being overcome. Only very small amounts of substance (1 mg or less) are needed. The cost of equipment is high, but labor saving justifies initial expenditures (petroleum industry, etc.).

Mass spectrograms for a large number of compounds are available in the literature.[37,38]

b. *Mass and Abundance Measurements—Isotope Separation.* The first application of mass spectrometry, namely, the determination of the relative abundance of isotopes, is not within the realm of analytical chemistry, and details will not be given here. Much progress has been made in this field, and even such a difficult separation as that of HD and He[3] has been achieved.[39,40] Mass spectrometers have also been utilized in precise

[32]E. E. Roper, *U. S. Patent*, No. 2,412,359 (1946).

[33]B. W. Thomas and W. D. Seyfried, *Anal. Chem.*, **21**, 1022 (1949).

[34]A. V. Grosse, S. G. Hindin, and A. D. Kirshenbaum, *Anal. Chem.*, **21**, 386 (1949).

[35]S. G. Hindin and A. V. Grosse, *ibid.*, **20**, 1019 (1948).

[36]G. C. Eltenton, *J. Chem. Phys.*, **10**, 403 (1942); **15**, 455 (1947); *J. Phys. Colloid Chem.*, **52**, 463 (1948).

[37]*Catalog of Mass Spectral Data*, Am. Petroleum Institute Research Project 44, National Bureau of Standards, Washington, D.C.

[38]S. M. Rock, *Anal. Chem.*, **23**, 261 (1951), gives data for 279 compounds.

[39]L. T. Aldrich and A. O. Nier, *Phys. Rev.*, **70**, 983 (1946). This separation is difficult because the peaks for He[3] and HD are very close.

[40]See also the two-ion-beam method of A. O. Nier, E. P. Ney, and M. G. Inghram, *Rev. Sci. Instruments*, **18**, 294 (1947).

mass measurements[41] and in accurate determinations of the packing fractions of the elements.[42]

Isotopes can be separated by mass spectrometry, and although quantities produced in this manner are rather small, the method has received much attention. This application has been reviewed in detail by Dawton and Smith.[43]

c. Tracer Studies and Isotopic Dilution Method. Isotopes are often utilized in the elucidation of reaction mechanisms, and the reader is certainly familiar with the principle of the tracer method. Perhaps the first application was made by Polanyi and Szabo[44] in their classical work on the mechanism of saponification. They hydrolyzed amyl acetate with water containing oxygen–18 and found that this isotope was not present in the resulting amyl alcohol, thus proving that the reaction is

$$\text{R.C} \diagup_{\boxed{O - R' + H}}^{O} - O - H \longrightarrow R - CO_2H + R'OH \qquad (13\text{-}9)$$

and not

$$\text{R.C} \diagup_{O - \boxed{R' + H - O} - H}^{O} \longrightarrow R - CO_2H + R'OH \qquad (13\text{-}10)$$

Numerous applications involving one of the isotopes D, N^{15}, C^{13}, O^{18} have now been made, particularly in biochemistry (see Chapter 14 for the case of radioactive isotopes). A good historical account of the pioneering work can be found in a review by von Hevesy.[45]

The labeling of a compound by an isotope provides an elegant method for the analysis of complex mixtures by the *isotopic dilution method*. The principle is as follows:

Suppose that a component in a mixture is to be determined quantitatively. A known amount of this component, labeled with an isotope, is added to the mixture, and the amount of tracer is then determined (for instance, by mass spectrometry) in a known weight of the pure component isolated from the mixture. The pure component need not be separated quantitatively, and this greatly simplifies the analytical procedure. The method was intro-

[41]J. Mattauch, National Burea of Standards, *Circ.* **522,** 1 (1953); *Naturwissenschaften* **39,** 557 (1952).

[42]P. I. Richards, E. E. Hayes, and S. A. Goudsmit (abstract only), *Phys. Rev.,* **76,** 180 (1949). The packing fraction is defined by the ratio (atomic weight − mass number)/(mass number).

[43]R. H. V. M. Dawton and M. L. Smith, *Quart. Revs.,* **9,** 1 (1955); see also M. L. Smith, Ed., *Electromagnetically Enriched Isotopes and Mass Spectrometry,* Academic, Press, New York, 1956.

[44]M. Polanyi and A. L. Szabo, *Trans. Faraday Soc.,* **30,** 508 (1934).

[45]G. von Hevesy, *Cold Spring Harbor Symposia on Quant. Biol.,* **13,** 129 (1948).

duced by von Hevesy and Hobby[46] and developed particularly by Rittenberg and his co-workers[47] for the determination of certain amino acids in proteins. Application to oxygen elementary analysis has been investigated.[48]

d. Appearance Potentials. Bond dissociation energies can be calculated from appearance potentials. The dissociation energy of a substance AB is the heat, at absolute zero temperature, of the reaction

$$AB \text{ (gas)} = A \text{ (gas)} + B \text{ (gas)}.$$

If AB yields ions by electron impact, the appearance potential is the sum of the ionization potential of A and the bond dissociation energy $D(A\text{-}B)$, at least if the kinetic and excitation (electronic, vibrational, and rotational) energies of the fragments can be neglected. Numerous papers have dealt with appearance potentials, and the reader may study Stevenson's investigation,[49] for instance, as representative of present activity in this field. There are some difficulties which are partially caused by the relative uncertainty of defining exactly the appearance potential in plots of ion current versus electron accelerating voltage (Fig. 117). This difficulty can be overcome by measuring the difference between two appearance potentials for the same ion in the same state and in two similar processes.[50]

13-5. NEW METHODS OF MASS SPECTROMETRY

Two groups of new methods of sorting ions have been developed: (1) time of flight and velocity selection methods; and (2) methods based on the principle of the cyclotron. The resolution in the former group of methods is rather low, whereas it is excellent (up to 3500) for instruments of the cyclotron type. These newer methods have not supplanted the conventional mass spectrometer, but much effort is being spent in their improvement. Details are beyond the scope of this text, but the reader may study the principle of these new modes of approach[51-54] as an exercise.

13-6. OTHER INSTRUMENTAL METHODS OF GAS ANALYSIS

Several methods of gas analysis (thermal conductivity, magnetic susceptibility, velocity of sound, gas chromatography, etc.), which often require

[46]G. von Hevesy and R. Hobby, *Z. Anal. Chem.*, **88**, 1 (1932).

[47]See review of D. Rittenberg, *J. Appl. Phys.*, **13**, 561 (1942).

[48]A. D. Kirshenbaum, A. G. Streng, and A. V. Grosse, *Anal. Chem.*, **24**, 1361 (1952).

[49]D. P. Stevenson, *Discussions Faraday Soc.*, **10**, 35 (1951).

[50]J. A. Hipple and D. P. Stevenson, *Phys. Rev.*, **63**, 121 (1943).

[51]S. A. Goudsmit, *Phys. Rev.*, **74**, 622 (1948).

[52]W. H. Bennett, *Phys. Rev.* (abstracts only), **74**, 1222 (1948); **78**, 332 (1950); **79**, 222 (1950); *J. Appl. Phys.*, **21**, 143, 723 (1950).

[53]H. Sommer, H. A. Thomas, and J. A. Hipple, *Phys. Rev.*, **76**, 1877 (1949); **82**, 697 (1951).

[54]For additional references, see Barnard's monograph and the periodic reviews in *Analytical Chemistry* (Section 13-7).

much simpler equipment than mass spectrometry, have been devised. Some of these methods find extensive application in industry, and the reader may find it profitable to study them as literature survey problems (see Section 13–8). A good and simple survey is given by Mullen,[55] and periodic reviews can be found in *Analytical Chemistry.*[56]

13–7. BIBLIOGRAPHY

a. Books and Articles

F. W. Aston, *Mass Spectra and Isotopes*, 2nd ed., Longmans, Green and Co., New York, 1942.

G. P. Barnard, *Modern Mass Spectrometry*, Institute of Physics, London, 1953.

H. Ewald and H. Hinterberger, *Methods and Applications of Mass Spectrometry*, Verlag Chemie, Weinheim, 1953.

F. H. Field and J. L. Franklin, *Electron Impact Phenomena and the Properties of Gaseous Ions*, Academic Press, New York. (In preparation.)

J. A. Hipple, article in *Recent Advances in Analytical Chemistry*, Vol. VII, Interscience, New York, 1949.

J. J. Mitchell, chapter in *Physical Chemistry of Hydrocarbons*, A. Farkas, Ed., Vol. I, Academic Press, New York, 1950.

A. J. B. Robertson, *Mass Spectrometry*, Wiley, New York, 1954.

H. W. Washburn, article in *Physical Methods in Chemical Analysis*, W. G. Berl, Ed., Vol. I, Academic Press, New York, 1950.

b. Review Articles

V. H. Dibeler, *Anal. Chem.*, **26**, 58 (1954); **28**, 610 (1956).

V. H. Dibeler and J. A. Hipple, *Anal. Chem.*, **24**, 27 (1952).

W. J. Dunning, *Quart. Revs.*, **9**, 23 (1955).

J. A. Hipple and M. Shepherd, *Anal. Chem.*, **21**, 32 (1949).

J. Kistemaker, *Anal. Chim. Acta.*, **2**, 522 (1948).

K. I. Mayne, *Repts. Progr. Phys.*, **15**, 24 (1952).

A. O. C. Nier, *Ann. Rev. Nuclear Sci.*, **1**, 137 (1952).

M. Shepherd and J. A. Hipple, *Anal. Chem.*, **22**, 23 (1950).

H. G. Thode and R. B. Shields, *Rept. Progress Phys.*, **12**, 1 (1948–49).

J. W. Wachter and F. L. Sachs, *U.S. Atomic Energy Commission*, Rept. **Y-958** (1954). A detailed bibliography.

13–8. PROBLEMS

1. Discuss the design of a mass spectrometer for the analysis of solids. See A. E. Shaw and W. Rall, *Rev. Sci. Instruments*, **18**, 278 (1947).

2. Compare the features of 180-deg mass spectrometers with sector instruments. See Barnard's monograph (Section 13–7a), pp. 154–158.

3. Discuss the method of internal standards in mass spectrometry. See references in footnotes 32 to 35 in text.

[55]P. W. Mullen. *Modern Gas Analysis*, Interscience, New York, 1955.
[56]L. K. Nash, *Anal. Chem.*, **22**, 108 (1950); **23**, 74 (1951).

4. Show how the mass spectrometer can be utilized as a microeffusiometer. See M. Eden, B. E. Burr, and A. W. Pratt, *Anal. Chem.*, **23**, 1735 (1951).

5. Discuss the design of a mass spectrometer for the separation of isotopes on a production scale, and review some applications. See C. P. Keim, *J. Appl. Phys.*, **24**, 1255 (1953); R. H. V. M. Dawton and M. L. Smith, *Quart. Revs.*, **9**, 1 (1955).

6. Discuss the principles of the newer methods of mass spectrometry, and compare their essential features with those of conventional mass spectrometers. See references in footnotes 51 to 54 in text.

7. Discuss the determination of the bond energy $D(CH_3—H)$ from appearance potentials. See D. P. Stevenson, *Discussions Faraday Soc.*, **10**, 35 (1951).

8. Review some typical applications of the isotope dilution method in biochemistry. See D. Rittenberg, *J. Appl. Phys.*, **13**, 561 (1942).

9. Study the paper of M. Shepherd [*Anal. Chem.*, **19**, 635 (1947)] on the accuracy obtained in mass spectrometry.

10. Study how the rate of recombination of methyl radicals was measured by mass spectrometry by K. U. Ingold and F. P. Lossing, *J. Chem. Phys.*, **21**, 368, 1135 (1953).

11. Discuss the principles of gas analysis by thermal conductivity measurements. See reference in footnote 55 in text and the article by E. R. Weaver in *Physical Methods in Chemical Analysis*, W. G. Berl, Ed., Vol. II, Academic Press, New York, 1951. Further details can be found in the classical work of H. A. Daynes, *Gas Analysis by Measurement of Thermal Conductivity*, Cambridge University Press, London, 1933.

12. Discuss the principle of gas analysis by measurement of the velocity of sound. See reference in footnote 55 in text and the article by C. E. Crouthamel and H. Diehl, *Anal. Chem.*, **20**, 515 (1948).

13. Discuss the method of oxygen analysis based on the measurement of the magnetic susceptibility of this gas. See L. Pauling, R. E. Wood, and J. H. Sturdivant, *J. Am. Chem. Soc.*, **68**, 795 (1946); C. A. Dyer, *Rev. Sci. Instruments*, **18**, 696 (1947).

14. Prepare a seminar on gas chromatography. Use as a source, C. Phillips, *Gas Chromatography*, Academic Press, New York, 1956.

14

Nuclear Radiation Methods

14–1. RADIOACTIVE DECAY

Most elements are not naturally radioactive, and purely analytical applications of nuclear radiation measurements would be of very limited scope if it were not for the possibility of transforming many elements into radioactive ones (*activation analysis*) or to analyze mixtures by addition of compounds tagged (tracers) with a radioactive element (*isotopic dilution method*). Even so, strictly analytical applications of radioactivity are far less general than for other methods such as absorption spectrometry and polarography.

The detailed discussion of nuclear radiation (*nucleonics*) is not within the province of this book, and the following treatment is limited (1) to some of the methods for nuclear radiation measurements, (2) to analytical applications of tracers, and (3) to activation analysis. Some of the fundamentals of radioactive decay are covered in this introductory section.

The disintegration rate of a radioactive element is proportional to the number of its atoms present in the sample. Thus,

$$\frac{dN}{dt} = -\lambda N, \tag{14–1}$$

where λ is the *decay constant*. Upon integration equation (14–1) yields the number of radioactive atoms at time t,

$$N = N_0 e^{-\lambda t}, \tag{14–2}$$

where N_0 is the number of radioactive atoms present at time $t = 0$.

The unit for rates of disintegration is the *curie*, which corresponds to

3.7×10^{10} disintegrations per second. The millicurie is the unit most commonly used. Samples are sometimes characterized by their *specific activity*, which is expressed in curies or millicuries per gram.

It is convenient to discuss the decay of a radioactive element in terms of its *half-life* τ, i.e., the time interval after which the disintegration rate has dropped to one-half of its value. Half-lives[1] range from a fraction of a second to more than 10^9 years (Table XX).

TABLE XX

Some Properties of a few Radioactive Isotopes[a]

ATOMIC NUMBER	SYMBOL	ATOMIC WEIGHT	HALF-LIFE	ENERGY, MEV[b]
1	H	3	12.5 *yr*	0.018
6	C	14	5720 *yr*	0.15
11	Na	24	14.9 *hr*	1.39
15	P	32	14.3 *d*	1.72
16	S	35	87 *d*	0.166
27	Co	60	5.2 *yr*	0.31[c]
53	I	131	8.0 *d*	0.32, 0.60[d]
88	Ra	226	1600 *yr*	4.79 (β), 4161 (β) 0.188 (γ)
92	U	235	8.8×10^8 *yr*	4.5 (a), 0.16 (γ)
		238	4.5×10^9 *yr*	4.2

[a]From *Nuclear Data*, Circular 499, National Bureau of Standards, Washington, D. C., 1950.
[b]10^6 ev.
[c]Maximum energy for beta-ray emission; this is followed by further disintegration with gamma emission (1.17 mev and 1.33 mev). A small fraction (<10%) disintegrates with beta emission of higher energy (1.56 mev).
[d]Two simultaneous beta emissions, which are followed by gamma emission.

The half-life can readily be expressed in terms of the decay constant. Thus, the combination of equations (14–1) and (14–2) yields

$$\frac{dN}{dt} = -\lambda N_0 e^{-\lambda t}, \qquad (14\text{--}3)$$

where $-\lambda N_0$ is the rate of disintegration at time $t = 0$. At time $t = \tau$

$$-\frac{1}{2}\lambda N_0 = -\lambda N_0 e^{-\lambda \tau}, \qquad (14\text{--}4)$$

by definition of τ, and therefore,[2]

$$\tau = \frac{0.693}{\lambda}. \qquad (14\text{--}5)$$

[1]A survey of nuclear data is given in Circular 499 (and supplements) of theNational Bureau of Standards. See also the articles by K. Way *et al.*, *Nucleonics*, **2**, No. 5, 82 (1948) and J. M. Hollander, I. Perlman, and G. T. Seaborg, *Rev. Mod. Phys.*, **25**, 469 (1953). Some data are conveniently summarized in a chart available from Dept. 6-221 of the General Electric Co., Schenectady 5, N.Y.

[2]$\frac{1}{2} = e^{-\lambda \tau}$, or $-\lambda \tau \log e = \log \frac{1}{2}$, i.e., $-0.434\lambda \tau = -0.301$ and $\lambda \tau = 0.693$.

The disintegration rate given by equation (14–3) may now be written in terms of the half-life as

$$\frac{dN}{dt} = \left(\frac{dN}{dt}\right)_{t=0} e^{-0.693(t/\tau)}, \qquad (14\text{–}6)$$

where $(dN/dt)_{t=0}$ is the rate at time $t = 0$.

It follows from equation (14–6) that a plot of the decimal logarithm of disintegration rate against time should yield a straight line whose slope is $-(0.693/\tau)\log e$, or $-0.301/\tau$. It is possible to ascertain from such a plot whether only a single element is disintegrating; when several radioactive elements are present, the logarithmic plot is composed of several linear segments, at least if the half-lives are different enough from each other (Fig. 119).

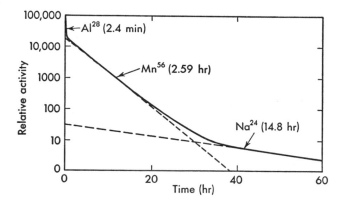

Fig. 119. Semilogarithmic plot of rate of disintegration against time for a mixture of Al^{28}, Mn^{56}, and Na^{24} in the activation analysis of an aluminum alloy. [From G. E. Boyd, *Anal. Chem.*, **21**, 335 (1949).]

In general, disintegration rates are determined by counting the number of disintegrations over a certain time t_m. If t_m is negligibly small as compared with the half-life τ, the rate is simply the ratio of the number of disintegrations to the time t_m. When t_m is of the order of τ, as is the case for elements having a short half-life, rates obtained by the foregoing procedure must be corrected. It can be demonstrated (see problem 1, Section 14–7) that this correction does not exceed a few per cent for $t_m < 0.1\tau$.

Further details about radioactive decay, and in particular about the complex disintegration schemes of certain elements, can be found in the classical work of Rutherford, Chadwick, and Ellis and in the other books listed in Section 14–6.

14-2. COUNTING EQUIPMENT

a. Classification of Detectors. Detection of nuclear radiation is based on the interaction of radiation with matter, and a detailed treatment of detection should begin with a review of the interaction of neutrons, electromagnetic radiation (γ- and X-rays), and charged particles (α and β) with matter. This approach will not be followed here, for the sake of briefness, and it will suffice to know that the following effects of nuclear radiation are generally applied to detection: (1) chemical reaction; (2) ionization of a gas, liquid, or solid; (3) emission of light. Initiation of a chemical reaction is applied, for instance, in detection by the photographic plate, a method which will not be discussed here.[3] Ionization is at the basis of several important detectors: *ionization chambers, proportional and Geiger-Müller counters.* Light emission is applied in *scintillation counters.*

b. Ionization Chambers. An ionization chamber is essentially composed of a vessel with two electrodes connected to a power supply. The chamber is filled with a gas which often is at atmospheric pressure. The sample is placed either inside the chamber or outside in front of a transparent window. Radioactive gases (carbon dioxide labeled with carbon-14, for instance) are conveniently studied by introducing them in the chamber.

Ionization of the gas in the chamber liberates electrons and positive ions, which migrate in the electric field between the electrodes. These charged particles recombine before they reach the electrode when the electrical field between the electrodes is very low, and the current in the electrode circuit is extremely small. The effect of recombination decreases as the field strength is increased, and a saturation plateau is reached in the current-voltage characteristic of the chamber at field intensities of the order of 10 volts per centimeter. Virtually all ions produced in the chamber are then captured at the electrodes. Each disintegration produces in the saturation range, on the average, a constant number of ions and causes the flow of a certain quantity of electricity in the electrode circuit. The number of ionizing events caused by a nuclear particle or photon increases with the gas pressure, and the current in the electrode circuit increases accordingly.

Currents through ionization chambers are very low (10^{-10} to 10^{-16} amp) and are measured with d-c amplifiers (with electrometer tube in the input circuit), with vibrating reed electrometers,[4] or with electrometers. The latter type of instrument is perhaps the most sensitive, particularly the quartz-fiber instrument devised by the Lauritzens.[5,6] The pulses are

[3]See, for instance, A. Beiser's review of nuclear emulsion techniques in *Rev. Mod. Phys.*, **24**, 273 (1952).

[4]See footnote 25 in Chapter 13.

[5]C. C. Lauritzen and T. Lauritzen, *Rev. Sci. Instruments*, **8**, 438 (1937).

[6]See the design of F. C. Henriques, Jr., G. B. Kistiakowsky, C. Margnetti, and W. G. Schneider, *Ind. Eng. Chem., Anal. Ed.*, **18**, 349 (1946).

counted or integrated over a given period. The counting method requires a measuring device (generally with d-c amplifier) with a sufficiently fast response (Section 14–2f). Integration is generally performed by charging the chamber at a given voltage in the saturation range, and by following with an electrometer or a vibrating reed electrometer (with pen-and-ink recorder) the drift in voltage which results from ionization. A correction must be made for the leakage current observed without sample. This leakage current is made very low by proper insulation of the electrodes (amber, teflon, etc.) and by removal of air moisture.

Ionization chambers played an important role in early investigations on radioactivity. They still are utilized in alpha and gamma ray determinations, but other counters, and particularly Geiger-Müller counters, are generally preferred because they lend themselves more readily than ionization chambers to routine work. Pocket ionization chambers are utilized in radiation monitoring.

c. Proportional Counters. When the voltage applied to an ionization chamber is raised above the saturation voltage, *ion multiplication* is observed and the current in the electrode circuit increases. In the process of ion multiplication an electron produced by the initial ionization event has sufficient energy to ionize the molecules with which it collides, and this results in the further production of electrons and positive ions. This *avalanche process* greatly amplifies the pulse size, perhaps by a factor 10^5, in comparison with the pulse obtained in the saturation region. If the field strength is not too high, the pulse size is proportional to the energy of the incident particle or photon, and the instrument therefore is called a *proportional counter.*

A proportional counter tube is essentially composed of a thin tungsten wire (diameter as small as 0.002 mm) which is exactly concentric to a metallic cylinder having a diameter of several centimeters (Fig. 120). The wire is the anode of the tube. This arrangement is used for two reasons:

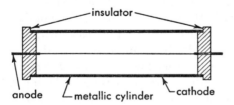

Fig. 120. Schematic diagram of proportional counter.

1. The electric field along the radius of the tube varies hyperbolically,[7] and in the immediate vicinity of the wire, reaches the rather high value (10^4 volts cm^{-1}) required for ion multiplication; high field strengths are produced, although the total voltage applied between wire and cylinder is perhaps only 1000 volts,

[7]See an electricity text; for instance, L. Page and N. I. Adams, *Principles of Electricity,* 2nd ed., Van Nostrand, New York, 1949.

whereas this would not be the case with a counting tube composed of two parallel plates, for instance.

2. The zone of ion multiplication is limited to a thin sheath around the anode and the multiplication factor is constant; the volume of gas in which electrons are produced by primary ionization events is very much greater than the multiplication zone, and the multiplication factor is independent of the position in the tube where an electron is generated by primary ionization. This would not be the case with parallel plate electrodes.

Samples of low activity, such as compounds tagged with carbon-14 and sulfur-35, are generally placed inside the counter tube, preferably as a gas but often as a solid in a small dish. In the latter case it is convenient to pass a gas at a constant rate through the counter (*flow-type counter*) rather than to have the complications of filling a hermetically sealed tube. Many gases could be used, but mixtures of methane and argon or butane and helium are generally utilized in flow counters.[8]

Proportional counters [and scintillation counters (see Section 14–2e)] are utilized rather than Geiger-Müller counters whenever the measurement of pulse sizes is of importance. Even when pulse sizes need not be known, flow-type counters are more advantageous than Geiger-Müller counters in the determination of weak alpha or beta emitters, mainly because of increased sensitivity. Proportional counters are particularly advantageous in the measurement of alpha radiation because these particles have a short range (a few centimeters in air) and dissipate their energy in a small volume of gas, thus causing high local ionization. Beta and gamma rays have a much lower ionization power than alpha particles and give pulse sizes much smaller than alpha particles. The counting system can be made (see Section 14–2f) to register only pulses above a certain size, and thus it will count the alpha particles to the exclusion of beta and gamma rays.

d. Geiger-Müller Counters. When the voltage applied to a proportional counter is sufficiently increased, the pulse size corresponding to each ionizing event becomes constant and independent of the energy of the particle or quantum causing the primary ionization event. The counter then operates in the *Geiger-Müller region*. A simple explanation for the constancy of the pulse size is as follows:

As the gas is ionized in the counting tube, the quanta emitted in the ultraviolet range cause photoelectric emission of electrons by the cathode. These secondary electrons are attracted by the anode, where they cause ion multiplication at points outside the area where the avalanche process initiated by the primary ionization event first occurred. As a result, ion

[8]For the reasons for the use of this gas mixture, see Sharpe's monograph listed in Section 14–6.

multiplication spreads to a complete sheath around the anode, and the same pulse size is observed for each primary ionizing event.

Positive ions produced by ionization have much lower mobilities than electrons and they do not move far from the anode in the time interval required for the electrons to cross the space between electrodes. Positive ions therefore form a space charge around the anode and considerably decrease the field strength in the vicinity of this electrode. Conditions no longer prevail for ion multiplication, at least momentarily, but positive ions soon reach the cathode where they are neutralized with emission of ultraviolet quanta which cause photoelectric emission of electrons by the cathode. A new avalanche process is initiated, and the discharge continues. The discharge can be interrupted electronically, and the counter is then restored to conditions in which it can register a new count. However, the gas (argon) in most counting tubes contains a small fraction of a *quenching agent* which automatically interrupts the discharge, perhaps, 50 to 300 μ sec after primary ionization. Quenching agents are substances (ethyl alcohol, chlorine, bromine, etc.) having a lower ionization potential than argon, the main gas in the counter. Argon ions transfer their charge to the quenching agent with the formation of positive ions which are neutralized at the cathode. The quantum of light being emitted during neutralization of these ions has too low an energy to cause photoelectric emission of electrons, and the discharge extinguishes itself.

The number of ions produced per count is of the order of 10^9 per centimeter of anode. Large pulse sizes are generated, and the counting equipment can be quite simple. This is a marked advantage of Geiger-Müller counters over other counters.

A fraction of a quenching agent such as ethyl alcohol is decomposed by cracking during each discharge, and the life of Geiger-Müller counting tubes is limited to perhaps 10^8 to 10^9 counts.[9] Halogens simply dissociate during ionization and recombine afterwards, and the life of counting tubes in which chlorine or bromine is the quenching agent should be much longer than for tubes filled with ethyl alcohol or other organic derivatives. The halogen, however, may be consumed by reaction with the electrodes and other metallic parts of the tube. Counting tubes filled with a halogen have the further advantage of being usable at low temperatures (prospecting, etc.), while this is not the case with tubes filled with ethyl alcohol because of condensation of the quenching agent.

The characteristic of Geiger-Müller tubes showing count rate against voltage between electrodes exhibits a plateau. The tube works in this

---

[9] The volume of counting tube per centimeter of anode wire is perhaps 10 cm^3. Since the pressure of quenching agent is approximately 10^{-3} atm, there are about $(10 \times 10^{-3} \times 6 \times 10^{23})/(2.24 \times 10^4) \approx 3 \times 10^{17}$ molecules per centimeter of anode wire. Each discharge causes the decomposition of about 10^9 molecules, and the life of the counting tube is $(3 \times 10^{17})/10^9$, or 3×10^8 counts; i.e., 10^8 to 10^9 counts.

voltage range (Fig. 121). Below this plateau the voltage is too low to produce constant pulse size, and beyond the plateau the count rate increases because of breakdown and spurious discharges through the tube. Actually the plateau has a slope of perhaps 0.02 to 0.05 per cent per volt,

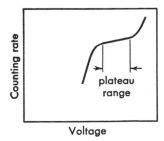

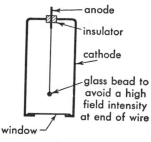

Fig. 121. Characteristics of Geiger-Müller counter.

Fig. 122. Schematic diagram of end-window Geiger-Müller counter.

and the voltage applied to the tube must be properly stabilized. The plateau generally covers a range of 200 to 300 volts for commercial tubes and is observed between 800 and 1400 volts. Tubes used in battery-operated portable detectors exhibit their plateau at a lower voltage, perhaps 400 volts. The count rate for a given voltage varies with temperature, and proper correction should be made in accurate work.

Geiger-Müller counting tubes of varied design are available: end-window type (Fig. 122), immersion type, etc. Windows are made of materials quite transparent to radiation, such as mica or aluminum, and their thickness is rated in milligrams per square centimeter. Counting tubes with a window as thin as 1 mg cm^{-2} are utilized in the counting of weak emitters, such as carbon-14 and sulfur-35.

Geiger-Müller tubes are undoubtedly utilized more often than any other counter, mainly because they require only rather simple counting equipment in view of their large pulse size. Application to the counting of beta-ray emitters is most frequent, but Geiger-Müller tubes can also be used in the measurement of the intensity of X-rays and gamma radiation. Ionization, then, is caused by the secondary electrons emitted as a result of radiation absorption (see Section 12–1). Under these conditions the efficiency of an ordinary counting tube is low (1 per cent), but it can be increased by proper selection of the nature and the pressure of the gas in the counter. Beta radiation can be filtered out by fitting the counter with a beryllium window, which is quite transparent to X-rays and gamma radiation but opaque to beta particles.

e. Scintillation Counters. The phosphorescence exhibited by certain substances, such as zinc sulfide, upon irradiation by nuclear radiation was applied to detection in the early days of radioactivity. The phosphor was observed with a microscope and individual scintillations were counted. The method was almost entirely disregarded with the development of Geiger-Müller counters, but it was revived after the invention of the photomultiplier tube (see Section 8–7).

In a scintillation counter a layer of phosphor is deposited on the window of a photomultiplier tube; each flash of the phosphor generates a pulse in the circuit of the tube, which is counted. Since the response of photomultiplier tubes is linear and the intensity of the flash is proportional to the energy of the incident particle or photon, scintillation counters can be utilized for energy measurements. This is a particularly valuable feature which they have in common with proportional counters.

The nature of the phosphor depends on the radiation to be measured: zinc sulfide activated by silver for alpha particle; naphthalene, anthracene, and other organic phosphors for beta rays; sodium iodide activated by thallium for gamma radiation. Neutrons can be counted by means of a liquid phosphor containing an element (boron, cadmium) which strongly absorbs neutrons. Details are beyond the scope of this text, but data can be found in Birks' monograph and other books listed in Section 14–6.

f. Counting Equipment. Pulses given by the counting tube are amplified[10] and either counted with a mechanical register or transformed in such a manner as to give a direct reading of the counting rate. Mechanical registers cannot follow more than a few hundred counts per second, and a *scaling unit* must generally be inserted between the counter amplifier and the register (Fig. 123). A scaler transmits to the register only one

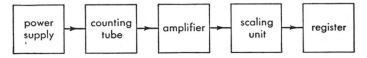

Fig. 123.   Block diagram of counting equipment.

pulse out of a given number. The basic circuit is a "scale of two" which transmits only every other pulse. By connecting scales of two in series it is possible to transmit only one pulse out of 2, 4, 8, 16, 32 . . . pulses. Scales of ten which transmit one pulse out of each 10, 100, 1000 . . . pulses are designed by combination of scales of two. They simplify the counting and often are utilized in commercial instruments. New electronic counting devices, such as the *decatron*, eliminate the necessity of having scaling units, but the discussion of these new developments is beyond the scope of this text.

[10]Except for the combination electrometer-ionization chamber.

In proportional and scintillation counters, a *discriminator* is generally connected between the counter amplifier and the scaling unit in such a manner that only pulses whose size exceeds a given and adjustable limit are transmitted to the scaling unit and register. This enables one, for instance, to count alpha particles with a proportional counter in a sample also emitting beta and/or gamma radiation. The discriminator can be set up to transmit pulses whose heights cover a narrow range (1 volt), and the variations of counting rate with pulse height can then be studied. Such *nuclear radiation spectrometers* are useful tools for qualitative and quantitative analysis.[11,12] The nuclear radiation spectrum can be determined point by point with a single channel instrument whose range of transmitted pulses is varied after the counting corresponding to each point. Instruments with twenty, forty, or even a larger number of channels cover the whole spectrum in a single operation. Details about beta- and gamma-ray spectrometers can be found in the monograph edited by Siegbahn (Section 14–6).

Counting units are often equipped with relays which stop the operation either after a given time or when the count number has reached a preselected value; this allows the operator to leave the counting unit unattended. More elaborate devices have been designed in which the counting of a sample is automatically repeated at regular intervals and the results are recorded on different registers. The data required for the construction of a complete decay curve for relatively short-lived isotopes are collected in this fashion. Such automatic instruments considerably reduce the labor required in routine activation analysis (see Section 14–5). Counting units with automatic sample changers are also useful in work involving many similar determinations.

Many commercial counting units are available in the United States and abroad (see advertisements in *Nucleonics* and other journals).

Continuous reading of the counting rate is obtained with a *counting-rate meter* whose operating principle is as follows (Fig. 124):

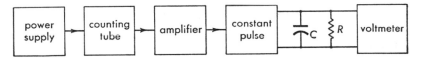

Fig. 124. Block diagram of counting-rate meter.

Each pulse of the counter is transformed into a pulse of constant height and width, which is applied to a capacitor C in such a manner that each pulse supplies a constant charge to C. Capacitor C is continuously dis-

[11]B. Kahn and W. S. Lyon, *Nucleonics*, **11**, No. 11, 61 (1953).
[12]R. E. Connally and M. B. LeBoeuf, *Anal. Chem.*, **25**, 1095 (1953).

charged through a resistance R. The voltage across C, under these conditions, depends on the charge supplied per unit of time and, consequently, on the counting rate. The latter is read directly on the vacuum-tube voltmeter connected across R. Counting-rate meters are particularly valuable in portable survey instruments. Commercial equipment is available.

g. Absolute Measurements. The measured counting rate[13] is generally smaller than the disintegration rate of the sample for several reasons: (1) absorption by the sample, by the air gap between sample and counter, and by the window of the counter; (2) the relatively poor geometry of the sample holder-counter assembly prevents all particles or photons being emitted to reach the inside of the counter; and (3) efficiency of the counter smaller than 100 per cent. The discrepancy between measured counting rates and disintegration rates is generally unimportant in analytical applications because comparative measurements are made. Whenever necessary, as in medical applications of radiotracers, counters can be calibrated with standards available from the National Bureau of Standards for some of the most commonly used isotopes. Methods have been developed for absolute activity measurements (see problem 3 in Section 14–7).

h. Sample Mounting. Three important points should be kept in mind in the mounting of samples: (1) the background radiation should be minimized; (2) the position of the sample with respect to the counter should remain the same in comparative measurements; and (3) back scattering of radiation (beta) should be kept constant.

Background radiation, which is caused by local contamination and by cosmic rays, is reduced by shielding the sample holder and counting tube with lead (free of radium) bricks. The effect of cosmic rays cannot be eliminated by ordinary shielding devices, and the counting rate cannot be reduced below a certain limit, perhaps 5 to 10 counts per minute for Geiger-Müller counters.

The position of the sample with respect to the counting tube should be rigorously fixed and reproducible in the case of weak emitters (carbon-14, sulfur-35, etc.) because of the relatively strong absorption of radiation by air in the gap between tube and holder. This air gap also must be reduced to a minimum for weak emitters.

Back-scattering of beta rays is minimized by proper selection of the material in the construction of the sample holder. Aluminum and lucite, which have a low back-scattering power, are selected in general.

14–3. COUNTING ERRORS AND CORRECTIONS

Counting rates are affected by three principal errors: (1) the error caused by background radiation; (2) the error resulting from the finite resolution time of the counting tube and counting equipment; and (3) the statistical

[13]It is assumed that the background correction discussed in Section 14–3a is made.

error. Self-absorption by samples of a weak emitter must also be taken into account.

a. Correction for Background Radiation. The counting rate for the sample is calculated by subtracting the counting rate for the background, as measured in a separate experiment, from the total counting rate obtained with the sample.

b. Error Caused by the Finite Resolution Time of Counters. If the interval between two disintegrations is shorter than the resolution time of the counting tube and counting equipment, some counts are lost. Detailed studies of this error, which is appreciable above 2000 to 20,000 counts per minute (depending on the tube) have been made, and the reader may consult a paper by Kohman[14] as a guide for further study. Only a simplified analysis will be given here.

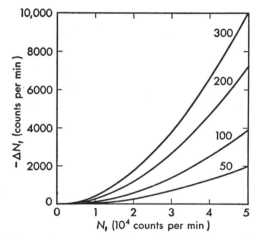

Fig. 125. Variations of error on counting rate with true counting rate for different resolution times of the counter, according to equation (14-8). Resolution times in microseconds.

Let N_t be the true counting rate; N_m, the measured rate; and t_r, the resolution time of the counter. Then the counter is not sensitive during the total interval $N_m t_r$ each unit of time, and $N_t N_m t_r$ counts are lost per unit of unit. Hence,

$$N_t = N_m + N_t N_m t_r, \qquad (14\text{-}7)$$

or

$$N_m = \frac{N_t}{1 + N_t t_r}. \qquad (14\text{-}8)$$

The rate N_m is smaller than N_t and the resulting error $-\Delta N_t$ is plotted in Fig. 125 against the true counting rate N_t for varying resolution times.

[14]T. P. Kohman, *Anal. Chem.*, **21**, 352 (1949).

The error becomes significant above 20,000 counts per minute. Larger counting rates can be avoided by dilution of the sample in most analytical applications. Otherwise, either a correction must be introduced or comparative measurements must be made.

The foregoing treatment is very approximate and gives only the order of magnitude of the counting error. This is why several methods have been developed for the experimental determination of correction curves of the type in Fig. 125. Details can be found in Kohman's paper.[14] One obvious method is to have two identical sources and count them separately and together. A complete curve is constructed by employing paired sources of varying activity.

c. Statistical Error. The counting of randomized events such as disintegrations is affected by a statistical error. The calculation of this error and the selection of conditions for minimizing it are very important in counting experiments. The following discussion must be limited to the essential points, and the reader is referred to reviews for further details.[15] Numerous references to general books on statistics can be found in reviews by Wernimont,[16] and Hader and Youden.[17]

A series of measurements of a given datum is characterized by the *standard deviation,* which is defined as the square root of the average value of the square of the individual deviations. It can be shown that the standard deviation Δ for a total of N counts is

$$\Delta = \sqrt{N}. \qquad (14\text{–}9)$$

For instance, if 10,000 counts are registered, the standard deviation is $\sqrt{10,000}$, or 1 per cent. The significance of the standard deviation may better be grasped by noting the relationship between this datum and the *probable and reliable errors.* Thus, the probable error, whose probability of not being exceeded is 0.5, is equal to 0.67Δ. The reliable error, which has a probability of 0.9 of not being exceeded, is equal to 1.64Δ.

Two types of counting procedures can be followed, depending on whether the duration of counting or the total count is controlled. The following discussion pertains to time-controlled counting, but the same ideas can be applied to count-controlled counting (see problem 4 in Section 14–7).

Let N_t be the total count for background and sample in a time interval t, and N_b the count for the background alone in the same interval. Then the counting rates are

$$\frac{N_t \pm N_t^{1/2}}{t} \text{ and } \frac{N_b \pm N_b^{1/2}}{t},$$

[15] L. J. Rainwater and C. S. Wu, *Nucleonics,* **1,** No. 2, 60 (1947).
[16] G. Wernimont, *Anal. Chem.,* **21,** 115 (1949).
[17] R. J. Hader and W. J. Youden, *ibid.,* **24,** 120 (1952).

respectively. The counting rate for the sample is

$$\frac{N_t - N_b}{t} \pm \left[\left(\frac{N_t^{1/2}}{t}\right)^2 + \left(\frac{N_b^{1/2}}{t}\right)^2\right]^{1/2},$$

and the standard deviation is

$$\Delta = \frac{100(N_t + N_b)^{1/2}}{N_t - N_b - (N_t + N_b)^{1/2}} \text{ per cent.} \qquad (14\text{--}10)$$

By introduction of the counting rates $R_t = N_t/t$ and $R_b = N_b/t$ in equation (14–10), there results,

$$\Delta = \frac{100(R_t + R_b)^{1/2}}{t^{1/2}(R_t - R_b) - (R_t + R_b)^{1/2}} \text{ per cent.} \qquad (14\text{--}11)$$

The time t for given values of R_b and Δ can be readily calculated as a function of $R_t - R_b$ from equation (14–11). The result can be presented

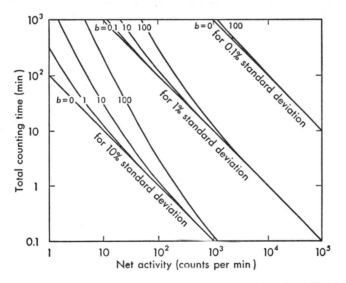

Fig. 126. Diagram for the determination of total counting time. Total time is for counting of sample and background, these two counting times being equal. [From T. P. Kohman, *Anal. Chem.*, **21**, 352 (1949).]

in a diagram (Fig. 126) which is most useful in evaluating the time required for counting a given background and standard deviation. It is seen from this chart that a counting time of approximately 100 min would be required for the determination of a sample giving 100 counts per minute with a standard deviation of 1 per cent at a background rate of 10 counts per minute.

When the background counting rate is much smaller than the sample

counting rate, the influence of errors on the former rate become quite
negligible, as can be seen from equation (14–11). It is then not practical
to spend as much time for counting the background as for the sample,
and it can be shown (see problem 5 in Section 14–7) that the optimum
ratio of background counting time to the total time for counting the background and the sample plus background is

$$\frac{(R_t/R_b)^{1/2} - 1}{(R_t/R_b) - 1}$$

Thus, for $R_t/R_b = 20$, the above ratio is 0.183, and the counting time
for the background should be approximately one-fifth of the total time
spent for counting. A chart for the determination of counting time in
which the foregoing considerations are taken into account is given by
Browning.[18]

d. Correction for Self-Absorption.   Soft radiation is partially absorbed by the sample emitting it, and a correction of the counting rate
must be made.[19] The derivation of the correction requires the knowledge
of a relationship between radiation absorption and sample thickness, and
this matter will be taken up first.

Equation 9–9, for the absorption of light can be applied, as a first
approximation, to the absorption of nuclear radiation by matter. In an
experiment similar in its principle to filter photometry, the activity of a
sample is measured with and without a layer of absorbing material interposed between radioactive sample and detector. Then,

$$P = P_0 e^{-\mu b}, \tag{14–12}$$

where P_0 and P are the counting rates without and with absorbing layer,
respectively; μ is the *linear absorption coefficient*; and b, the thickness of
the absorbing layer. Values of μ have been determined experimentally,
but for orientation purposes in the case of *soft* beta emitters, the approxi-
mative equation proposed by Libby,[19]

$$\mu = \frac{750\delta}{E^{5/3}}, \tag{14–13}$$

can be applied. There, μ is in reciprocal centimeters, δ is the density of
the absorbing medium, and E is the maximum energy of the beta particle
in kiloelectronvolts. For instance, μ for barium carbonate ($\delta = 4.29$) and
for beta rays emitted by carbon-14 ($E = 150$ kev) is 0.76 cm^{-1}.

The relationship between surface activity of a sample absorbing its own
radiation and the sample thickness can be established by considering a

18W. E. Browning, Jr., *Nucleonics*, 9, No. 3, 63 (1951).
19W. F. Libby, *Anal. Chem.*, 19, 2 (1947).

layer of uniform sample thickness b and specific activity A (Fig. 127). The contribution to the surface activity per square centimeter of sample area is for a slab of thickness dx at a depth x,

$$P = \frac{1}{2}A\delta\, e^{-\mu x}\, dx. \qquad (14\text{-}14)$$

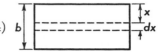

Fig. 127. Diagram for discussion of self-absorption.

There, $\delta\, dx \times 1$ is the mass of the layer of thickness dx and $A\delta\, dx$ is the activity of this layer. Since the activity is measured on one side of the slab, one-half of the radiation is lost and the total activity of the slab of thickness dx must be multiplied by 1/2. The activity at the surface of the slab of thickness b is calculated by integrating P over the slab thickness. The surface activity per square centimeter is

$$P = \int_0^b \frac{1}{2}A\delta e^{-\mu x}dx$$

$$= \frac{A\delta}{2\mu}(1 - e^{-\mu b}). \qquad (14\text{-}15)$$

As the thickness increases, P approaches the value $A\delta/2\mu$, which is the activity of an infinitely thick sample.

If the sample did not absorb, the surface activity P' per square centimeter would be simply one-half of the product of the specific activity multiplied by the sample mass per square centimeter, i.e.,

$$P' = \frac{A\delta b}{2}. \qquad (14\text{-}16)$$

The correction factor for self-absorption is then P/P', or in view of equations (14–15) and (14–16), $(1-e^{-\mu b})/\mu b$. Values of this factor are plotted against the dimensionless variable μb in Fig. 128.

EXAMPLE. Calculate the activity at the surface of a layer of barium carbonate labeled with carbon-14 for the following data: $b = 0.25$ cm; $\delta = 4.29$; $A = 10^{-5}$ millicurie g^{-1}. The maximum energy of beta ray from carbon-14 is 150 kev (see Table XX). Calculate the correction factor for self-absorption.

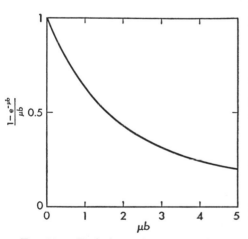

Fig. 128. Variations of correction factor for self-absorption.

According to equation (14–13), one has

$$\mu = \frac{750 \times 4.29}{150^{5/3}}$$
$$= 0.76 \text{ cm}^{-1},$$

and the surface activity is, in view of equation (14–15),

$$P = \frac{10^{-5} \times 4.29}{2 \times 0.76}(1 - e^{-0.76 \times 0.25})$$
$$= 4.9 \times 10^{-6} \text{ millicurie per sq cm.}$$

Since a curie corresponds to 3.7×10^{10} disintegrations per second (see Section 14–1), $P = 1.09 \times 10^4$ disintegrations per square centimeter and per minute.

The correction factor is

$$\frac{1 - e^{-0.76 \times 0.25}}{0.76 \times 0.25} \quad \text{or} \quad 0.91.$$

The effect of dilution of a radioactive substance with the same inactive compound can be readily determined from the correction factor. The method of calculation will be illustrated by an example.

EXAMPLE. A layer of anhydrous sodium sulfate, 0.15 cm thick and labeled with sulfur-35, has a surface activity of 7540 disintegrations per square centimeter and per minute. This sample is mixed with nine times its weight of inactive anhydrous sodium sulfate. Calculate the surface activity of the dilute sample on the assumption that it is spread in a layer ten times as thick as the original sample. The densities of the tagged and untagged compound are virtually the same ($\delta = 2.70$). Furthermore, $E = 167$ kev for sulfur-35 (Table XX).

From equation (14–13) one deduces $\mu = 0.40$ cm^{-1} for sodium sulfate. The correction factor $(1 - e^{-\mu b})/\mu b$ for the original sample is

$$\frac{1 - e^{-0.40 \times 0.15}}{0.40 \times 0.15} \quad \text{or} \quad 0.967,$$

and this factor is

$$\frac{1 - e^{-0.40 \times 1.5}}{0.40 \times 0.15} \quad \text{or} \quad 0.75$$

for the sample. Hence the surface activity of the dilute sample is

$$7540 \times \frac{0.75}{0.967} \quad \text{or} \quad 5850 \text{ disintegrations per sq cm and per min}$$

The decrease in surface activity resulting from the increase in layer thickness is quite pronounced.

14–4. TRACER METHODS

a. Fundamentals. A substance can be labeled by substituting a radioactive isotope (*tracer*) for some of the atoms of one of its elements. Analytical studies, mechanisms of reactions, diffusion processes, and other phenomena can be studied in this manner by following the path of the tagged compound. The tracer method has been applied for many years, and an authoritative survey of the early work can be found in Paneth's monograph.[20] Some general considerations on the use of tracers are given in a review by Yankwich,[21] and further details can be found in some of the books listed in Section 14–6.

Only very minute quantities of tracer are needed to produce a measurable activity, as is apparent from the following simple calculation. The absolute value of the disintegration rate of the tracer is, in view of equations (14–1) and (14–5),

$$\left| \frac{dN}{dt} \right| = 0.693 \frac{N}{\tau}, \tag{14–17}$$

where N is the number of radioactive atoms in the sample and τ is their half-life. The number N is related to the weight w of the tracer and to its gram atomic or molecular weight W_a by

$$N = \frac{6.02 \times 10^{23} w}{W_a}. \tag{14–18}$$

By combination of equation (14–17) and (14–18) there follows

$$w = 2.40 \times 10^{-24} W_a \, \tau \frac{dN}{dt}, \tag{14–19}$$

where the same unit of time is used to express τ and dN/dt.

EXAMPLE. Calculate the weight of sodium iodide (containing only iodine-131) having a counting rate of 1360 counts per minute with a counting tube having an efficiency of 0.12. The half-life of iodine-131 is 8.0 days.

One has
$$\frac{dN}{dt} = \frac{1360}{0.12}$$
$$= 11{,}330 \text{ disintegrations per min}$$
$$\tau = 8.0 \times 24 \times 60$$
$$= 11{,}520 \text{ min}$$
$$W_a = 149.9$$

Hence [equation (14–19)],
$$w = 2.40 \times 10^{-24} \times 149.9 \times 11{,}520 \times 11{,}330$$
$$= 4.70 \times 10^{-14} \text{ gram.}$$

[20]F. A. Paneth, *Radioelements as Indicators*, McGraw-Hill, New York, 1928.
[21]P. E. Yankwich, *Anal. Chem.*, **21**, 318 (1949).

Very small amounts of radioactive substance handled in tracer studies can be easily lost because of adsorption on the wall of containers, precipitates, etc. This serious source of error is eliminated by the addition of a sufficient quantity (perhaps 20 mg) of *carrier*. This often is the inactive form of the tracer substance, but the carrier may also be another inactive substance having similar properties to those of the tracer. For example, barium ion is used as a carrier in the precipitation of radium sulfate because the sulfates of these two elements behave similarly in the precipitation process. In most cases it is essential that the tracer and its carrier be present as the same chemical species because, otherwise, separation of the tracer and carrier from other substances is very difficult. Such a separation is achieved by the usual methods of analytical chemistry: precipitation followed by centrifugation and or filtration, liquid-liquid extraction, distillation, ion-exchange separations, chromatography and related methods, electrodeposition, etc. Recovery of the tracer element is generally not complete, and the counting rate must be corrected accordingly.

While carriers are generally added to tracers, *carrier-free tracers*[22] are of great usefulness in the study of coprecipitation phenomena, electrolytic deposition of less than a monolayer of deposit, and in general, in the investigation of very dilute solutions. In such studies one must be on the alert for the formation of *radiocolloids* by absorption of the tracer on colloids such as silica or dust which are present as impurities. The solution of tracer then exhibits the properties of a colloidal solution, and there is the danger of misinterpretation of experimental results.

There is a slight difference in behavior between the tracer and the corresponding inactive substance because of *isotopic effect*. For example, the equilibrium constant for

$$C^{13}O_2 + C^{12}O_3^{--} = C^{12}O_2 + C^{13}O_2^{--}$$

is[23] 1.012 at 25°C. The isotopic effect is quite pronounced for hydrogen, deuterium, and titrium, but it can be neglected for heavier elements in most cases. However, there are applications, particularly in kinetics, in which the isotopic effect is used to great advantage.

b. Isotopic Dilution Method. The principle of the isotopic dilution method and a brief historical note were given in Section 13–4c. The method allows the analysis of one or even several compounds in a mixture by the following procedure:

The substance which is to be determined in the mixture is tagged with a tracer having a specific activity of A disintegrations per minute and per

[22]For a review of the methods of production and isolation of carrier-free tracers, see W. M. Garrison and J. G. Hamilton, *Chem. Revs.*, **49**, 237 (1951).

[23]A. C. Wahl and N. A. Bonner, Eds., *Radioactivity Applied to Chemistry*, Wiley, New York, 1951, p. 3.

gram. A weight of a grams of this tagged compound is added to the mixture, and a known weight of the substance to be determined is isolated from the mixture. The specific activity A' of this isolated fraction is measured. One then has

$$A' = \frac{a}{a + x} A, \tag{14-20}$$

and the weight x of analyzed substance is

$$x = a\left(\frac{A}{A'} - 1\right). \tag{14-21}$$

The isotopic dilution method has the great advantage of not requiring quantitative separation of the analyzed substance from the mixture but only the isolation of a known weight of this substance. The method has proven most valuable, particularly in the analysis of complex mixtures in biochemical studies.

There are variations in the procedure outlined above. Instead of diluting the inactive compound with the tagged compound, one can do the opposite; one can also utilize two tracers of elements whose radioactive properties are sufficiently different to allow differentiation. Application to the analysis of several compounds has been made.[24]

The precision of the method is discussed by Radin in a series of articles.[25]

c. Applications. Besides their use in the isotopic dilution method, other important applications of tracer methods to analytical chemistry are the determination of solubilities and the study of the efficiency of separation methods (coprecipitation phenomena, ion-exchange, chromatography, etc.). Most applications of tracers are not within the realm of analytical chemistry, and only a brief enumeration can be made here: determination of reaction rates in the vicinity of equilibrium by isotopic exchange, study of reaction mechanisms, measurement of the rate of self-diffusion, investigation of absorption processes, study of the behavior of solutions at very low concentrations, etc. A few typical applications may be discussed as problems (Section 14-7, problems 12, 13, 18 to 21, 23, and 24). A particularly elegant application is the radiocarbon dating of archeological specimens which was developed by Libby[26] (see problem 14, Section 14-7).

14-5. ACTIVATION ANALYSIS

a. Fundamentals. It was pointed out in Section 14-4a that very small amounts (10^{-14} gram) of radioactive substances have measurable

[24] F. C. Henriques, Jr., and C. Margnetti, *Ind. Eng. Chem., Anal. Ed.*, **18**, 420 (1946). See also a good discussion in the book of Kamen referred to in Section 14-6.

[25] N. S. Radin, *Nucleonics*, **1**, No. 1, 24 (1947); **1**, No. 2, 48 (1947); **1**, No. 4, 51 (1947); **2**, No. 1, 50 (1948); **2**, No. 2, 33 (1948).

[26] W. F. Libby, *Radiocarbon Dating*, 2nd ed., University of Chicago Press, Chicago, 1955.

counting rates. Conversely, traces of certain elements in a nonradioactive sample can be determined by making them radioactive through some suitable nuclear reaction. This method of *activation analysis* was soon applied after the discovery of artificial radioactivity (1934), and the earliest application probably was made by von Hevesy and Levi,[27] who determined dyspronium and europium in rare earths by activation with slow neutrons. Shortly afterwards, Seaborg and Livingood[28] determined traces of gallium in iron by bombarding the sample with deuterons from a cyclotron. The development of nuclear piles gave a great impetus to activation analysis, which is now a well established, but not widely applied, method of trace analysis. Only the essential points are mentioned here, and the reader is referred to reviews by Boyd[29] and Smales[30] for further details.

The rate of production dN^*/dt of a radioactive element (*nuclide*[31]) by irradiation by neutrons, deuterons, and other particles is proportional to the number of target atoms N and to the flux φ of particles. The proportionality factor is called the *cross section σ of the target atom* for the nuclear reaction being applied. Furthermore, the radioactive isotope being produced disintegrates continuously at a rate which is proportional to the number of radioactive atoms. Hence,

$$\frac{dN^*}{dt} = \varphi\sigma N - \lambda N^* \tag{14-22}$$

where λ is the decay constant defined by equation (14-1). Units in equation (4-22) are: φ in particles per square centimeter and per second, σ in square centimeters per target atom. Furthermore, $N = N_0 - N^*$, N_0 being the initial number of target atoms. By introducing this value of N in equation (4-22) and integrating[32] the resulting equation, one obtains

$$N^* = N_0 \frac{\varphi\sigma}{\varphi\sigma + \lambda} \left[1 - e^{-(\varphi\sigma + \lambda)t}\right] . \tag{14-23}$$

As t tends to infinity, the exponential vanishes in equation (14-23), and the fraction of target atoms converted to the radionuclide is $\varphi\sigma/(\varphi\sigma + \lambda)$. This fraction increases with the flux, with the cross section of the target atoms, and with the half-life of the nuclide ($\lambda = 0.693/\tau$). However, the ratio N^*/N_0 is, in general, very small in comparison with

[27]G. von Hevesy and H. Levi, *Kgl. Danske Videnskab. Selskab. Math-fys. Medd.*, **14**, No. 5 (1936); **15**, No. 11 (1938).

[28]G. T. Seaborg and J. J. Livingood, *J. Am. Chem. Soc.*, **60**, 1784 (1938).

[29]G. E. Boyd, *Anal. Chem.*, **21**, 335 (1949).

[30]A. A. Smales, *Ann. Repts. Chem. Soc.*, **46**, 285 (1949); *Atomics*, **4**, No. 3, 55 (1953); E. N. Jenkins and A. A. Smales, *Quart. Revs.*, **10**, 83 (1956).

[31]This term was coined by T. Kohman, *Am. J. Phys.*, **15**, 356 (1947).

[32]Set $y = N_0 - \dfrac{\varphi\sigma + \lambda}{\varphi\sigma} N^*$, and note that $y = N_0$ at $t = 0$.

unity because λ is much larger than $\varphi\sigma$ even for intense fluxes and large cross-sectional areas; for instance, $N^*/N_0 = 3 \times 10^{-5}$ for $t \to \infty$ in the case of gold-198 and for $\varphi = 10^{12}$ neutrons cm^2 sec^{-1} (see data in Table

TABLE XXI
Some Properties of a few Radionuclides[a]

ELEMENT	ATOMIC WEIGHT	RADIO-NUCLIDE	HALF-LIFE	CROSS SECTION, BARNS[b]	ABUNDANCE OF PARENT NUCLIDE
Ag	107.9	Ag^{108}	2.3 *min*	34	51.4
As	74.9	As^{76}	26.8 *hr*	4	100
Au	197.2	Au^{98}	2.7 *d*	95	100
Br	79.9	Br^{80}	18 *min*	8.5	50.6
Co	58.9	Co^{60}	5.3 *yr*	34	100
Cs	132.9	Cs^{134}	2.3 *yr*	26	100
Cu	63.5	Cu^{64}	12.9 *hr*	4.3	69
I	126.9	I^{128}	25 *min*	6.1	100
In	114.8	In^{116}	54 *min*	52	95.8
La	138.9	La^{140}	40 *hr*	9	99.9
Mn	54.9	Mn^{56}	2.6 *hr*	12	100
Na	23	Na^{24}	14.8 *hr*	0.48	100

[a]Data from A. A. Smales, *Atomics*, **4**, No. 3, 55 (1953).
[b]1 barn = 10^{-24} cm^2; values are for neutron activation.

XXI). It is therefore permissible to write equation (14–23) in the approximate form generally quoted in the literature[29,30]

$$N^* \approx N^0 \frac{\varphi\sigma}{\lambda}[1 - e^{-\lambda t}]. \tag{14-24}$$

By introducing in equation (14–24) the half-life $\tau [\lambda = 0.693/\tau$, see equation (14–5)] and noting that $N^*\lambda$ is the disintegration rate, one obtains

$$A = \varphi\sigma N(1 - e^{-0.693 t/\tau}) \tag{14-25}$$

for the disintegration rate at time t of irradiation. The activity grows with the quantity between parentheses (*saturation factor*). The saturation factor is practically equal to unity (Fig. 129) for irradiation times equal to a few half-lives. Conversely, the saturation factor is much smaller than unity for reasonable irradiation periods for nuclides having very long half-lives.

The activity for a given weight w of the target element is calculated by substituting N in equation (14–25) by the value

$$N = \frac{6.02 \times 10^{23} fw}{W_a}, \tag{14-26}$$

where f is the abundance fraction of the target isotope yielding the nuclide $(0 < f \leqslant 1)$, and W_a is the atomic weight of the target element.

As soon as irradiation is stopped, the activity of the sample decreases according to equation (14–2), at least if there are no complications in the disintegration scheme. Decay curves are plotted in Fig. 129 (dashed curves) for irradiation times equal to 1, 2, and 4 times the half-life τ.

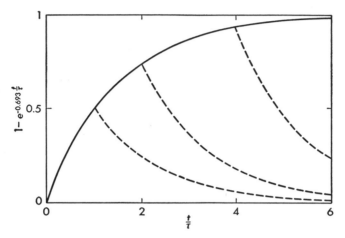

Fig. 129. Variations of saturation factor with the ratio, t/τ, of the irradiation time to the half-life of the element being produced.

Data needed for application of equations (14–25) and (14–26) are listed in Table XXI, and much more extensive compilations are available in the literature.[1,33]

EXAMPLE. Calculate the activity of a sample containing 2×10^{-10} grams of copper 45 min after a 28-hr irradiation in a flux of 6×10^{11} neutrons cm^{-2} sec^{-1} of a uranium pile. $\tau = 12.9$ hr, $f = 0.69$, $\sigma = 4.3 \times 10^{-24}$ cm^2 (Table XXI), and $W_a = 63.5$.

The activity immediately after irradiation is from equations (14–25) and (14–26)

$$A = \frac{6 \times 10^{11} \times 4.3 \times 10^{-24} \times 6.02 \times 10^{23} \times 0.69 \times 2 \times 10^{-10}}{63.5}(1 - e^{-0.693 \times 28/12.9})$$

= 3.38 disintegrations per sec

= 203 disintegrations per min.

Forty-five minutes after irradiation is terminated the activity drops to [see equation (14–2) and (14–5)]

$$A = 203e^{-0.693(45/60 \times 12.9)}$$

= 195 disintegrations per min.

[33]A useful chart showing activation cross sections as a function of the half-life of radio-nuclides is given by W. W. Meinke and R. E. Anderson, *Anal. Chem.*, **25**, 778 (1953).

It is seen from this example that quantities of an element in the milli-microgram range or even smaller amounts can be determined by activation analysis. The sensitivity of the method increases with the flux of nuclear particles and the activation cross section of the target element. Fluxes of 10^{12} neutrons $cm^{-2}sec^{-1}$ are produced in uranium piles, and the newer piles may generate fluxes as high as 10^{14} neutrons $cm^{-2}sec^{-1}$. If one sets as the lower rate 100 disintegrations of the radionuclide per minute, one calculates that the *theoretical* limit of sensitivity for irradiation to saturation in a flux of 10^{12} neutrons $cm^{-2}sec^{-1}$ is between 10^{-10} and 10^{-12} gram according to the element[30] (see problem 9 in Section 14-7). In practice, the sensitivity may be somewhat lower because of losses in the chemical operations following irradiation.

b. Experimental Methods. Three essential steps can be distinguished in activation analysis: (1) preparation and irradiation of the sample and standard; (2) chemical treatment of sample and standard; (3) radioactivity measurements and possibly differentiation between radionuclides when several nuclides are produced and are not separated chemically.

Among the possible methods, irradiation by slow neutrons in uranium piles is unquestionably the most advantageous because of the high fluxes available ($10^{12} - 10^{14}$ neutrons $cm^{-2}sec^{-1}$) and the corresponding high sensitivity.[34] Other sources of neutrons[35] and other particles are also useful, but fluxes are lower than in piles and the most important advantage of activation analysis (namely, its high sensitivity) is lost. Other sources are the cyclotron with fluxes of $10^8 - 10^9$ particles $cm^{-2}sec^{-1}$, the van de Graaff accelerator with fluxes up 10^7 particles $cm^{-2}sec^{-1}$, radium-beryllium and antimony-beryllium sources yielding from 10^2 to 10^6 neutrons $cm^{-2}sec^{-1}$, depending on the quantity of radium or radioactive antimony. Although these sources produce lower fluxes than the pile, it should not be overlooked that particles other than neutrons may have a nuclear reaction more advantageous than neutrons (shorter irradiation time, elimination of interfering reactions, etc.).

In general, solid samples and standards are dissolved after irradiation, and the inactive isotope of the nuclide is added as carrier. The nuclide and inactive isotope are then transformed into the same chemical species and separated from the major constituents of the sample by the usual techniques of analytical chemistry.[36] The radiochemical purity of the isolated products must be verified when several radioactive elements are produced

[34]The U.S. Atomic Energy Commission provides facilities for irradiation; similar services are rendered by government agencies in England and France.

[35]T. I. Taylor and W. W. Havens, Jr., *Nucleonics*, **6**, No. 4, 54 (1950).

[36]See the compilation of radiochemical separation techniques by W. W. Meinke, Atomic Energy Commission *AECD* 2738, August 30, 1949, and *AECD* 3084, March 15, 1951; see also the review of G. B. Cook and H. Seligman, *Forschr. Chem. Forsch.* **3**, 411 (1955).

by irradiation. This is done by following the decrease of the counting rate of the sample with time and by preparing a plot of the logarithm of the sample activity against time. A straight line should result if only one radioactive element is present (Section 14–1) unless the different radionuclides thus produced have nearly the same half-lives.

It is sometimes possible to avoid chemical separations and determine directly several elements in the irradiated sample by one of the following methods or by both:

1. The logarithm of the counting rate of the sample is plotted against time and the contribution of each nuclide is determined on this plot (Fig. 119). This procedure is applicable when the nuclides have sufficiently different half-lives.

2. Advantage is taken of differences in the energy of the radiation emitted by the nuclides. The activity of the sample is measured with a spectrometer which is adjusted at the various energy levels of the nuclides being sought. If a spectrometer is not available, advantage can be taken of the differences in the penetrating power of the radiation of the nuclides.

The activity of the sample is measured with aluminum foil of different thicknesses between sample and counting tube, and the results of the analysis can be computed directly. The method will be discussed by first considering two samples of a single nuclide, namely, sodium-24 and potassium-42 (Fig. 130). These two elements have about the same half-

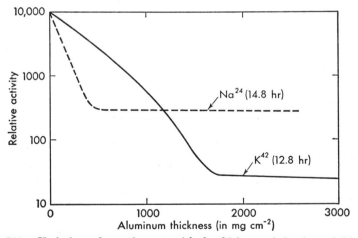

Fig. 130. Variations of counting rate with the thickness of aluminum foil interposed between sample and counting tube. [After G. E. Boyd, *Anal. Chem.*, **21**, 335 (1949).]

life (14.9 hr for sodium, 12.8 hr for potassium), but the beta particles emitted by sodium-24 have a lower energy (1.39 mev) than those of potassium (3.58 mev). It is seen in Fig. 130 that the beta radiation of sodium is almost completely stopped with an aluminum thickness of 700 mg cm^{-2}, whereas 1700 mg cm^{-2} are required for potassium. The almost constant counting rate of sodium at thicknesses larger than 700 mg cm^{-2} corresponds to gamma radiation which is hardly stopped by aluminum. If a sample contains both sodium-24 and potassium-42, the counting rate of potassium can readily be calculated by measuring the activity of the sample with screens of 700 and 1700 mg cm^{-2} aluminum, respectively. The counting rate at 1700 mg cm^{-2}, which only corresponds to gamma radiation, can be subtracted from the rate of 700 mg cm^{-2}, and the counting rate for beta radiation from potassium is obtained directly. A minor correction for the slightly greater absorption of gamma radiation at 1700 mg cm^{-2} than at 700 mg cm^{-2} may be made to improve the accuracy.

c. Potentialities and Limitations. The potentialities of activation analysis as a powerful tool of trace analysis were indicated in Section 14–5a. Most elements are transformed in radionuclides by the n, γ *reaction*, in which a radionuclide is formed from the target atom with a gain of one unit of mass (Table XXII). The radionuclide disintegrates with gamma-

TABLE XXII

Elements Producing Radionuclides with Measurable Activity[a,b,c]

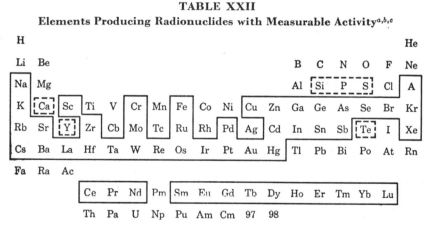

[a]From G. H. Morrison and J. F. Cosgrove, *Anal. Chem.*, **28**, 320 (1956).
[b]For a flux of 3.4 x 10^{12} neutrons per sq. cm. per sec.; measurement of radioactivity within 8 to 10 hours after removal from pile.
[c]Elements in solid blocks form gamma-emitters; elements in broken blocks form only beta-emitters.

ray emission. Some elements, particularly the light ones, cannot be determined by activation analysis because either they yield nuclides having too short a half-life or the radiation emitted by the nuclide is too soft for practical measurements. Furthermore, in trace analysis, the activation cross section of the trace element should be much smaller than that of the major constituents. Some elements such as cadmium, which strongly absorb neutrons, may cause an error because of *self-shielding* and the resulting decrease in flux from the periphery of the sample to its center. Self-shielding can often be avoided by dilution. One serious limitation is the possible formation of a given nuclide by several nuclear reactions involving not only the element to be determined but also *other* elements. Smales[30] cites as example the following interfering reactions caused by selenium in the analysis of arsenic by neutron activation $(As_{33}^{75} + n_0^1 \rightarrow As_{33}^{76})$:

$$Se_{34}^{76} + n_0^1 \longrightarrow As_{33}^{76} + H_1^1$$

$$Se_{34}^{76} + \gamma \longrightarrow As_{33}^{76} + H_1^1$$

$$\xrightarrow{\;n_0^1\;} As_{33}^{76}$$

$$Se_{34}^{77} + \gamma \longrightarrow As_{33}^{76} + H_1^1$$

One obvious limitation is the necessity of having a source producing a high flux of nuclear particles, but this disadvantage will disappear progressively as the number of atomic piles increases.

Despite its limitations, activation analysis has proven most valuable in trace analysis, as can be readily ascertained from the variety of analysis that have been reported.[29,30,37] A few typical applications may be discussed as an exercise (problems 16 and 17 in Section 14–7).

14–6. BIBLIOGRAPHY

a. Books

J. Birks, *Scintillation Counters*, McGraw-Hill, New York, 1953.

E. Bleuler and G. J. Goldsmith, *Experimental Nucleonics*, Rhinehart, New York, 1952.

J. F. Bonner, article in *Physical Methods of Organic Chemistry* 2nd ed., Vol. I, Part III, A. Weissberger, Ed., Interscience, New York, 1954. Review of scintillation counters.

J. R. Bradford, *Radioisotopes in Industry*, Reinhold, New York, 1953.

M. Calvin, C. Heidelberger, J. C. Reid, B. M. Tolbert, and P. E. Yankwich, *Isotopic Carbon*, Wiley, New York, 1949.

C. L. Comar, *Radioisotopes in Biology and Agriculture*, McGraw-Hill, New York, 1955.

G. B. Cook and J. F. Duncan, *Modern Radiochemical Practice*, Oxford University Press, London, 1952.

C. D. Coryell and N. Sugarman, Eds., *Radiochemical Studies—The Fission Products*, 3 vols., McGraw-Hill, New York, 1951.

S. C. Curran, *Luminescence and the Scintillation Counter*, Butterworths, London, 1953.

S. C. Curran and J. D. Craggs, *Counting Tubes*, Butterworths, London, 1949.

[37]C. L. Gordon, *Anal. Chem.*, **26**, 176 (1954).

G. E. Francis, W. Mulligan, and A. Wormall, *Isotopic Tracers*, Athlone Press, London, 1954.

G. Friedlander and J. W. Kennedy, *Nuclear and Radiochemistry*, 2nd ed., Wiley, New York, 1955.

R. Glascock, *Labelled Atoms*, Interscience, New York, 1951.

S. Glasstone, *Sourcebook on Atomic Energy*, Van Nostrand, New York, 1950.

A. C. Graves and D. K. Froman, *Miscellaneous Physical and Chemical Techniques of the Los Alamos Project*, McGraw-Hill, New York, 1952.

G. H. Guest, *Radioisotopes*, Pitman, New York, 1951.

M. D. Kamen, *Radioactive Tracers in Biology*, Academic Press, New York, 1947.

S. A. Korff, *Electron and Nuclear Counters*, Van Nostrand, New York, 1946.

A. Langer, article in *Physical Methods in Chemical Analysis*, W. G. Berl, Ed., Academic Press, New York, 1951. Methods of measurement in tracer work.

P. B. Moon, *Artificial Radioactivity*, Cambridge University Press, London, 1949.

A. F. Reid, *Preparation and Measurement of Isotopic Tracers*, Edwards, Ann Arbor, Michigan, 1946.

B. B. Rossi and H. H. Straub, *Ionization Chambers and Counters*, McGraw-Hill, New York, 1949.

J. Sacks, *Isotopic Tracers in Biochemistry and Physiology*, McGraw-Hill, New York, 1953.

G. K. Schweitzer and I. Whitney, *Radioactive Tracer Techniques*, Van Nostrand, New York, 1949.

G. T. Seaborg and J. J. Katz, *Actinide Elements*, McGraw-Hill, New York, 1954.

E. Segre, Ed., *Experimental Nuclear Physics*, 2 vols., Wiley, New York, 1953.

J. Sharpe, *Nuclear Radiation Detectors*, Wiley, New York, 1955.

K. Siegbahn, Ed., *Beta- and Gamma-ray Spectroscopy*, Interscience, New York, 1955.

W. Siri, *Isotopic Tracers and Nuclear Radiations*, McGraw-Hill, New York, 1949.

D. Taylor, *The Measurement of Radio Isotopes*, Wiley, New York, 1951.

G. von Hevesy, *Radioactive Indicators*, Interscience, New York, 1948.

A. C. Wahl and N. A. Bonner, Eds., *Radioactivity Applied to Chemistry*, Wiley, New York, 1951. Application of tracers in a wide variety of fields; with detailed bibliography.

W. J. Whitehouse and J. L. Putman, *Radioactive Isotopes*, Oxford University Press, London, 1953.

R. R. Williams, Jr., *Principles of Nuclear Chemistry*, Van Nostrand, New York, 1950.

D. W. Wilson, A. O. C. Nier, and S. P. Riemann, *Preparation and Measurement of Isotopic Isomers*, Edwards, Ann Arbor, Michigan, 1946.

H. Yagoda, *Radioactive Measurements with Nuclear Emulsions*, Wiley, New York, 1949.

b. Some Books on Nuclear Physics

H. A. Bethe, *Elementary Nuclear Theory*, Wiley, New York, 1947.

M. Born, *Atomic Physics*, translation by J. Dougall, Blackie, London, 1951.

N. Feather, *An Introduction to Nuclear Physics*, Cambridge University Press, London, 1948.

E. Fermi, *Nuclear Physics*, compiled by J. Orear, A. H. Rosenfeld, and R. A. Schluter, University of Chicago Press, Chicago, 1950.

D. Halliday, *Introductory Nuclear Physics*, Wiley, New York, 1950.

I. Kaplan, *Nuclear Physics*, Addison-Wesley Publishing Co., Cambridge, Mass., 1955.

R. E. Lapp and H. L. Andrews, *Nuclear Radiation Physics*, 2nd ed., Prentice-Hall, New York, 1954.

F. K. Richtmeyer and E. H. Kennard, *Introduction to Modern Physics*, 5th ed., McGraw-Hill, New York, 1955.

E. Rutherford, J. Chadwick, and C. D. Ellis, *Radiations from Radioactive Substances*, Cambridge University Press, London, 1951.

c. Reviews and Abstracts

C. L. Gordon, *Anal. Chem.*, **21**, 96 (1949); **23**, 81 (1951); **26**, 176 (1954).

W. W. Meinke, *Anal. Chem.*, **28**, 736 (1956).

Symposium on Nucleonics, *Anal. Chem.*, **21**, 318–368 (1949).

Annual Review of Nuclear Science, Annual Reviews, Inc., Stanford, Cal. (since 1952).

Nuclear Science Abstracts, U.S. Atomic Energy Commission Information Service, Oak Ridge, Tenn. (since 1948).

14–7. PROBLEMS

a. Extension of Theory

1. Calculate the correction to be made in the measurement of disintegration rates when the duration of counting t_m is not negligible in comparison with the half-life. Plot the correction (in per cent) against the ratio t_m/τ. Note that the average rate of disintegration is

$$\frac{dN}{dt} = \frac{1}{t_m} \int_0^{t_m} \frac{dN}{dt} \, dt ,$$

where dN/dt can be expressed in terms of $(dN/dt)_{t=0}$ by means of equation (14–6).

2. Calculate the average life of a radioactive element of half-life τ.

3. Discuss the principles of the coincidence counter and the four-pi counting method for absolute radioactivity measurements. See Siegbahn's monograph and articles by J. Barnothy and M. Forro, *Rev. Sci. Instruments*, **22**, 415 (1951); and H. H. Seliger and L. Cavallo, *J. Research Natl. Bur. Standards*, **47**, 41 (1951). For the calibration of counters with standards of known activity see L. F. Curtiss, *Circular* **473**, Nat. Bur. Standards, 1948.

4. Calculate the standard deviation in the counting method in which the same total number of counts is measured for the background alone and the sample and background. Plot standard deviation against the ratio of the counting times for varying count number (100, 500, 1000, 5000, 10,000).

5. Show that the standard deviation Δ is minimum when the ratio, y, of background counting to the total counting time for background, and background plus sample, is

$$\frac{(R_t/R_b)^{1/2} - 1}{(R_t/R_b) - 1}$$

where R_t is the counting rate for sample and background, and R_b the counting rate for background alone.

Note: Express Δ as a function of the ratio y and minimize the resulting function by equating its first derivative to zero.

b. Application of Theory

6. The adsorption of stearic acid on metals can be studied by labeling this substance with carbon-14 and by measuring the counting rate for a monolayer of adsorbed acid. Calculate the specific activity of the solid stearic acid which is required for making measurements with a standard deviation of 5 per cent and a background counting rate of 10 counts per minute. Duration of counting of the sample is 30 min.; area of sample in counting tube (gas flow type), 3.5 cm²; specific gravity of stearic acid, 0.85; area covered per molecule, 2×10^{-15} cm. Assume a complete monolayer.

7. The surface activity of solid samples of monohydrated potassium oxalate labeled with carbon-14 is 466 and 647 counts per minute for a sample thickness of 0.50 cm and 1.00 cm, respectively. Calculate: (a) the linear absorption coefficient of the sample; (b) the activity at infinite thickness. Specific gravity of sample is 2.13.

Note: It is useful to make a plot of

$$y(\mu) = \frac{1 - e^{-\mu b_1}}{1 - e^{-\mu b_2}},$$

where b_1 and b_2 are the sample thicknesses.

8. A sample containing several aminoacids is analyzed for α-alanine (α-aminopropionic acid) by the isotopic dilution method; 0.065 gram of carbon-14 labeled α-alanine, having a specific activity of 38,400 counts per minute and per gram, is added to 0.527 gram of the sample. The fraction of the α-alanine which is isolated subsequently from the sample has a specific activity of 19,400 counts per minute and per gram. Calculate the weight per cent of α-alanine in the sample.

9. Calculate the *theoretical* highest sensitivity for neutron activation analysis of bromine, copper, gold, and iodine. A minimum rate of 100 disintegrations per minute is prescribed. Conditions of activation: irradiation to saturation; flux of neutrons, 10^{12} neutrons cm^{-2} sec^{-1}.

10. A sample containing 3.1×10^{-9} gram of bromine and 8.8×10^{-9} gram of copper is irradiated for 10 hr in a flux of 10^{12} neutrons cm^{-2} sec^{-1}. Prepare a plot of the logarithm of disintegration rate against time, and verify that one can deduce from this plot the half-lives of the two nuclides produced by irradiation.

11. A sample of aluminum containing traces of sodium is analyzed by neutron activation analysis. The surface activity of the sample, as measured 10 min after an 18-hr irradiation period, is 910 counts per minute and per square centimeter for an aluminum sheet 0.14 cm thick. Calculate the amount of sodium in the aluminum sample in parts per million. The linear absorption coefficient of aluminum for the beta radiation of sodium-24 is 21 cm^{-1} (it is *assumed* that the counter is insensitive to the gamma radiation of sodium-24); specific gravity of aluminum, 2.70; irradiation in a flux of 7.1×10^{11} neutrons cm^{-2} sec^{-1}.

c. Literature Survey Problems

12. Discuss the application of tracers to the study of the separation of rare earths. See articles by G. E. Boyd and co-workers in *J. Am. Chem. Soc.*, **69**, 2800, 2818, 2849 (1947).

13. Review some of the industrial applications of radionuclides. See J. W. Irvine, Jr., *Anal. Chem.*, **21**, 364 (1949).

14. Discuss the principle of radiocarbon dating. See W. F. Libby, *Radiocarbon Dating*, 2nd ed., The University of Chicago Press, Chicago, 1955.

15. Study the principle and the characteristics of neutron activation analysis with a van de Graaf accelerator. See G. J. Atchison and W. H. Beamer, *Anal. Chem.*, **28**, 237 (1956).

16. Review the neutron activation analysis of arsenic in biological material and sea water. See A. A. Smales and B. D. Pate, *Analyst*, **77**, 188, 196 (1952); *Anal. Chem.*, **24**. 717 (1952).

17. As examples of activation analysis, discuss the determinations of antimony, thallium, and zirconium. See, for antimony, J. E. Hudgens, Jr., and P. J. Cali, *Anal. Chem.*, **24**, 171 (1952); for thallium, C. J. Delbecq, L. E. Glendenin, and P. H. Yuster, *Anal. Chem.*, **25**, 350 (1953); for zirconium, J. E. Hudgens, Jr., and H. J. Dabagian, *Nucleonics*, **10**, No. 5, 25 (1952).

18. Discuss adsorption effects in the handling of very dilute solutions. See H. M. Hershenson and L. B. Rogers, *Anal. Chem.*, **24**, 219 (1952).

19. Examine some of the possible radiotracer methods for the study of adsorption of organic substances on metals. See D. E. Beischer, *J. Phys. Chem.*, **57**, 134 (1953); and F. P. Bowden and A. C. Moore, *Trans. Faraday Soc.*, **47**, 900 (1951).

20. Discuss some typical applications of radiotracers to the investigation of the aging of precipitates. See references in A. C. Wahl and N. A. Bonner, *Radioactivity Applied to Chemistry*, Wiley, New York, 1951, pp. 38–43.

21. Discuss the principle of the measurement of self-diffusion coefficients in solids by tracer methods. See pp. 62–74 of the reference in problem 20.

22. Discuss the isotopic dilution method involving dilution with an *inactive* compound. See A. S. Keston, S. Udenfriend, and R. K. Cannan, *J. Am. Chem. Soc.*, **68**, 1390 (1946); *ibid.*, **71**, 249 (1949).

23. As an example of application of the tracer method to the study of reaction mechanisms, discuss the study of the Willgerodt reaction by W. C. Dauben, J. C. Reid, P. E. Yankwich, and M. Calvin, *J. Am. Chem. Soc.*, **68**, 2117 (1946).

24. Discuss the application of hafnium-181 ($\tau = 46$ days) to the study of zirconium-hafnium separations by ion-exchange. See K. Street, Jr., and G. T. Seaborg, *J. Am. Chem. Soc.*, **70**, 4268 (1948); E. H. Huffman and R. C. Lilly, *ibid.*, **71**, 4147 (1949); K. A. Kraus and G. E. Moore, *ibid.*, **71**, 3263 (1949).

15

Laboratory Experiments

15-1. PURPOSE AND SCOPE OF LABORATORY WORK

Two different modes of approach can be followed in laboratory work in instrumental analysis: The essential points of theory can be verified experimentally or the instrumental methods can be applied to a variety of analyses of "practical" value. When the second approach is followed, the instrumental determination often comes at the end of a series of operations, such as dissolution of sample, precipitation, filtration, and evaporation, which are taught in courses in quantitative analysis. Further work on these operations is generally beneficial in helping the student to improve his experimental skill, but these manipulations consume the major fraction of the laboratory time, which could otherwise be devoted to the experimental study of theory. This consideration has determined the type of experiments described in this chapter. Application of instrumental methods to practical cases is not made, but it is strongly suggested that one or possibly a few applications be part of the laboratory work. In this manner the student will be able to see how instrumental methods are integrated in the general scheme of an analysis. Any recent issue of one of the analytical journals generally contains procedures for practical analyses which can be carried out in one afternoon.

Laboratory work requires the use of commercial instruments such as filter photometers, spectrophotometers, etc., which often are designed for maximum simplicity of operation. This feature of commercial instruments is excellent in routine work, but it is a disadvantage if the student faithfully follows the manufacturer's instructions without understanding them.

327

Instruments as simple as possible are recommended for the laboratory course.

Instructions for commercial instruments are not included in this text because of the great variety of instruments now on the market. Abridged versions of the manufacturers' instructions, possibly with additional comments on the purpose of each step, can be prepared easily and made available to students.

Some methods discussed in the course have not been included in the laboratory exercises because instruments for their study are not available for instruction purposes in most laboratories, or because the use of these instruments requires a specialized training which cannot be acquired in a brief laboratory period. Demonstrations are recommended and suggestions for further work are made.

Experimental procedures are quite detailed, but the student is not guided so firmly as to deprive him of any initiative.

15-2. ELECTRODE POTENTIALS

Equipment. Student potentiometer with accessories, and if possible, the simple potentiometer described below; silver, platinum, and calomel electrodes; bridge filled with 1 *M* ammonium nitrate; magnetic stirrer or conventional stirrer with small glass propeller; three 100-ml beakers; three 100-ml volumetric flasks; 1-ml, 10-ml and 50-ml pipettes; wash bottle; and stirring rod.

It is suggested that the principle of the potentiometric method and the effect of overvoltage be studied with the simple equipment described below. The other measurements can be made with a student potentiometer.

The principle of the potentiometric method can be studied profitably and quite accurate measurements can be made with the simple apparatus of Fig. 131. There,

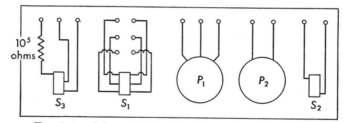

Fig. 131.   Schematic diagram of potentiometer lay-out.

P and R are 100-ohm Helipot potentiometers;[1] S_1 is a double-pole double-throw toggle switch; S_2, a single-pole single-throw toggle switch; and S_3 a single-pole double-throw toggle switch with spring action for automatic return to the central position. The potentionmeters and switches are mounted on a transparent Lucite panel which is attached to a metal frame. Connections between the potentiometers and switches are made on the back of the panel. Binding posts for banana plugs

[1]Available from Beckman Instruments Inc., Fullerton, California.

are utilized for external wirings. Connections are made with flexible wires fitted with banana plugs with lateral wire outlets.[2] Several plugs can be connected to a single binding post. The panel is designed to permit easy operation of the switches and potentiometers without interference from the connecting wires. The potentiometer circuit is fed with a 3-volt dry cell and is standardized to make 1000 divisions of P_1 correspond to 2 volts.

Reagents. Two-tenths molar silver nitrate; 1 M potassium nitrate; 1 M potassium iodide; 1 M potassium iodate; 0.2 M sodium hydroxide; saturated solution of potassium chloride with an excess of solid potassium chloride and solid calomel (1 gram); solid potassium chloride; mercury in a 60-ml bottle with medicine dropper.

a. Principle of the Potentiometric Method. Prepare a saturated calomel electrode. Fill the bottom of the electrode with mercury; add approximately 2 to 3 grams of solid potassium chloride and perhaps 0.1 gram of calomel (mercurous chloride); fill the electrode with a solution saturated with potassium chloride and calomel.

Prepare the following cell

$$\text{Ag} \quad \Big| \quad \text{AgNO}_3(0.1\ M) \quad \Big| \quad \begin{matrix} \text{bridge with} \\ 1\ M\ \text{NH}_4\text{NO}_3 \end{matrix} \quad \Big| \quad \text{calomel electrode.}$$

The silver-silver ions electrode is prepared in a 100-ml beaker with a mechanical stirrer (magnetic or glass propeller type).

Set up the potentiometer according to the basic diagram of Fig. 10 in Chapter 2, with all switches open during the wiring. Connect the above cell to the potentiometer. Be sure to verify the polarity of the cell: the calomel electrode is connected to the negative terminal of the potentiometer.

Determine the voltage of the cell without stirring the solution and by following the procedure outlined in Section 2–10b.

b. Influence of Overvoltage on Electrode Potential Measurements. After completion of the preceding experiment, start the stirrer. (Why?) Set the potentiometer off balance, and take enough readings of the current by varying the voltage applied to the cell to prepare a plot similar to that of Fig. 12 in Chapter 2. Cover the full scale of the galvanometer on both sides of the zero.

Prepare 100 ml of a solution 0.1 M in potassium iodide, 0.1 M in potassium iodate, and 0.1 M in sodium hydroxide, and make the same measurements for the cell,

$$\text{Pt} \quad \Big| \quad \text{KIO}_3 + \text{KI} + \text{NaOH} \quad \Big\| \quad \text{calomel electrode,}$$

as for the cell with the silver electrode. Note that the platinum electrode is

[2]Available from General Radio Co., Cambridge, Mass.

now the positive terminal of the cell. The potential of the platinum electrode may drift if the electrode is not clean. This source of error can be eliminated by immersion of the electrode in a solution of potassium dichromate in sulfuric acid. The electrode is washed with water after the cleaning in the chromic acid solution.

Be sure to use different bridges for the measurement with the silver electrode and the iodate-iodide system. (Why?)

Plot the current-potential relationship for the iodate-iodide couple, and compare this plot with the one for the silver electrode. Explain the difference.

Note that a stirrer is *not* needed in potentiometric measurements in which only the equilibrium potential is being determined.

c. Influence of Ionic Strength on Electrode Potentials. Prepare the same cell as in experiment 15–2a, but with solutions 0.01 M in silver nitrate, and 0.01 M, 0.05 M, 0.1 M, and 0.5 M in potassium nitrate. Measure the voltage of these cells, and plot the cell voltage against the square root of the ionic strength. Interpret the results. Is the liquid-liquid junction potential constant?

d. Verification of the Nernst Equation. Prepare the same cell as in experiment 15–2a, but with solutions 0.5 M in potassium nitrate, and 0.001 M, 0.01 M, and 0.1 M in silver nitrate. Use a fresh bridge for these measurements, and begin the measurements with the lowest concentration of silver ions. (Why?) Calculate the shift in potential for each tenfold change in silver ion concentration, and compare the results with the theoretical value at the temperature of the room.

15–3. pH MEASUREMENTS WITH THE GLASS ELECTRODE AND ACID-BASE TITRATIONS

Equipment. Commercial pH meter, preferably of the potentiometric type; calomel electrode (industrial model); ordinary glass electrode and electrode for high pH's (industrial model); 5-, 10-, and 25-ml pipettes; 1-ml pipette graduated in tenths of a milliliter; 50-ml burette; three 100-ml volumetric flasks; two 25-ml volumetric flasks; 125-ml beaker; wash bottle; and stirring rod.

Reagents. One-tenth molar acetic acid; 0.1 M sodium acetate; 0.1 M hydrochloric acid; 0.1 M phosphoric acid; 0.1 M sodium hydroxide; 0.05 M sodium carbonate; 0.05 M potassium hydrogen o-phthalate; 0.01 M sodium tetraborate decahydrate (borax, $Na_2B_4O_7 \cdot 10H_2O$); solid potassium chloride.

a. Buffering Action. Prepare 100 ml of solutions of acetate buffer having the following compositions: 0.05 M in acid and salt, and 0.01 M and 0.09 M in acid and salt, respectively. Measure the pH of these solutions, using a 0.05 M potassium hydrogen o-phthalate solution (pH = 4.01 $\pm$ 0.01 at 25°) as standard. Measure then the pH of the mixtures of 0.5-ml

0.1 M hydrochloric acid and 24.5 ml of either buffer (use 25-ml flasks for dilution). Calculate the change of pH for each buffer.

b. Influence of Dilution, Ionic Strength, and Temperature. Dilute ten times the above buffer 0.05 M in acid and salt, and compare the pH's of the concentrated and dilute buffers.

Add enough solid potassium chloride to the buffer 0.05 M in acid and salt to make the final solution 0.1, 0.5, and 1 molar in this salt, respectively; determine the pH of the solution. Compare this pH with the value obtained without potassium chloride.

Measure the pH of 0.1 M hydrochloric acid at 25° and in the vicinity of 40°, and deduce the average temperature coefficient for the pH in the range 25° to 40°. Make the measurements with a glass electrode of the industrial type which is directly immersed in the beaker in which the solution is heated. Also immerse a thermometer in the solution. Standardize the electrode with 0.05 M potassium hydrogen o-phthalate at 25°, and do not forget to change the temperature setting on the pH meter for the measurement at 40°.

Repeat these measurements for 0.01 M sodium hydroxide with the special glass electrode for high pH's, and deduce the pH temperature coefficient as above. Standardize the electrode with a 0.1 M borax solution at 25° ($pH = 9.18 \pm 0.01$).

Explain the results by noting that at constant pressure and concentration the pH changes with temperature because of variations of the activity coefficient and the ionic product of water[3] (sodium hydroxide).

c. Error in Alkaline Solution. Standardize an ordinary glass electrode with 0.01 M borax solution ($pH = 9.18 \pm 0.01$ at 25°), and measure the pH of a 0.05 M sodium carbonate solution. Repeat the pH determination with a special electrode (lithium glass) for high pH's. Compare the experimental values with the calculated pH; second ionization constant of carbonic acid at 25°, $K_2 = 4.84 \times 10^{-11}$.

d. Acid-base Titrations. Carry out the following potentiometric titrations: 25 ml 0.1 M hydrochloric acid with 0.1 M sodium hydroxide; 25 ml 0.1 M acetic acid with 0.1 M sodium hydroxide; and 10 ml 0.1 M phosphoric acid with 0.1 M sodium hydroxide. Make the pH measurements with glass and calomel electrodes of the industrial type which are directly immersed in the beaker containing the solution being titrated. Before titration, add approximately 10 ml of distilled water to the phosphoric acid solution to avoid incomplete immersion of the tip of the glass electrode.

Determine before titration the volumes of titrant for which readings

[3]See, for instance, R. G. Bates, *Electrometric pH Determinations*, Wiley, New York, 1954, pp. 108–112.

ought to be made for precise plotting of the titration curves. If the concentration of reagents is not accurately known, determine the equivalence point in a preliminary titration, and then determine the complete titration curve.

Plot the titration curves and indicate the pH ranges in which the color of common indicators changes; for example, methyl red (pH 4.2 to 6.2) and phenolphthalein (pH 8.0 to 9.8).

e. Suggestion for Further Work. It is suggested that an acid-base titration in nonaqueous solvent with potentiometric end point be carried according to the procedure given by Fritz.[4]

15–4. POTENTIOMETRIC TITRATIONS INVOLVING PRECIPITATION

Equipment. Potentiometer (of the type, for instance, in Fig. 131); direct-reading vacuum-tube voltmeter (pH meter), or galvanometer with a 1-megohm adjustable resistance (radio type) in series; silver electrode; calomel electrode of the industrial type; 50-ml burette; 2-ml and 25-ml pipettes; two 100-ml volumetric flasks; 125-ml beaker; 25-ml graduated cylinder; wash bottle; and stirring rod.

If the combination galvanometer-resistance is adopted as direct reading voltmeter, the scale of the galvanometer should be at least 10 to 20 cm to achieve a reasonable degree of precision. The variable resistance in series with the galvanometer is adjusted to cause full deflection for the maximum cell voltage during titration. It is a good precaution to insert in series with the variable resistance a fixed 100,000-ohm resistance (radio type, 2 watts) to avoid any excessive current through the galvanometer when the adjustable resistance is set accidentally at its lowest value (perhaps only a few ohms).

Reagents. One-tenth molar sodium chloride; 0.1 M potassium iodide; and 0.1 M silver nitrate.

Procedure for the Titration of Silver Nitrate with Sodium Chloride and Potassium Iodide. Titrate 25 ml of 0.1 M silver nitrate with 0.1 M sodium chloride, and plot the titration curve. Repeat the experiment with 25 ml of 0.1 M potassium iodide as titrant, and plot the results on the diagram with the chloride titration curve. Discuss the influence of the solubility of the precipitate on the shape of titration curves.

Prepare 0.002 M solutions of sodium chloride and silver nitrate by dilution of the 0.1 M reagents. Titrate 25 ml of 0.002 M silver nitrate with 0.002 M sodium chloride, and plot the titration curve. Replot on this diagram the titration curve previously obtained with the 0.1 M reagents, and discuss the effect of dilution on the shape of titration curves.

Be sure to calculate in advance the volumes of titrant at which voltage readings must be taken for reliable plotting of titration curves. If the reagent concentrations are not known exactly, determine the equivalence point in a preliminary titration.

[4] J. S. Fritz, *Acid-Base Titrations in Nonaqueous Solvents*, The G. Frederick Smith Chemical Company, Columbus, Ohio, 1952, pp. 24–42.

15-5. OXIDATION-REDUCTION COUPLES AND TITRATIONS

Equipment. Student potentiometer and accessories, or simple potentiometer of Fig. 131; direct-reading instrument for voltage measurements (vacuum-tube voltmeter or galvanometer-resistance combination) for the titrations; pH meter with glass and calomel electrodes; platinum and calomel electrodes of the industrial type; two 50-ml burettes; 25-ml and 50-ml pipettes; four 50-ml graduated cylinders; five 100-ml volumetric flasks; one weighing bottle; wash bottle; and stirring rod. Note that a pH meter may be substituted for the student potentiometer.

Reagent. One-tenth molar acetic acid; 0.2 M sodium acetate; 0.5 M potassium ferrocyanide (freshly prepared); 0.5 M potassium ferricyanide (freshly prepared); 2 M potassium chloride; 0.1 M hydrochloric acid; 0.1 M sodium hydroxide; 0.1 M potassium hydrogen o-phthalate; 0.2 M acetic acid; 0.1 M monopotassium phosphate; 1 M sulfuric acid; 0.1 M ceric sulfate; solid quinhydrone; solid ferrous ammonium sulfate $FeSO_4 \cdot (NH_4)_2SO_4 \cdot 6H_2O$.

The standard solution of ceric sulfate is prepared by dissolving the proper amount of ceric ammonium sulfate in 1 M sulfuric acid. The solution may be standardized against sodium oxalate or arsenious oxide.[5]

a. Verification of the Nernst Equation. Fill two 50-ml burettes with 0.2 M potassium ferrocyanide and 0.2 M potassium ferricyanide, and prepare the following mixtures:

> 0.001 M $K_3Fe(CN)_6$, 0.1 M $K_4Fe(CN)_6$, 1 M KCl
> 0.01 M $K_3Fe(CN)_6$, 0.1 M $K_4Fe(CN)_6$, 1 M KCl
> 0.1 M $K_3Fe(CN)_6$, 0.1 M $K_4Fe(CN)_6$, 1 M KCl
> 0.1 M $K_3Fe(CN)_6$, 0.01 M $K_4Fe(CN)_6$, 1 M KCl
> 0.1 M $K_3Fe(CN)_6$, 0.001 M $K_4Fe(CN)_6$, 1 M KCl

Measure with a potentiometer the equilibrium potentials for these solutions with a platinum electrode coupled with a calomel electrode, and prepare a diagram similar to Fig. 4 of Chapter 2. In the same diagram plot the calculated curve showing potential against composition by using the experimental value of the formal potential.

Explain why the solution is made 1 M in potassium chloride.

b. Influence of pH on the Potential of Oxidation-Reduction Reactions Involving Hydrogen Ions. Prepare the following buffer mixtures in 50-ml graduate cylinders:

> 50 ml 0.1 M hydrochloric acid
> 10 ml 0.1 M hydrochloric acid + 25 ml 0.1 M potassium hydrogen o-phthalate, and dilute to 50 ml with distilled water
> 10 ml 0.2 M acetic acid, and dilute to 50 ml with 0.1 M sodium hydroxide
> 20 ml 0.1 M sodium hydroxide + 25 ml 0.1 M monopotassium phosphate, and dilute to 50 ml with distilled water.

[5]See I. M. Kolthoff and E. B. Sandell, *Textbook of Quantitative Inorganic Analysis,* 3rd ed., Macmillan, New York, 1952, p. 582.

Add to each solution a few small crystals of quinhydrone, and shake the graduated cylinders to accelerate dissolution. Measure the pH of each solution with a pH meter with glass electrode. Measure the potential of a platinum electrode, coupled with a saturated calomel electrode, for each solution; and plot the potential of the platinum electrode against pH. Compare the slope of the resulting line (straight) with the theoretical slope at the temperature of the room.

Since quinhydrone is an addition compound of one mole of quinone per mole of hydroquinone, the ratio of the concentration of quinone to that of hydroquinone is equal to unity in each experiment.

c. Titration of Ferrous Ion with Ceric Ion. Weigh to the milligram about 1 gram of ferrous ammonium sulfate $FeSO_4(NH_4)_2SO_4 \cdot 6H_2O$, and dissolve the sample in 25 ml of 1 M sulfuric acid. Titrate the solution with 0.1 M ceric sulfate, using a platinum electrode as indicator electrode and a saturated calomel electrode (industrial model) as reference.

Be sure to determine in advance the volumes of titrant at which readings should be taken. If the concentrations are not known with accuracy, carry out a preliminary titration to determine the equivalence point.

Plot the results and indicate on the titration curve the theoretical potential at the equivalence point. The titration curve should be symmetrical with respect to the equivalence point. If this is not the case, give the reason for the distortion of the titration curve.

d. Suggestion for Further Work. Titrations with a strong reductant such as chromous ion or titanous ion can be carried out in air-free medium. See examples, for instance, in Müller's book.[6]

15–6. POLAROGRAPHIC TECHNIQUES

Equipment. A manual polarograph, for instance the potentiometer of Fig. 131, which is designed with a sufficient low internal resistance (why?); galvanometer with an Ayrton shunt;[7] polarographic cell assembly which is installed in a large photographic or stainless steel tray *to avoid the spilling of mercury on the bench and the floor;* timer; polarographic *H*-cell; nitrogen tank with regulator; 50-ml volumetric flask; 5-ml and 10-ml pipettes; 1-ml pipette graduated in 0.1-ml units; 100-ml beaker; stirring rod; test tube (15 cm); Bunsen burner with support and gauze; wash bottle; filter paper.

Reagents. One-tenth molar potassium nitrate; 10^{-2} M lead nitrate, 10^{-2} M potassium iodate; 1 per cent methyl red in 95 per cent ethyl alcohol; solution saturated with potassium chloride and calomel with an excess of both salts (only 1 gram of calomel); solid potassium chloride; anhydrous sodium sulfite; solid potassium nitrate; gelatin; mercury in a 60-ml bottle with medicine dropper.

---

[6]E. Müller, *Die Elektrometrische Massanalyse,* 6th ed., Steinkopff, Dresden, 1942, pp. 228–253. Book reprinted by Edwards, Ann Arbor, Michigan, 1945.

[7]Easily constructed with a commutator of the radio type and carbon resistors (radio type, 2 watts).

Care of Dropping Mercury Electrodes. A dropping mercury electrode can render long service provided that it is properly washed with distilled water and dried with filter paper after completion of each experiment. The capillary is conveniently inserted in a test tube when it is not used. The flow of mercury is stopped with a clamp on the rubber tube connecting the capillary to the mercury reservoir. It is not a sound practice to interrupt the flow of mercury when the capillary is immersed in a solution because of the danger of crystallization of salt in the bore of the capillary.

a. Oxygen Waves and Oxygen Removal.

Prepare the calomel electrode of the polarographic *H*-cell (Fig. 38B in Chapter 4). The agar-agar plug is not needed in this and the following experiments if the fritted glass disk is of sufficiently fine porosity. However, in accurate analytical work the use of an agar-agar plug is advisable to avoid dilution of the analyzed solution by the potassium chloride solution seeping through the fritted glass disk.

Fill the dropping mercury electrode arm of the *H*-cell with 0.1 *M* potassium nitrate to which are added three drops of a 1 per cent methyl red alcoholic solution. Insert the capillary electrode, and adjust the head of mercury to obtain a drop-time between 3 and 5 sec. Set the galvanometer shunt at its lowest sensititivity, and connect the cell to the polarograph, the dropping mercury electrode being connected to the negative terminal of the potentiometer. Adjust the output voltage of the potentiometer to 1.3 volts, and increase the galvanometer sensitivity until the average current during drop life corresponds approximately to two-thirds of the full scale of the galvanometer. This is the sensitivity at which measurements will be made.

Vary the potential of the dropping mercury electrode between 0.1 and -1.8 to -1.9 volts (versus S.C.E.), and take enough readings to be able to plot reliably the oxygen double wave and the initial segment of the current-potential for the reduction of the supporting electrolyte. The foot of the oxygen wave is poorly defined when the electrolyte contains chloride ions. (Why?)

Set the potential of the dropping mercury electrode at a value in the upper plateau of the second wave, and measure the current. Bubble nitrogen for 1 min and measure again the current *after the stirring of the liquid has stopped*. Never measure a polarographic current while bubbling nitrogen through the solution because stirring interferes with diffusion at the mercury drop electrode. Bubble nitrogen for another minute and measure the current again. Repeat these operations until the current has dropped to a small fraction of its initial value. Plot current against time of nitrogen bubbling. The points may not fit a curve very well because nitrogen is not bubbled exactly in the same fashion after each interruption.

Renew the potassium nitrate solution in the polarographic cell, and measure the current at the same potential as in the study of oxygen removal by nitrogen. Prepare in a test tube approximately 2 ml of a saturated solution of sodium sulfite, and add this solution to the potassium nitrate solution in the H-cell. Stir with a glass rod, and replace the dropping electrode. Follow the decrease of the oxygen diffusion current with time, and take current readings until the current has dropped to perhaps a few per cent of its initial value. Increase the sensitivity of the galvanometer toward the end. Plot the diffusion current against time.

Wash the cell (D.M.E. arm) immediately after completion of the experiment to avoid diffusion of sulfite in the arm of the cell with the calomel electrode.

Note that the procedure followed in the study of oxygen removal does not yield the exact diffusion current because a correction is not made for the residual current. This approximate method suffices here, although its use is not advisable in analytical determinations.

b. Maximum Suppressors. Transfer 10 ml of $10^{-2} M$ lead nitrate to a 50-ml volumetric flask, and dilute to 50 ml with 0.1 M potassium nitrate. Fill the D.M.E. arm of the H-cell with this solution, and remove oxygen by bubbling nitrogen for 10 min. Set the polarograph at -0.8 volt (versus S.C.E.), and determine the proper galvanometer sensitivity as in experiment 15–6a, except that the diffusion current for lead should correspond to not more than 20 to 30 per cent of the full scale. Determine the current-potential curve, point by point, in the range -0.2 to -0.8 volt (versus S.C.E.). Take enough points to obtain a good definition of the wave and its maximum, but do not waste time by taking too many readings.

Boil 50 ml of distilled water, and add 0.5 gram gelatin. Stir until gelatin is completely dissolved. Transfer a few millimeters to a test tube and cool under water. Add 0.2 ml of the cold gelatin solution to the lead solution in the H-cell, and determine the current-potential curve again.

Note that the maximum may not be observed with old solutions. (Why?)

c. Migration Current. Prepare in a 50-ml volumetric flask a $10^{-3} M$ solution of lead nitrate. Fill the H-cell as usual, and add 0.2 ml of the 1 per cent gelatin solution previously prepared. Remove oxygen by bubbling nitrogen through the solution for 10 min. Measure the current at -0.8 volt (versus S.C.E.), with the galvanometer sensitivity adjusted at a value corresponding to 60 to 80 per cent of the full-scale deflection. Add enough solid potassium nitrate to make the solution in the H-cell approximately 0.1 M (a few small crystals), and bubble nitrogen a few minutes to speed up dissolution of the salt. Measure again the diffusion current at -0.8 volt (versus S.C.E.). Compare the currents before and after addition of the supporting electrolyte, and explain the results.

Repeat this experiment with $10^{-3} M$ potassium iodate by measuring the diffusion current at -1.4 volts (versus S.C.E.). The galvanometer deflection should not exceed 25 to 35 per cent of the full scale before the addition of supporting electrolyte. Compare the diffusion currents before and after the addition of supporting electrolyte, and explain the difference between this case and that of lead.

See the remark at the end of the Section 15–6a about the error on the diffusion current when a correction for the residual current is not made.

15–7. FACTORS CONTROLLING DIFFUSION CURRENTS

Equipment. Use the same polarographic equipment as in experiment 15–6 or a recording polarograph; H-cell; calibrated 100,000-ohm resistance or decade box; dropping mercury electrode assembly with index for the reading of the head of mercury on a ruler attached to the support of the mercury reservoir; nitrogen tank with regulator; four 100-ml volumetric flasks; 1-ml, 5-ml, 10-ml, and 25-ml pipettes; small cup for collecting mercury (measurement of m); 5-cm watch glass; thermometer (0° to 110°); crystallization dish about 15 cm in diameter (to immerse the H-cell in an ice bath); stirring rod; wash bottle; and filter paper.

Reagents. One-tenth molar potassium nitrate; $10^{-2} M$ lead nitrate; solution saturated with potassium chloride and mercurous chloride with an excess of both salts (only 1 gram of calomel); 1 per cent methyl red in alcohol in 60-ml bottle with medicine dropper; acetone; mercury in 60-ml bottle with medicine dropper.

a. Influence of Potential on Drop Time. Prepare a polarographic H-cell, and fill the D.M.E. arm with 0.1 M potassium nitrate. Adjust the head of mercury for a drop time of 3 to 4 sec at −0.8 volt (versus S.C.E.), and note the mercury level on the scale on the mercury reservoir support. The drop time is determined by measuring with a timer, graduated in tenths of a second, the time required for the fall of 10 or 20 drops. Measure the drop time with the mercury drop polarized at 0, −0.2, −0.4 . . . −1.6, −1.8 volts (versus S.C.E.), and plot the drop time τ and $\tau^{1/6}$ against potential.

b. Measurement of m. Measure the rate of flow of mercury with the D.M.E. at −0.40 volt (versus S.C.E.). This potential is selected because the result of this experiment is needed in Section 15–7c. The value of m is determined by collecting in a small glass cup (Fig. 132) the mercury flowing from the capillary for an accurately timed interval of perhaps 10 min. The mercury globule is transferred on a previously weighed watch glass; then washed twice with a few drops of distilled water; and finally dried with filter paper. A drop of acetone is added with a glass rod and is removed with filter paper. The dry mercury globule is then weighed, and m is calculated.

Fig. 132. Glass cup for the determination of m.

c. Determination of Diffusion Coefficients and Diffusion Current Constants. Transfer exactly 10 ml of $10^{-2} M$ lead nitrate in a 100-ml volumetric flask; add 2 to 3 drops of a 1 per cent alcoholic solution of methyl red, and dilute to 100 ml with 0.1 M potassium nitrate. Use this solution to wash the D.M.E. arm of the H-cell used in the preceding experiment, and fill the cell. De-aerate with nitrogen as usual, and determine the current-potential curve by taking enough current readings between -0.2 and -0.8 volt (versus S.C.E.). Plot the wave and determine graphically the diffusion current by the method of Fig. 34 (left).

Calibrate the galvanometer for the sensitivity selected for the above experiment. Substitute for the cell a calibrated 100,000-ohm resistance (or a decade box set at this value), and take a few current readings for different applied voltages. Calculate the current from Ohm's law, and use the average sensitivity in further calculations.

Calculate the diffusion current constant at the temperature of the experiment (preferably 25°) by using the values of m and τ previously determined. The drop time should be taken at the half-wave potential from the plot of drop time against potential. Calculate the polarographic diffusion coefficient for lead ion.

d. Influence of the Head of Mercury. Study the effect of the head of mercury on the diffusion current for lead by using the same solution as in the preceding experiment. Adjust the head of mercury at different levels corresponding to drop times between 2 and 6 sec, and measure the current at -0.8 volt (versus S.C.E.) for each head of mercury. Read the head of mercury on the ruler attached to the support of the mercury reservoir. Correct the current readings for the residual current by taking for the latter current the extrapolated value at -0.8 volt (versus S.C.E.) which is read on the polarogram plotted in experiment 15–7c. This procedure saves time, but the value is approximate because the residual current depends on the head of mercury. (Explain why.) Plot diffusion current against the square root of the head of mercury, and explain the results.

In all rigor the head of mercury ought to be corrected for the back pressure,[8] but this minor correction can be neglected here.

After completion of this experiment bring back the mercury level to the same setting as in experiment 15–7c.

e. Influence of Concentration of Reducible Substance. Transfer in 100-ml volumetric flasks 1, 5, and 25 ml of $10^{-2} M$ lead nitrate. Add a few drops of a 1 per cent alcoholic solution of methyl red, and dilute to 100 ml with 0.1 M potassium nitrate. Take the polarograms of these solutions as in experiment 15–7c by starting with the lower concentration (Why?). It is not necessary to renew the calomel electrode for each concentration. Select the proper galvanometer sensitivity on the basis of the results obtained in experiment 15–7c, and calibrate the galvanometer for each

[8]See I. M. Kolthoff and J. J. Lingane, *Polarography*, 2nd ed., Vol. 1, Interscience, New York, 1952, p. 79.

sensitivity. It is not necessary to take many points to have a good definition of each wave. Determine graphically the diffusion current for each concentration, and plot diffusion current against concentration of lead nitrate, including the result obtained in experiment 15–7c.

Do not empty the cell after the measurement with the $5 \times 10^{-3} M$ lead nitrate solution.

f. Influence of Temperature. Immerse the cell with the $5 \times 10^{-3} M$ lead nitrate solution used in the last determination of experiment 15–7e, and cool the solution to approximately 0° to 2° while bubbling nitrogen through the solution. (Why? The solution is already de-aerated.) Note the temperature, and determine the current-potential curve. Determine graphically the diffusion current. Compare this current with the current obtained at room temperature, and calculate an *average* temperature coefficient for the diffusion current.

By making the approximation that the diffusion coefficient of lead ion and the diffusion current have the same temperature dependence, calculate from the data on hand an approximate value of the heat of activation of the diffusion coefficient of lead ion. Use the result to compute the temperature coefficient of the diffusion current at room temperature. Compare this value with the average temperature coefficient previously computed.

g. Suggestions for Further Work. The following experiments are suggested for advanced students: kinetic current for the reduction of dextrose, catalytic current for the reduction of titanic ion in presence of hydroxylamine, and determination of the number of electrons involved in the polarographic reduction of nitromethane.

The following equipment is needed: the same polarographic equipment as in the other experiments in this group; timer; polarographic cells of the Erlenmeyer and H types; dropping mercury electrode assembly with ruler attached to the support of the mercury reservoir and pointer for the reading of the head of mercury; polarographic microcell (Fig. 38C); dropping mercury electrode with ground conic tip; gas washing bottle for the control of the nitrogen flow; nitrogen tank with regulator; 1-ml pipette; two 50-ml volumetric flasks; 10-ml graduated cylinder; 600-ml beaker; weighing bottle.

The following reagents are needed: 0.01 M lithium hydroxide or 0.01 M tetramethylammonium hydroxide;[9] $10^{-2} M$ titanic chloride or sulfate in 3 M hydrochloric acid; $10^{-2} M$ nitromethane; 0.1 M hydrochloric acid; saturated solution of oxalic acid with excess of solid acid; 1 M hydroxylamine hydrochloride; solution saturated with potassium chloride and mercurous chloride with an excess of both salts (only 1 gram of calomel); dextrose; gelatin; mercury in 60-ml bottle with medicine dropper; wash bottle; and filter paper.

[9]This reagent, especially purified for polarographic analysis, is available from Southwestern Analytical Chemicals, 1107 W. Gibson Street, Austin, Texas. The solution should be kept in a plastic container, not in a glass bottle. (Why?)

KINETIC CURRENT FOR THE REDUCTION OF DEXTROSE. Prepare 50 ml of 0.2 M dextrose in 0.01 M lithium hydroxide or, preferably, 0.01 M tetramethylammonium hydroxide. Fill a polarographic cell (Fig. 38A) with mercury pool as anode (why not an H-cell with saturated calomel electrode?) with this solution, and record the polarogram with a drop time of 1 to 2.5 sec at −1.9 volts with respect to the mercury pool. (Why is the drop time quite short?) Note the mercury level on the ruler attached to the mercury reservoir. (Why is the limiting current so small for such a concentrated solution as 0.2 M dextrose?)

Record again the current-potential curve but with drop times of 2 to 3 sec and, if possible, 3 to 4 sec. All drop times are measured with the mercury drop at −1.9 volts with respect to the mercury pool. Measure the limiting current for the different drop times, and explain the results.

Set the mercury reservoir at the level corresponding to the shortest drop time previously selected, and immerse the cell in a beaker filled with water at 60° to 70°. Let the solution warm up while bubbling nitrogen through it. (Why?) Open the cell and measure the temperature within 0.5°. Close the cell rapidly when the solution has reached 35° to 40°, and immediately measure the current at −1.90 volts with respect to the mercury pool. Measure the temperature again, and take as the temperature of the solution the average of the readings before and after the current measurement. Note that it will be necessary to use a sensitivity lower than that needed at room temperature. Calculate the *average* temperature coefficient for the limiting current, and compare this result with the coefficient obtained in experiment 15–7f. Explain the difference.[10]

CATALYTIC CURRENT FOR THE REDUCTION OF TI (IV) IN PRESENCE OF HYDROXYLAMINE. Transfer exactly 5 ml of a $10^{-2}\,M$ titanic chloride (or sulfate) solution to a 50-ml volumetric flask and dilute to 50 ml with a saturated solution of oxalic acid. Fill the D.M.E. arm of an H-cell with this solution, and record the polarogram. The galvanometer sensitivity is adjusted to produce a deflection of 25 to 35 per cent of the full scale with the mercury drop at −0.40 volt (versus S.C.E.). Add to the solution in the H-cell 1 ml of 1 M hydroxylamine hydrochloric measured with a 10-ml graduated cylinder (hydroxylamine is a poison). Determine the current-potential curve again.

Plot on the same diagram the current-potential curves obtained before and after the addition of hydroxylamine. Explain the results by noting that titanium (III) is oxidized by hydroxylamine. This reaction was investigated by Evans and coworkers.[11] A quantitative study of the kinetics of this reaction can be made by polarography.[12]

[10]See K. Wiesner, *Collection Czechoslov. Chem. Communs.*, **12**, 64 (1947).
[11]P. Davis, M. G. Evans, and W. C. E. Higgins, *J. Chem. Soc.*, 2563 (1951).
[12]A. Blazek and J. Koryta, *Collection Czechoslov. Chem. Communs.*, **18**, 326 (1953).

DETERMINATION OF n WITH A POLAROGRAPHIC MICROCELL. Determine the number of electrons involved in an electrode reaction by following with a polarographic microcell the decrease in concentration of reducible (oxidizable) substance in an electrolysis at constant potential. The number of electrons is readily deduced from a plot of the logarithm of the diffusion current against time (see problem 6 in Chapter 6).

Transfer 5 ml of $10^{-2}\,M$ nitromethane in a 50-ml volumetric flask, and dilute to 50 ml with 0.1 M hydrochloric acid. Fill the microcell of Fig. 38C in Chapter 4 with mercury, and transfer in it exactly 0.3 ml of the $10^{-3}\,M$ nitromethane solution. Insert the capillary of the dropping mercury electrode in the solution, and adjust the level of the tip to avoid contact between the mercury drop and the mercury pool. Pass nitrogen above the solution for at least 30 min. The rate of flow of nitrogen is controlled with a gas washing bottle which is inserted between the tank regulator and the cell. To avoid air re-entry a slow stream of nitrogen may be maintained during the electrolysis even when oxygen is removed.

Connect the cell to a manual polarograph, but be sure to leave open the switch controlling the electrolysis current. The D.M.E. is connected to the negative terminal of the polarograph. Adjust the voltage across the cell at 0.90 volt. Start the electrolysis and a timer simultaneously, and adjust the galvanometer sensitivity *rapidly*. Read the current as soon as possible after the beginning of electrolysis. Measure the current at regular time intervals, and stop the electrolysis when the current has dropped to perhaps three-fourths to two-thirds of its initial value. Plot the logarithm of current against time, and deduce from the slope of the resulting straight line the number of electrons involved in the reduction of nitromethane in 0.1 M hydrochloric acid (see problem 6 in Chapter 6).

The foregoing method is discussed in articles by Gilbert and Rideal[13] and by Meites *et al.*[14] Further details on the polarography of nitromethane can be found in an article by Petru.[15]

15-8. POLAROGRAPHIC CURRENT-POTENTIAL CURVES

Equipment. Use the same polarographic equipment as in experiments 15–6 and 15–7; pH meter with glass electrode; timer; nitrogen tank with regulator; H-cell; five 100-ml volumetric flasks; 100-ml graduated cylinder; 1-ml (graduated in 0.1 ml), 2-ml, 5-ml, 10-ml and 25-ml pipettes; wash bottle; and filter paper.

Reagents. One-hundredth molar p-nitroaniline in a mixture of 35 per cent by volume of ethyl alcohol and water; 95 per cent ethyl alcohol; 0.2 M hydrochloric acid; 0.8 M glycine; 0.8 M potassium chloride; 0.25 M monopotassium phos-

[13]G. A. Gilbert and E. K. Rideal, *Trans. Faraday Soc.*, **47**, 396 (1951).

[14]S. Bogan, L. Meites, E. Peters, and J. M. Sturtevant, *J. Am. Chem. Soc.*, **73**, 1584 (1951).

[15]F. Petru, *Collection Czechoslov. Chem. Communs.*, **12**, 620 (1947).

phate; 0.25 M boric acid; $10^{-2} M$ cadmium sulfate; 1 M potassium nitrate; 4 M ethylenediamine (standardized by acid-base titration); $10^{-2} M$ potassium iodate; 1 M sodium hydroxide; 0.05 M potassium hydrogen o-phthalate (for pH meter standardization); solution saturated with potassium chloride and mercurous chloride with an excess of both salts (only 1 gram of calomel); gelatin; mercury in 60-ml bottle with medicine dropper.

a. Analysis of Reversible Waves. Prepare a plot of log $[(\bar{\imath}_d - \bar{\imath})/\bar{\imath}]$ against potential for the current-potential curve obtained in experiment 15–7c for the reduction of the plumbous ion. Do not consider points for which $(\bar{\imath}_d - \bar{\imath})/\bar{\imath}$ is smaller than 0.05 and larger than 20. (Why?) Compare the slope of the straight line thus obtained with the theoretical slope.

b. Influence of pH on Half-Wave Potentials. The electrolytic reduction of most organic substances involves hydrogen ions, and consequently the half-wave potential may be pH dependent. The relationship between $E_{1/2}$ and pH is readily established when the Nernst equation is applicable. However, this equation cannot be applied for reduction or oxidation of most organic substances, and the dependence of $E_{1/2}$ on pH can be determined only by experiment. In some cases the half-wave potential is virtually independent of pH although the electrode reaction involves hydrogen ions. In other cases $E_{1/2}$ varies more rapidly with pH than one would expect from the Nernst equation. The dependence of $E_{1/2}$ on pH is often affected by the presence of salts and by the nature of the solvent.

The pH of the medium is adjusted with a buffer mixture *with a good buffering capacity*. For instance, a mixture of $5 \times 10^{-3} M$ acetic acid and $10^{-1} M$ sodium acetate would be a poor buffer in the polarographic study of a 10^{-3} molar solution of a substance whose reduction involves two hydrogen ions per molecule. With a poor buffer the pH in the immediate vicinity of the drop may differ from the pH in the bulk of the solution by several pH units.

The effect of pH on half-wave potentials can be studied, for example, for the six electron reduction of p-nitroaniline in water-alcoholic mixtures.[16]

Prepare the following solutions (ionic strength of approximately 0.1) in 100-ml volumetric flasks by adding to exactly 5 ml of $10^{-2} M$ p-nitroaniline (see reagents), 35 ml of 95 per cent ethyl alcohol, 2 ml of 1 per cent gelatin solution (see preparation in experiment 15–6b), and the following reagents:

    10 ml 0.2 M hydrochloric acid, and dilute to 100 ml with distilled water
    10 ml 0.2 M hydrochloric acid + 10 ml 0.8 M glycine, 10 ml 0.8 M potassium chloride, and dilute to 100 ml with distilled water
    10 ml 0.25 M potassium hydroxide, 10 ml 0.5 M monopotassium phosphate, and dilute to 100 ml with distilled water
    10 ml 0.25 M potassium hydroxide, 10 ml 0.8 M potassium chloride, 25 ml 0.25 M boric acid, and dilute to 100 ml with distilled water

[16] O. D. Shreve and E. C. Markham, *J. Am. Chem. Soc.*, **71**, 2993 (1949).

Note that all volumes in the preparation of the buffers can be measured with a graduated cylinder.

Measure the pH's of these solutions with a pH meter with glass electrode. Determine the current potential-curve for each solution. The galvanometer sensitivity, which is the same for the different solutions, is adjusted with the dropping mercury electrode at -0.5 volt (versus S.C.E.) for the solution of lowest pH. The solubility of oxygen in water-alcohol mixtures is greater than in water, and sufficient time should be allowed for oxygen removal. Time is saved by the use of a fritted glass gas disperser for the nitrogen inlet in the cell. (Why? How do you determine whether oxygen is practically removed?)

Determine the half-wave potential for each wave, and plot $E_{1/2}$ against pH. Compare the slope of the resulting line, if it is a straight line, with the theoretical slope.

c. Reduction of Complex Ions. Prepare in 100-ml volumetric flasks solutions which contain 0.01 per cent gelatin and are $10^{-2}\,M$ in cadmium sulfate, 0.1 M in potassium nitrate, and which have the following molarities in ethylenediamine: 2.5 M, 1 M, 0.5 M, and 0.1 M. The volumes of standard ethylenediamine solution should be measured exactly. (Why?) Determine or record the current-potential curves. The galvanometer sensitivity, which is the same for all the solutions, is adjusted with the dropping mercury electrode at -1.15 volts (versus S.C.E.).

Determine the half-wave potentials of each wave. Ascertain that the Nernst equation is obeyed (how?), and plot half-wave potentials against the logarithm of the concentration of ethylenediamine. Calculate the coordination number for the ethylenediamine cadmium complex on the assumption that a single complex is formed. Compute the instability constant of the complex, knowing that $E_{1/2} = -0.58$ volt (versus S.C.E.) for cadmium in 0.1 M potassium nitrate. Compare your result with the one in the literature.[17]

d. Analysis of Irreversible Waves. Transfer exactly 10 ml of $10^{-2}M$ potassium iodate in a 100-ml volumetric flask; add 0.5 ml of a 1 per cent gelatin solution, and dilute to 100 ml with 1 M sodium hydroxide. Prepare an H-cell with saturated calomel electrode and an agar-agar plug[18] (saturated potassium chloride). An agar-agar plug is needed here to decrease the rate of diffusion of sodium hydroxide in the calomel electrode compartment. (Why?) Record the polarogram of this solution with a drop time of 2 to 3 sec.[19] The galvanometer sensitivity is adjusted with the mercury drop at

---

[17]B. E. Douglas, H. A. Laitinen, and J. C. Bailar, Jr., *J. Am. Chem. Soc.*, **72**, 2484 (1950).

[18]For a simple technique, see I. M. Kolthoff and J. J. Lingane, *Polarography*, 2nd ed , Vol. 1, Interscience, New York, 1952, p. 362.

[19]A short drop time is selected here because comparison with data obtained with longer drop times will be made later.

−1.4 volts (versus S.C.E.). Measure the drop time at −1.2 volts (versus S.C.E.). Plot the current-potential curve, and analyze it by the method of Koutecky.[20] This method was discussed in problem 8 of Chapter 4 for the case in which maximum currents during drop life are measured (pen-and-ink recorder). If the average current is measured (as is the case for instruments equipped with a galvanometer), the current-potential curve can be represented by the following approximate equation,

$$\frac{\bar{\imath}}{\bar{\imath}_d} = \frac{0.87[(k_f\tau^{1/2})/D^{1/2}]}{1 + 0.87[(k_f\tau^{1/2})/D^{1/2}]}, \qquad (15\text{–}1)$$

where $\bar{\imath}$ is the average current along the wave, $\bar{\imath}_d$ is the diffusion current, τ is the drop time, D is the diffusion coefficient of iodate ion, and k_f is the rate constant at the potential corresponding to the current $\bar{\imath}$. The rate constant k_f is potential-dependent. Discuss in a general way, and without going into the details, the ideas involved in the derivation of the equation showing the dependence of k_f on potential.

Calculate k_f for $\bar{\imath}/\bar{\imath}_d = 0.1, 0.2, \cdots 0.9$ for the experimental iodate wave, and plot log k_f against potential. Verify that k_f varies exponentially with potential. The value of D needed in this computation is calculated from the average diffusion current by application of the Ilkovic equation.

With the solution previously used, record the current-potential curve again with the same galvanometer sensitivity as before, but with a drop time of 5 to 6 sec. Measure the drop time at −1.2 volts (versus S.C.E.). Determine the half-wave potential, and calculate the shift in $E_{1/2}$ with respect to the half-wave potential for a drop time of 2 to 3 sec. Calculate the shift in half-wave potential from equation (15–1), and compare the result with the experimental shift. To calculate this shift, write k_f in the form [see equation (4–32)]

$$k_f = k_f{}^0 \exp(-\lambda E), \qquad (15\text{–}2)$$

where $-\lambda$ is the slope of the plot of log k_f against E. Thus, at $E_{1/2}$,

$$(k_f)_{E_{1/2}} = k_f{}^0 \exp(-\lambda E_{1/2}), \qquad (15\text{–}3)$$

and

$$\frac{\bar{\imath}}{\bar{\imath}_d} = 0.5. \qquad (15\text{–}4)$$

Express $E_{1/2}$ as a function of drop time by combining equations (15–1), (15–3), and (15–4).

15–9. VOLTAMMETRIC TITRATIONS

Equipment. Manual polarograph; H-cell for amperometric titrations; dropping mercury electrode; rotated platinum electrode assembly; electrode assembly for dead-stop end point; nitrogen tank with regulator; 10-ml and 50-ml burettes;

[20]J. Koutecky, *Collection Czechoslov. Chem. Communs.*, **18**, 597 (1953).

2-ml, 5-ml, and 25-ml pipettes; 50-ml graduated cylinder; 150-ml beaker; wash bottle; and filter paper.

The H-cell for amperometric titrations is similar to the cell of Fig. 38B except that the D.M.E. arm has a capacity of approximately 100 ml. A silver-silver chloride electrode made of heavy silver wire may be used for reference electrode. The electrode is cleaned in 1:1 nitric acid for a few seconds and is oxidized anodically in 1 M HCl for a few minutes at perhaps 1 to 10 milliamp.[21] The silver wire coated with silver chloride is immersed in 0.1 M potassium chloride in one of the arms of the H-cell. The tip of the burette is adjusted in the stopper of the H-cell, and a platinum wire (Fig. 133) is attached to the tip with a short (5 mm) narrow

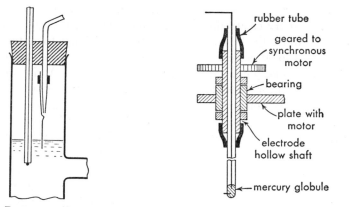

rubber tube
geared to synchronous motor
bearing
plate with motor
electrode hollow shaft
mercury globule

Fig. 133. Burette-cell assembly for amperometric titrations with the dropping mercury electrode.

Fig. 134. Shaft for rotated platinum electrode.

rubber tube to prevent the formation of droplets. The burette inlet also serves as an outlet for nitrogen.

The rotated platinum electrode assembly is composed of the electrode of Fig. 37 and a 600-rpm synchronous motor. The glass tube is inserted in a hollow shaft geared to the synchronous motor (Fig. 134). Contact to the platinum electrode is made with a mercury globule.

The electrode assembly for dead-stop end point is simply composed of two platinum wires (0.5 by 5 mm) sealed in glass tubes which are inserted in a rubber stopper. The cell is a 150-ml beaker with a glass propeller stirrer.

Reagents. One-tenth molar potassium chloride; 0.1 M lead nitrate; 0.1 M potassium nitrate; 5×10^{-2} M potassium dichromate; 5×10^{-3} M arsenious acid in 1 M hydrochloric acid;[22] 1 M hydrochloric acid; 5 M potassium bromide; 1/600 M potassium bromate; 0.1 M freshly prepared sodium thiosulfate; 0.1 M

[21]For more refined methods, see the review of G. L. Janz and H. Taniguchi, *Chem. Revs.*, **53**, 397 (1953).
[22]Dissolve the required weight of arsenious oxide in 2 to 3 M sodium hydroxide, and add enough 6 M hydrochloric acid to make the solution, upon dilution, approximately 1 M in acid.

iodine;[23] $10^{-2} M$ freshly prepared potassium ferrocyanide; $10^{-2} M$ ceric sulfate; $1 M$ sulfuric acid.

a. Amperometric Titration of Lead Nitrate with Potassium Chromate with the Dropping Mercury Electrode. Prepare the silver-silver chloride electrode ($0.1 M$ potassium chloride) of a special H-cell for amperometric titrations. Transfer exactly 5 ml $0.1 M$ lead nitrate in the D.M.E. arm of the H-cell, and add approximately (graduated cylinder) 50 ml of $0.1 M$ potassium nitrate. Fill the 10-ml burette of the cell assembly with $5 \times 10^{-2} M$ potassium dichromate. Adjust the stopper of the H-cell, and insert the tip of the burette in the cell. Bubble nitrogen for 10 min to remove oxygen from solution. After oxygen removal, set the dropping mercury electrode at -1.0 volt (versus the silver-silver chloride electrode), and adjust the galvanometer sensitivity to obtain a current reading at 70 to 90 per cent of full-scale deflection. Note the current reading. Use the same potential setting during titration. Add 1 ml of titrant. Bubble nitrogen for 10 to 20 sec to stir the solution, and read the current. Repeat the operation for total volumes of titrant of 2, 3, $\cdots$ 6, and 7 ml. It is advisable to take readings at each 0.1 ml in the immediate vicinity of the equivalence point to detect the effect of the solubility of the precipitate on the shape of the titration curve. This need not be done in routine work, but it is of interest here. Wait a few minutes before reading the current near the equivalence point to let the precipitation reaction reach equilibrium. Plot current against volume of titrant, and determine the equivalence point.

Repeat the same experiment, but with the dropping mercury electrode at 0 volt (versus the silver-silver chloride electrode). Plot the titration curve, and explain its difference[24] from the curve previously obtained.

b. Amperometric Titration of Arsenic (III) with Potassium Bromate—Use of the Rotated Platinum Electrode. Transfer exactly 5 ml of the $5 \times 10^{-3} M$ arsenic (III) solution (see reagent) to the H-cell for amperometric titrations. Dilute to approximately 40 ml with $1 M$ hydrochloric acid, and add 10 ml (graduated cylinder) of a $5 M$ potassium bromide solution. Start the motor of the rotated platinum electrode, and adjust its potential at 0.2 volt (versus the silver-silver chloride electrode). Oxygen is virtually not reduced at this potential on a platinum electrode, and therefore the cell can be left open. Set the galvanometer sensitivity at one-tenth of the value selected for the lead dichromate titration. Determine the titration curve point by point, noting that the current does not increase until the equivalence point is reached. Plot the titration curve, and determine the equivalence point.[25]

[23]Dissolve 12.7 grams of iodine in a solution of 50 grams of potassium iodide in 40 ml water. Dilute to 1 lit. after dissolution of iodine.

[24]I. M. Kolthoff and Y. D. Pan, *J. Am. Chem. Soc.*, **61**, 3402 (1939).

[25]H. A. Laitinen and I. M. Kolthoff, *J. Phys. Chem.*, **45**, 1079 (1941).

c. Dead-Stop End Points. Set up the electrodes for dead-stop end point and connect them to a manual polarograph. Adjust the galvanometer sensitivity to obtain full-scale deflection for a current of 10 to 25 ma. Set the voltage applied to the electrodes at 0.025 volt.

Transfer exactly 25 ml 0.01 M sodium thiosulfate in the cell; add 10 ml of distilled water and start the stirrer. Add slowly with a 50-ml burette 0.1 M iodine, and observe the galvanometer scale. Stop the addition of titrant when the current begins to increase, and then add the titrant by small increments of perhaps 0.1 ml. Note the current after each addition of titrant. The current increases rapidly with the volume of titrant beyond the equivalence point. Plot the titration curve and explain the results.

Repeat the experiment for the titration of potassium ferrocyanide with $10^{-2}\,M$ ceric sulfate in 1 M sulfuric acid. Transfer 25 ml of $10^{-2}\,M$ potassium ferrocyanide to the titration cell, and dilute to approximately 50 ml with 1 M sulfuric acid. Add with the burette 12.5 ml of $10^{-2}\,M$ ceric sulfate, and start the stirrer of the cell. Set the galvanometer sensitivity to its lowest value; apply 0.05 volt between the electrodes, and adjust the sensitivity to obtain a deflection of 60 to 80 per cent of the full scale. Empty and clean the cell, and fill it again as before, but without addition of ceric solution. Also refill the burette. Add the titrant by increments of 2.5 ml, and read the current after each addition of titrant. Use increments of 0.1 ml of titrant in the immediate vicinity of the end point. Plot the titration curve, and explain the results.

Further examples of titration curves can be found in an article by Stone and Scholten.[26]

d. Suggestion for Further Work. Titrate ferric ion with titanium (III) in tartrate medium.[27]

15-10. ELECTROGRAVIMETRY AND ELECTROLYSIS AT CONTROLLED POTENTIAL

Equipment. Electroanalyzer with platinum gauze electrodes and tall 250-ml beaker for electrodeposition; potentiostat and cell (250-ml beaker) for electrolysis at constant potential; magnetic stirrer; timer; oven adjusted at 110°; 10- and 50-ml pipettes; 10-ml graduated cylinder; and wash bottle.

Electroanalyzers are available from several manufacturers, and detailed instructions for the construction of an inexpensive unit are given in the literature.[28]

Among the variety of potentiostats described in the literature, it is suggested that the instrument of Lingane and Jones[29] be selected because its design is simple

[26]K. G. Stone and H. G. Scholten, *Anal. Chem.*, **24,** 671 (1952).

[27]M. Spalenka, *Collection Czechoslov. Chem. Communs.*, **11,** 146 (1939); see also I. M. Kolthoff and J. J. Lingane, *Polarography*, 2nd ed., Vol. 2, Interscience, New York, pp. 893–894 and 936–937.

[28]P. S. Farrington and R. L. Pecsok, *J. Chem. Education*, **30,** 461 (1953).

[29]J. J. Lingane and S. L. Jones, *Anal. Chem.*, **22,** 1169 (1950).

and directly derived from the principle of the "manual" set-up for electrolysis at constant potential. Thus, the galvanometer of the manual instrument is simply replaced by a galvanometer relay (Weston 534) which controls the operation of the unit feeding the electrolysis cell. It is suggested for pedagogic reasons to utilize a student potentiometer or, preferably, the unit of Fig. 131 for the control of potential. The galvanometer relay can also be separated from the main unit of the potentiostat (Fig. 135).

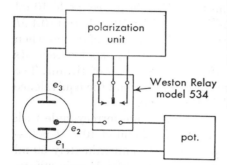

Fig. 135. Schematic diagram of potentiostat with galvanometer relay.

Because of the use of a galvanometer relay, the potential control of the Lingane-Jones instrument is quite poor when the

resistance of the reference electrode circuit exceeds a few thousand ohms. The calomel electrode should be designed accordingly (Fig. 136).

Reagents. One-tenth molar copper sulfate; concentrated sulfuric acid; and acetone.

a. Electrogravimetric Determination of Copper.

Weigh to the tenth of a milligram the larger of the two platinum electrodes (stationary electrode) supplied with the instrument for electrogravimetry. Transfer exactly 50 ml of 10^{-1} M copper sulfate into a 250-ml tall beaker for electro-

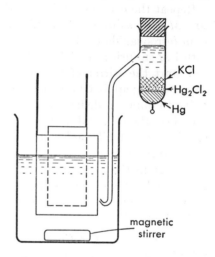

Fig. 136. Electrode assembly for the determination of potential - time curves in electrolysis at constant current. (After J. J. Lingane, *Electroanalytical Chemistry*, Interscience, New York, 1953, p. 252.)

deposition, and lower the electrodes in the cell. Add 1 ml concentrated sulfuric acid and then add water until the platinum gauze electrodes are immersed for two-thirds of their length. Start the stirrer and adjust the instrument settings to make the stationary electrode the cathode. Adjust the current to approximately 0.6 amp. Continue the electrolysis for 45 min or until the blue color has disappeared. Determine the completeness of deposition by adding a few milliliters of water and by noting whether a red deposit is formed on the electrode area freshly exposed to solution after 5 min of electrolysis. Continue the electrolysis if necessary.

When deposition is complete, raise the electrodes *without switching off the electrolysis circuit.* (Why?) Wash the cathode with a wash bottle filled with distilled water; remove the cathode, and dip it in a 250-ml beaker filled with pure acetone. (Why?) Save the acetone for later use.[30] Remove the electrode, and dry it for 10 min in an oven set at 105° to 110°. Remove the electrode from the oven and let it cool to room temperature (why?) before weighing it. Compare the weight of the deposit with its calculated value.

b. Determination of Copper by Electrolysis at Controlled Potential. Weigh to the tenth of a milligram the larger electrode of the cell of Fig. 136 for electrolysis at controlled potential. Adjust the tip of the calomel electrode within 1 mm of the outer platinum electrode. Transfer exactly 10 ml of 0.1 M copper sulfate in the cell, and add approximately 150 ml of distilled water and 1 ml concentrated sulfuric acid. Start the stirrer, and connect the electrodes to the potentiostat. Be sure that the polarity is correct: the outer electrode is the negative terminal of the electrolysis and potential control circuits. Verify that the switch controlling the electrolysis current is open, and turn on the power switch of the potentiostat. While the tubes of the instrument are warming up, set the potentiometer at 0.1 volt. Start simultaneously the electrolysis and a timer, and observe the pointer of the automatically controlled autotransformer. This pointer should reach its equilibrium position at about two-thirds to three-fourths of its full course. (Why?) If this is not the case, increase or decrease the output voltage of the manually controlled auto transformer. Reverse the direction of rotation of the motor of the potentiostat if necessary.

If too much time is required in the proper setting of the instrument, interrupt the electrolysis; clean and refill the cell, and start again.

Measure the current regularly during electrolysis, and plot the current and its logarithm against time. Explain the result. Ascertain that the copper is virtually removed (how?), and interrupt the electrolysis. Treat the electrode as in experiment 15–10a; determine its increase in weight, and compare this result with the theoretical weight increase.

c. Suggestions for Further Work. Two experiments in classical electrogravimetry are suggested: (1) the use of a complexing agent for the separation of one metal from another—for instance, the separation of copper from silver in cyanide medium; and (2) the separation of copper from lead by electrolysis in a nitric acid medium.

The study of the variations of potential of the cathode during the deposition of copper at constant current is suggested as an experiment for advanced students. The reagent concentrations and the cell assembly are

---

[30]In actual analytical determinations it is better to use a small wash bottle containing acetone, and to discard the used acetone.

the same as in experiment 15–10b, and the electrolysis is conducted at a constant current of 0.2 to 0.3 amp. The current may be continuously adjusted during electrolysis, but it is much more practical to apply the method used in coulometric titrations at constant current (see experiment 15–11a). The cell in series with an adjustable resistance is fed with a 50 to 200-volt, d-c power supply. This requires an electronic power supply, preferably with electronic voltage regulation and heavy duty resistors. Do not touch different parts of the electrical circuit with *both* hands. Determine with a student potentiometer the potential of the cathode during deposition, and plot the potential-time curve. Take frequent readings when deposition is almost complete. Explain the results.

15–11. COULOMETRIC METHODS

Equipment. Apparatus and cell for coulometric titrations at constant current with internal generation of titrant (Fig. 49); 50-ml graduated cylinder, 5-ml pipette.

The cell may be fed with 100- to 200-volt dry cells, but the current consumption is prohibitive in the titration described below. Titrations of very dilute solutions, which require only low currents (1 ma or a smaller current) may be performed with dry cells, but a commercial power supply with automatic voltage regulation is more practical than dry cells.

The double-pole toggle switch controlling the electrolysis and the timer circuits is mounted on the panel of a small box to minimize danger of electrocution. The timer circuit is fitted with male and female plugs. It is advantageous to mount another switch in parallel with this switch, with automatic return to the "off" position. Manipulation of this switch is easier than for an ordinary toggle switch when the current must be passed for short times, as is necessary in the vicinity of the equivalence point.

Resistance R_1 of the schematic diagram of Fig. 49 is most conveniently a set of wire-wound resistors connected to a commutator. Resistors permitting heavy loads should be selected to prevent heating over periods of 10 to 30 min. (Why?)

Resistance R_2 of Fig. 49 can be a decade box, but care must be taken not to overload the resistors of the box. A set of calibrated resistors of the plug-in type is very convenient.[31]

Reagents. Five-hundredths molar thiosulfate, $1\,M$ potassium iodide; and freshly prepared 0.2 per cent soluble starch solution.

a. Coulometric Titration of Thiosulfate with Generated Iodine. Prepare the cell for coulometric titrations with internal generation of titrant, and remove the nitrogen inlet (Fig. 51). Oxygen does not interfere in this titration. Transfer exactly 5 ml of $5 \times 10^{-2}\,M$ sodium thiosulfate in the cell, and dilute to 50 to 75 ml with $1\,M$ potassium iodide. Fill the cathodic compartment also with potassium iodide. Add 5 ml of a 0.2 per cent soluble starch solution to the anodic compartment.

---

[31]Inexpensive calibrated resistors are available from General Radio Co., Cambridge, Mass. The 10-ohm resistor, Model 500, is adequate for experiment 15–11a.

Set up the apparatus schematically as shown in Fig. 49. Connect together the wires normally attached to the cell electrodes, and adjust resistance R_1 to obtain a current corresponding to completion of the titration in 10 to 15 min. The ohmic drop in R_2 should be 0.5 to 1.0 volt under these conditions. (Why not a lower voltage?) Interrupt the current, and insert the cell in the electrolysis circuit. Note the reading on the timer; start the stirrer, and close the electrolysis switch. Measure exactly the ohmic drop in resistance R_2 during titration. Observe the solution, and periodically interrupt the electrolysis in the vicinity of the equivalence point. Let the current flow for short periods, perhaps a few seconds, near the equivalence point. Stop the electrolysis when the characteristic blue color appears in solution. Calculate the amount of thiosulfate initially present from the current and the duration of electrolysis.

A detailed study of this coulometric titration has been made.[32]

b. Suggestions for Further Work. Coulometric titrations with a variety of titrants and methods of equivalence-point detection can be performed. References can be found in the current literature and in the monographs of Lingane[33] and Delahay.[34]

The coulometric analysis of a lead nitrate solution by electrolysis at constant potential is an interesting exercise for advanced students. The procedure is as follows:

Set up the cell of Fig. 137, and transfer enough mercury to it to cover the bottom. Transfer 5 ml of 5×10^{-2} M lead nitrate and add 50 to 75 ml of 1 M potassium chloride. Adjust the stopper of the cell. Fill the silver-silver chloride electrode with 1 M potassium chloride, and insert the electrode tube in the stopper. The electrode should easily slide in the stopper. The stirrer is adjusted with its propeller *partially* immersed in mercury. The reference electrode is at a level at which the fritted glass disk is within 1 to 2 mm of the mercury surface when the stirrer is in operation. Avoid violent stirring.

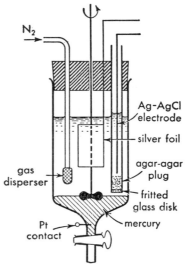

Fig. 137. Cell for coulometric determinations at constant potential.

Verify that the switch controlling the electrolysis circuit is open. Connect

[32]P. S. Tutundzic and S. Mladenovic, *Anal. Chim. Acta*, **8,** 184 (1953).

[33]J. J. Lingane, *Electroanalytical Chemistry*, Interscience, New York, 1953, pp. 377–430.

[34]P. Delahay, *New Instrumental Methods in Electrochemistry*, Interscience, New York, 1954, pp. 299–315.

the electrodes to the potentiostat and potentiometer as indicated schematically in Fig. 46, and insert a water coulometer (50-ml capacity) in the electrolysis circuit. Bubble nitrogen through the cell for 15 min. The bubbling of nitrogen is continued during the whole experiment, but the flow of gas can be somewhat reduced after removal of oxygen. (Why is it necessary to continue the bubbling of nitrogen?) Turn on the main switch of the potentiostat. While the tubes are warming up (1 min), set the potentiometer at 0.50 volt, the calomel electrode being connected to the positive terminal of the potentiometer. Adjust the water level at the bottom of the graduated burette of the coulometer, and read the volume exactly, both water columns being at the same level. Turn on the electrolysis circuit and start a timer simultaneously. Adjust the potentiostat as in experiment 15–10b.

Measure the current regularly during electrolysis, and plot the current and its logarithm against time. Interrupt the current when the current has reached 1 per cent of its initial value, and read the volume of gas evolved by bringing the water in both columns of the coulometer at the same level. Calculate the corresponding volume of gas under standard conditions (see problem 2 in Chapter 6), and compare this corrected experimental volume with the theoretical value calculated from the volume and concentration of the lead nitrate solution used in the electrolysis. Calculate also the error made by interrupting the current before completion of electrolysis. Assume that the current decreases exponentially with time in the computation of the error.[35]

15–12. CONDUCTOMETRY AND HIGH-FREQUENCY METHODS

Experiments in conductometry properly belong to the laboratory work in physical chemistry, and only applications of analytical character are covered here.

Equipment. Conductance bridge and cell (of the immersion type for convenience, Fig. 53B); thermometer; 10-ml burette; 2-ml and 5-ml pipettes; 100-ml beaker; wash bottle; and glass rod.

Inexpensive conductance bridges are available and the student potentiometer manufactured by Leeds and Northrup can be utilized as a bridge. It is preferable from a pedagogic point of view to let the student assemble the bridge.

Resistances R_1 and R_2 of the bridge in Fig. 54 are plug-in calibrated resistances (Genral Radio Co.). Resistance R_3 is a 0 to 111,111-ohm decade box, and C is a decade condenser box (in steps of 0.001 and 0.01 μf). The bridge is fed with a commercial oscillator operating at 1000 cps. Among the variety of balance indicators that may be used, the unit designed by Garman and Kinney[36] is particularly convenient. A similar balance indicator is available from General Radio Co. of Cambridge, Mass.

[35]See references in footnotes 33 and 34 for details.
[36]R. L Garman and G. Kinney, *Ind. Eng. Chem., Anal. Ed.,* **7,** 319 (1935).

Reagents. One-tenth molar potassium chloride; saturated solution of calcium sulfate (prepared in advance); 0.1 M hydrochloric acid; 0.1 M acetic acid; 0.1 M sodium hydroxide.

a. Determination of a Solubility Product and Calibration of the Cell. Set up the bridge of Fig. 54, and adjust the resistances R_1 and R_2 to 100 ohms. Immerse the conductance cell in, or fill it with, 0.1 M potassium chloride, and measure the temperature of the solution. Connect the cell to the bridge. Set the oscillator at 1000 cps, and adjust resistance R_3 and capacity C until balance is obtained. Calculate the cell constant (Table XXIII).

TABLE XXIII
Specific Conductance of 0.1 M Potassium Chloride[a]

T	0	18	20	25
ohms^{-1}cm^{-1}	0.007154	0.01119	0.01167	0.01289

[a]From H. S. Harned and B. B. Owen, *The Physical Chemistry of Electrolytic Solutions*, 2nd ed., Reinhold, 1950, p. 138.

Saturate distilled water (two distillations are preferable) with calcium sulfate, and measure the conductance of the solution. Also measure the conductance of the water used in the preparation of the calcium sulfate solution, and make the proper correction. Calculate the solubility and the solubility product of calcium sulfate from the conductance measurements (Table VIII).

Note that the conductance cell must be thoroughly cleaned to remove traces of salts before the conductance measurements with the calcium sulfate solution and distilled water.

b. Conductometric Titrations. Transfer 5 ml of 10^{-1} M hydrochloric acid in a 100 ml beaker and dilute with distilled water to approximately 50 ml. Insert the conductance cell in the solution, and measure the conductance. Titrate with 0.1 M sodium hydroxide, and determine the conductance after each addition of titrant. Make enough measurements to plot a reliable titration curve. Repeat the experiment with 5 ml of 0.1 M acetic acid and with a mixture prepared from 2 ml of 0.1 M hydrochloric acid and 2 ml of 0.1 M acetic acid.

c. Suggestions for Further Work. Determine the response of a high-frequency instrument (Sargent Oscillomcter) as the dielectric constant of the liquid in the cell is changed. Make measurements with benzene, chloroform, pyridine, acetone, ethanol, methanol, glycerol, and water; plot instrument response against dielectric constant (Table IX).

Determine the instrument response for water-ethyl alcohol mixtures of varying composition, and present the results graphically. Utilize these results in the analysis of an unknown mixture of these two substances.[37]

15-13. SOME INSTRUMENTAL CHARACTERISTICS OF FILTER PHOTOMETERS AND SPECTROPHOTOMETERS

Equipment. One-cell and two-cell filter photometers; spectrophotometer; autotransformer, 0-135 volts, 3 amp; 150-volt voltmeter; yellow, red, and blue filters; two 50-ml volumetric flasks; 50-ml burette or a set of pipettes.

The output voltage of the autotransformer should be limited to 115 volts to avoid the burning of the light bulb of the filter photometer.

Reagents. One-hundredth molar potassium chromate; 0.1 M sodium hydroxide.

a. Comparison of One-Cell and Two-Cell Instruments. On the basis of the data in Table XXIV and the available filters, prepare in 50 ml

TABLE XXIV
Molar Absorptivity of Potassium Chromate in 0.05 M Sodium Hydroxide[a]

λ (mμ)	325	350	372	375	400	425
log ϵ	2.65	3.42	3.67	3.66	3.29	2.57

[a]From the absorption spectrogram given by W. R. Brode, *Chemical Spectroscopy*, 2nd ed., Wiley, New York, 1943, p. 201.

volumetric flasks two solutions of potassium chromate in 0.05 M sodium hydroxide, having absorbancies of the order of 0.1 and 1, respectively. Connect a line operated one-cell filter photometer to an autotransformer, and connect an a-c voltmeter (0 to 150 volts) in parallel with the photometer. Set the voltage at 110 volts, and adjust the instrument at zero absorbancy with the blank (0.05 M sodium hydroxide). Measure the transmittancy of the more dilute chromate solution. Leave the instrument adjusted for $A = 0$ with the blank at 110 volts, but determine the absorbancy of the chromate solution at 105, 100, 95, and 90 volts, respectively. Plot absorbancy against line voltage, and determine the degree of voltage control corresponding to an error of 0.2 per cent for the absorbancy.

Repeat the preceding experiment with the two chromate solutions, using a two-cell filter photometer, and plot absorbancy against line voltage. Explain the results.

If the insulation of the autotransformer is not perfect, the galvanometer readings of the filter photometer may be unstable because of leaks and rectification in the circuit of the barrier layer cells. This source of error can be eliminated by installing the photometer on a grounded metallic plate.

b. Variations of Sensitivity with Wave Length. The energy output of the source and the sensitivity of the detector of a filter photometer or spectrophotometer vary with wave length. The slit of a spectrophotometer

[37]P. W. West, P. Senise, and T. S. Burkhalter, *Anal. Chem.*, **24**, 1250 (1952).

must therefore be varied with wave length. Study this effect by determining the slit width for a 100 per cent transmittance reading without absorption cell, as the wave length is changed. Plot the reciprocal of slit width against wave length, and replot the sensitivity curve of the detector on the same diagram. Data for the latter curve are supplied by the instructor.[38] Compare the two curves, and explain the results.

c. Transmittance of Filters. Determine the variations of transmittance with wave length for yellow, red, and blue filters, and plot the results on a single diagram. In what wave length ranges do orange, purple, and green filters absorb?

15–14. FACTORS CONTROLLING ABSORPTIVITIES

Equipment. Filter photometer and/or spectrophotometer; thermometer; 250-ml beaker; Bunsen burner with support; one 100-ml and eight 50-ml volumetric flasks; 1-ml, 2-ml, 5-ml, 10-ml, and 25-ml pipettes; 50-ml burette; 50-ml graduated cylinder.

Reagents. One-thousandth molar 2,4-dinitrophenol in 10^{-2} M sodium hydroxide; 10^{-2} M sodium hydroxide; 2.5 M potassium chloride; 10^{-3} M 2,4-dinitrophenol; 10^{-2} M ferric sulfate in 0.1 M sulfuric acid; 0.5 M and 10 M sulfuric acid; 0.5 M potassium thiocyanate; acetone.

a. Influence of Temperature. An increase of the temperature of a solution generally shifts its absorption band toward longer wave lengths. As a result, the influence of temperature may be quite pronounced when the absorbancy is measured at a given wave length in the ascending or descending branch of the curve showing absorbancy against wave length. The shift of this curve resulting from temperature variation then causes an appreciable error on the absorbancy. Conversely, the effect of temperature is minimized when absorbancy readings are taken in the range of wave lengths in which the absorbancy varies slowly with wave lengths, i.e., at the maximum or minimum in the plot of absorbancy against wave length. These conclusions can be verified for a solution of 2,4-dinitrophenol in sodium hydroxide.[39]

Prepare in a 50-ml volumetric flash a 10^{-4} M solution of 2,4-dinitrophenol in 10^{-2} M sodium hydroxide. Note the temperature of the solution and measure its absorbancy at 366 and 436 mμ, respectively. A spectrophotometer is more advantageous than a filter photometer in this experiment because of the possibility of fine adjustment of wave length.

Immerse the absorption cell with the 2,4-dinitrophenolate solution in a beaker with warm water, and raise the temperature of the solution by 5° to 10°. Measure the absorbancy immediately at the same wave lengths

[38] The response curves for several phototubes are given in a pamphlet of the Radio Corporation of America, Tube Department, Harrison, N.J.

[39] G. Kortüm and H. von Halban, *Z. physik. Chem.*, **A170**, 212 (1934).

as before. It is not necessary to warm the cell with the blank. Compare the absorbancies at the two temperatures, and explain the results.

A spectrogram of 2,4-dinitrophenolate may be supplied by the instructor or may be determined by the student.

b. Influence of Ionic Strength. Prepare in 50-ml volumetric flasks 10^{-4} M solutions of 2,4-dinitrophenolate in 10^{-2} M sodium hydroxide and 0 M, 0.1 M, 0.5 M, and 1.25 M in potassium chloride, respectively. Measure the absorbancies at 366 and 436 m$\ddagger$ by using for blank a 0.01 M sodium hydroxide solution having the same concentration of potassium chloride as the 2,4-dinitrophenol solution. Plot absorbancy against the square root of the ionic strength.

Further details on the effect of ionic strength can be found in a thorough investigation by Kortüm.[40]

c. Influence of a Shift in Equilibrium. The Beer-Lambert law is not obeyed when the absorbing species is involved in an equilibrium which is shifted upon dilution (Section 9–3f). This effect can be studied, for instance, for aqueous solutions of a weak acid whose anion has a much higher absorptivity than the nonionized acid. This is the case for 2,4-dinitrophenol.

Prepare in 50-ml volumetric flasks 2×10^{-5} M, 4×10^{-5} M, 6×10^{-5} M, 8×10^{-5} M, 10^{-4} M, 1.5×10^{-4} M and 2×10^{-4} M aqueous solutions of 2,4-dinitrophenol. Measure the absorbancy of these solutions, using water as a blank. Repeat the experiment with 5×10^{-5} M, 10^{-4} M, and 2×10^{-4} M solutions of nitrophenol which are 5 M in sulfuric acid. Plot absorbancy against concentration of 2,4-dinitrophenol for both sets of measurements. Plot also the difference between the two curves. Explain the results, and interpret them quantitatively.

Ionization constant of 2,4-dinitrophenol, $K = 10^{-4.0}$. Assume that K is the same in both experiments. Why is this a simplification?

d. Influence of Time. The formation of colored substances for photometric analysis may be relatively slow, and sufficient time should be allowed accordingly. In some instances the color may fade because of oxidation or reduction. This is the case for the colored complexes of ferric iron with thiocyanate. These complexes have the general formula $[\mathrm{Fe(CNS)}_n]^{+3-n}$ with $n = 1, 2, \cdots 6$ depending on the ratio of the concentrations of ferric iron and thiocyanate. The absorptivity of a solution of these complexes decreases with time because ferric iron is slowly reduced by thiocyanate.[41]

[40]G. Kortüm, *Z. physik. Chem.*, **B30**, 317 (1935).
[41]E. B. Sandell, *Colorimetric Determination of Traces of Metals*, 2nd ed., Interscience, New York, 1950, p. 367. Thiocyanate is a poor reagent for iron, but it is interesting for the study of some sources of error in photometry.

Prepare in a 50-ml volumetric flask a solution which is 10^{-4} M in ferric sulfate, 0.1 M in sulfuric acid and 0.1 M in potassium thiocyanate. Measure the absorbancy at 480 mμ immediately after preparation and after exposure to daylight for 5, 10, 15, and 20 min. Plot absorbancy against time.

e. Influence of Solvent. A change of solvent may markedly influence the absorption spectrogram of a substance. This effect can be observed with the complexes of iron (III) with thiocyanate when acetone is added to the solution. Prepare the same solution as in experiment 15–14d, but add 30 ml of acetone before diluting to 50 ml. Prepare also a blank with the same amount of acetone. Measure the absorbancy of the ferric solution, and compare the result with the absorbancy measured in experiment 15–14d before exposure to daylight.

f. Suggestions for Further Work. The absorbancy for systems involving hydrogen ions is often pH-dependent, as is the case, for instance, for colored indicators. The effect of pH may be studied by preparing solutions of an indicator in buffer mixtures at pH's which bracket by one pH unit the pK of the indicator. The absorbancy is measured at the two wave lengths corresponding to maximum absorption by the two forms of the indicator, and absorbancies are plotted against pH. The pK of the indicator can be determined from this plot.[42]

A liquid-liquid extraction, combined with photometric determination, is also suggested for further work. A determination with dithizone is of particular interest because of the practical significance of this reagent, but difficulties may be experienced because of the presence of traces of metals (lead, etc.) in the reagents and in distilled water. The determination of aluminum by extraction of aluminum hydroquinolate, according to Gentry and Sherrington,[43] can be carried out as an exercise. The procedure is summarized in Sandell's book.[44]

15–15. ERRORS IN FILTER PHOTOMETRY AND SPECTROPHOTOMETRY

Equipment. Filter photometer or, preferably, spectrophotometer; 50-ml burette; 10-ml pipette; five 50-ml volumetric flasks.

Reagent. One-thousandth molar potassium chromate; 0.25 M sodium hydroxide.

a. Absorbancy and Concentration. On the basis of the data of Table XXIV in experiment 15–13a and the available filters, calculate the concentration of a solution of potassium chromate in 0.05 M sodium hydroxide which has approximately an absorbancy of 1. Prepare this and

[42]See, for instance, W. R. Brode, *J. Am. Chem. Soc.*, **46**, 581 (1924).

[43]C. H. R. Gentry and L. G. Sherrington, *Analyst*, **71**, 432 (1946). See also S. Lacroix, *Anal. Chim. Acta*, **1**, 260 (1947).

[44]Sandell, *op. cit.*, pp. 153–154.

solutions in 0.05 M sodium hydroxide for which the concentrations of chromate are in the ratio 1:0.5:0.2:0.1:0.05, respectively. Measure the transmittancies and absorbancies of these solutions, and plot the absorbancy against chromate concentration. Prepare also a log-log plot for these data. Determine whether the Beer-Lambert law is obeyed.

b. Twyman-Lothian Plot. Verify the Twyman-Lothian relationship (Section 9-3e)

$$\frac{1}{C}\frac{dC}{dT} = \frac{0.434}{T \log T}. \tag{15-5}$$

By using the results of experiment 15–15a, plot the transmittancy of the chromate solution against the concentration of this substance. Trace tangents to the curve for six to eight values of T, and calculate dT/dC and dC/dT. Calculate the corresponding values of $(1/C)(dC/dT)$, and plot the results against transmittancy. Plot on the same diagram the values of $0.434/T \log T$ against transmittancy for T between 0.05 and 0.9. Compare the two curves and determine the range of transmittancies in which errors are minimized.

c. Ringbom Plot. Plot 1-T against log C for the results of experiment 15–15a, and indicate the range of transmittancies in which errors are minimized.

15–16. SIMULTANEOUS DETERMINATION OF TWO SUBSTANCES BY SPECTROPHOTOMETRY

Equipment. Spectrophotometer; three 50-ml volumetric flasks; 2-ml, 5-ml, and 25-ml pipettes; wash bottle.

Reagents. Two-thousandths molar potassium dichromate, 0.01 M potassium permanganate, 1 M sulfuric acid.

Procedure for the Determination of Dichromate and Permanganate. Prepare in a 50-ml volumetric flask a solution $2 \times 10^{-4}\ M$ in potassium dichromate and 0.5 M in sulfuric acid. Prepare also 50 ml of a $4 \times 10^{-4}\ M$ potassium permanganate solution which is 0.5 M in sulfuric acid. Determine the absorbancy of these solutions over the ranges 360 to 600 mμ. Plot the absorption spectrograms and determine the two optimum wave lengths for the simultaneous determination of potassium chromate and dichromate. Obtain from the instructor a solution containing both salts, and determine their concentrations.

Details on this determination can be found in a paper by Lacroix and Labalade.[45]

15–17. PHOTOMETRIC TITRATIONS

Equipment. Filter photometer or spectrophotometer; titration cell with mechanical stirrer (propeller type); column with cadmium amalgam reductor; 10-ml

[45]S. Lacroix and M. Labalade, *Anal. Chim. Acta*, **3**, 262 (1949).

burette; 50-ml graduated cylinder; 100-ml beaker; nitrogen tank with regulator and gas washing bottle (to control rate of flow).

Filter photometers or spectrophotometers are generally not fitted with a titration cell assembly, but adaptation to titration is very simple. The titration vessel is a 100-ml cylindric cell with a mechanical stirrer. The cell holder is such that stray light does not interfere with the photometric determination.[46] Quite obviously the propeller of the stirrer should not be in the light path of the instrument. The titration described below must be carried out in an air-free medium, and the cell must be closed with a stopper which has a nitrogen inlet. The opening for the stirrer serves as a nitrogen outlet.

The cadmium amalgam reductor is prepared[47] with approximately 20 grams of cadmium filings (30 to 60 mesh). Wash the filings with 1 N hydrochloric acid and treat them with the necessary volume of a 2 per cent mercuric chloride solution to bring the composition to 90 per cent cadmium and 10 per cent mercury. Wash the filings with 1 N hydrochloric acid, and pack them in a 20-cm column (0.5-cm internal diameter). Fill the column with very dilute hydrochloric acid (10^{-4} M) when it is not in use. When the column has not been used for several hours, wash it first with 100 ml of dilute (perhaps 0.01 M) sulfuric acid and then with 20 to 30 ml of 1 M sulfuric acid.

The tip of the column is inserted in a stopper which fits the titration cell.

Instructions for the use of reductor columns are given in Kolthoff and Sandell.[48]

Reagents. Five-thousandths molar uranyl sulfate; 1 M sulfuric acid; 10^{-2} M ceric sulfate.[49]

a. Titration of Uranium (IV) with Ceric Sulfate.

Transfer exactly 5 ml of 5×10^{-3} M uranyl sulfate to a 100-ml beaker, and dilute to approximately 25 ml with 1 M sulfuric acid. Wash the column with 20 to 30 ml of 1 M sulfuric acid. Collect the liquid, and make a blank determination by following the instructions for the actual titration. The blank correction should be negligible. Adjust the column stopper on the titration cell, and pass the uranyl solution over the column in an atmosphere of nitrogen at the rate of approximately 4 ml per minute. Wash the column with approximately 25 ml of 1 M sulfuric acid. Remove the column and place the cell in the photometer; adjust the stopper with the stirrer and the burette assembly, and pass nitrogen through the solution.

Adjust the sensitivity of the photometer or spectrophotometer (slit width) to obtain virtually a zero absorbancy reading at 360 mμ. Start the stirrer, and titrate with 10^{-2} M ceric sulfate. Take only a few absorbancy readings before and after the equivalence point, except in the immediate vicinity of this point where the titrant is added by increments of 0.1 ml.

[46]Information for adapting the Beckman Spectrophotometer Model B to photometric titrations is given by P. S. Sweetser and C. E. Bricker, *Anal. Chem.*, **25**, 253 (1953).

[47]C. E. Bricker and P. S. Sweetser, *Anal. Chem.*, **25**, 764 (1953).

[48]I. M. Kolthoff and E. B. Sandell, *Textbook of Quantitative Inorganic Chemistry*, 3rd ed., Macmillan, New York, 1952, pp. 568–571.

[49]See experiment 15–5 for the preparation of the ceric solution.

Plot absorbancy against volume of titrant, and determine the equivalence point.

Note: This titration was selected because it involves the application of reductor columns whose use is often not taught in laboratory exercises in quantitative analysis. The use of this column can be avoided by the selection of ferrous iron instead of uranium (IV) as the titrated substance. The ferrous solution is prepared in the cell by dissolving in air-free 1 M sulfuric acid (bubble nitrogen for 10 min) the required weight of ferrous ammonium sulfate. The solution is directly titrated with ceric sulfate as indicated above. Details on this titration are given by Bricker and Sweetser.[47]

b. Suggestions for Further Work. A variety of photometric titrations are discussed in the literature, and some of them may be performed as exercises. Some of these titrations were developed for purely analytical purposes, while others served in establishing the stoichiometry of reactions. An application of the latter type (the titration of cobalt (II) with thiocyanate,[50] for instance) may be made by advanced students.

A detailed bibliography on photometric titrations is given in a review by Goddu and Hume.[51]

15-18. METHOD OF CONTINUOUS VARIATIONS

Equipment. Filter photometer or spectrophotometer; ten 50-ml volumetric flasks; two 10-ml burettes; wash bottle.

Reagents. One-hundredth molar ferric sulfate in 0.1 M perchloric acid; 10^{-2} M sulfosalicylic acid in 0.1 M perchloric acid; 0.1 M perchloric acid.

a. Procedure for the Study of the Ferric Sulfosalicylic Acid Complex. Determine the complex of ferric iron with sulfosalicylic ion by the method of continuous variations.[52] Prepare in 50-ml volumetric flasks the following mixtures and dilute to 50 ml with 0.1 M perchloric acid:

1 ml sol. I + 9 ml sol. II
3 ml sol. I + 7 ml sol. II
5 ml sol. I + 5 ml sol. II
7 ml sol. I + 3 ml sol. II
1 ml sol. I + 9 ml sol. II

Solution I is 10^{-2} M ferric sulfate in 0.1 M perchloric acid, and solution II is 10^{-2} M sulfosalicylic acid in 0.1 M perchloric acid.

Prepare also blanks with the above amounts of solution I and dilute to 50 ml with 0.1 perchloric acid. Let the solutions of the ferric sulfosalicylic

[50]P. W. West and C. G. DeVries, *Anal. Chem.*, **23**, 334 (1951).
[51]R. F. Goddu and D. N. Hume, *ibid.*, **26**, 1740 (1954).
[52]R. T. Foley and R. C. Anderson, *J. Am. Chem. Soc.*, **70**, 1195 (1948).

complex stand for 30 min; measure their absorbancies at 500mµ. Plot absorbancy against the ratio of concentration of I to the sum of the concentrations of I and II, and deduce the formula of the complex thus formed.

b. Suggestion for Further Work. Examples of application of the method of continuous variations can be found in books by Charlot and Gauguin,[53] Martell and Calvin,[54] and Bailar.[55]

15-19. ULTRAVIOLET SPECTROPHOTOMETRY

Equipment. Spectrophotometer with ultraviolet range and two quartz cells; two 25-ml volumetric flasks; 1-ml pipette.

Reagents. A selection of aromatic compounds (see below); 95 per cent ethanol; isoöctane; cyclohexane; and 0.5 M potassium nitrate.

a. Identification from Ultraviolet Absorption Spectrogram. The instructor should have on hand a series of perhaps ten different aromatic compounds, preferably solid substances. The student will obtain a sample and will be given instructions for the preparation of a solution whose maximum absorbancy does not exceed 0.5 to 1 in such solvents as isoöctane, cyclohexane, and ethanol. It is convenient to prepare first a solution in a 25-ml volumetric flask, and then transfer 1 ml of this solution to another 25-ml volumetric flask and dilute with the solvent. The weight of substance is not too small under these conditions. The absorption spectrogram is determined, and the unknown substance is identified from the selection of absorption spectrograms made available to the student.

A wide selection of substances can be made from the spectrograms compiled by Friedel and Orchin.[56] The following compounds, with the corresponding solvent, are given for orientation purposes: anthracene, benzoic acid, o-, m-, and p-cresol, α-naphthol, and phenol in cyclohexane; carbazol, resorcinol, and naphthalene in 95 per cent ethanol.

b. Ultraviolet Absorption Spectrogram of an Inorganic Substance. Some inorganic substances can be determined by spectrophotometry in the ultraviolet range. As an example, the absorption spectrogram of 0.05 M potassium nitrate may be determined between 300 and 350 mµ.[57]

---

[53]G. Charlot and R. Gauguin, *Les Méthodes d'Analyse des Réactions en Solution,* Masson, Paris, 1951.

[54]A. E. Martell and M. Calvin, *The Chemistry of the Metal Chelate Compounds,* Prentice-Hall, New York, 1952.

[55]J. C. Bailar, Ed., *The Chemistry of the Coordination Compounds,* Reinhold, New York, 1956.

[56]R. A. Friedel and M. Orchin, *Ultraviolet Spectra of Aromatic Compounds,* Wiley, New York, 1951.

[57]A. Dolance and P. W. Healy, *Ind. Eng. Chem., Anal. Ed.,* **17,** 718 (1945).

c. Suggestion for Further Work. Two organic substances can be determined simultaneously as an alternative to experiment 15–16.

15–20. FLUOROMETRY, NEPHELOMETRY, AND TURBIDIMETRY

Equipment. Fluorophotometer with filters and cells; five 50-ml volumetric flasks; 10-ml burette; wash bottle.

Reagents. Solution of 10 ppm riboflavin in 5 per cent acetic acid (keep in darkness).

a. Fluorescence Intensity and Concentration. Determine the relative fluorescence intensities of solutions containing 0.2, 0.4, 0.6, 0.8, and 1 ppm of riboflavin. Prepare these solutions in 50-ml volumetric flasks by diluting with 5 per cent acetic acid a solution containing 10 ppm riboflavin in 5 per cent acetic acid. Plot fluorescence intensity against concentration.

b. Suggestions for Further Work. Determine aluminum by using pontachrome blue black R as reagent, according to Weissler and White.[58] The procedure is summarized in Sandell's book.[59]

Study the effect of time on the development of fluorescence for the preceding reaction by taking readings 5, 10, 15, and 30 min after the mixing of the reagents.

Study the effect of temperature on the fluorescence intensity of the aluminum morin complex. The procedure is described by White and Lowe.[60]

The nephelometric determination of sulfate may be carried out as an exercise. The instructions given by Yoe and Kleinmann[61] can be easily adapted to modern nephelometers.

15–21. CHARACTERISTICS OF SPECTROGRAPHS AND SOURCES

Equipment. Small Littrow and/or grating spectrograph; electrode holder; d-c source, and if possible, spark source; comparator; iron, copper, and aluminum rod electrodes; spectroscopic plates; and dark room facilities.

Spectroscopic plates with different characteristics can be selected from commercial brochures.[62] The Eastman Kodak emulsion Type 103-L is sensitive over a broad range of wave lengths and can be utilized in the following experiments. Plates of this type must be developed in complete darkness.

The spectrograph is focused and adjusted by the instructor before the laboratory sessions.[63]

[58]A. Weissler and C. E. White, *Ind. Eng. Chem., Anal. Ed.*, **18**, 530 (1946).

[59]See reference in footnote 41, pp. 151–152.

[60]C. E. White and C. S. Lowe, *Ind. Eng. Chem., Anal. Ed.*, **12**, 229 (1940).

[61]J. H. Yoe and H. Kleinmann, *Photometric Chemical Analysis*, Vol. 2, Wiley, 1929, pp. 157–167.

[62]*Materials for Spectrum Analysis*, Eastman Kodak Co., Rochester, N.Y., 2nd ed., 1954.

[63]See procedure, for instance, in W. R. Brode, *Chemical Spectroscopy*, 2nd ed., Wiley, New York, 1943, Chap. XII.

a. Influence of Excitation Conditions. Load the plate holder of the spectrograph; install two iron rod electrodes, and record the iron spectrum on the top of the plate with the exposure time indicated by the instructor. The correct exposure time varies with the conditions of excitation, the type of spectrograph, and the emulsion.

Move the plate and record an iron spectrum with the spark source if the latter is available. The conditions for spark excitation will be given by the instructor. Repeat the experiment for copper and aluminum rod electrodes, using both d-c and spark sources.

Develop the plate by following the standardized procedure (time of development and bath temperature) best suited to the emulsion, and compare the spectra.

b. Determination of the Linear Reciprocal Dispersion and Verification of the Hartmann Formula. Have the instructor identify one line of the iron spectrum obtained in experiment 15–21a with the d-c arc, and identify enough lines to prepare a plot of wave length against distance from a reference line. Measure all distances between lines with a comparator or with a good ruler if a comparator is not available. A plate or photograph of the iron spectrum with line assignment is supplied to the student.

By using the calibration curve, determine the wave length of a few of the strong lines of copper and aluminum, and compare your results with the corresponding data listed in tables of wave lengths (see Section 8–10c).

Verify the Hartmann formula (see problem 1, Chapter 8) for the wave length calibration curve previously prepared.

Determine the linear reciprocal dispersion at regular intervals along the calibration curve, and plot the resulting values against wave length.

15-22. QUALITATIVE ANALYSIS BY EMISSION SPECTROSCOPY

Equipment. The same equipment as in experiment 15–21 except that copper and aluminum electrodes are not needed; cup and pointed graphite electrodes.

Reagents. R.U. powder and sample of unknown composition. Samples can be conveniently prepared by the following procedure.[64]

A mixture of 25 parts of anhydrous silicic acid and 100 parts of alumina are ground together. This mixture is added to an aqueous solution of salts of the unknown elements to be determined, until a paste is formed. This paste is then dried and ground in a mortar. The concentration of the unknown elements (metals) may be varied from 0.001 to 1 per cent. Elements, such as iron, manganese, and nickel, which have very rich spectra should be avoided.

a. Procedure. By using d-c arc excitation, record on the same plate spectra of iron, the R.U. powder, and the powder of unknown compo-

[64] *Ibid.*, p. 314.

sition. The plate should be moved vertically after each exposure. The exposure time and arc current will be indicated by the instructor.

The spectra of the powder are obtained with the graphite electrodes, the lower electrode (cup) being connected to the positive terminal of the excitation source. The arc is struck by inserting in the electrode gap a graphite rod attached to an insulated holder. Handle the electrodes with forceps to avoid contamination.

Identify the elements in the powder of unknown composition by at least three lines, using the iron spectrum for wave length calibration. A series of photographs of the iron spectrum with the positions of lines of other elements is given by Brode.[65]

The experiment is simplified and the R.U. powder is not needed when a master plate with R.U. lines is available.

b. Suggestion for Further Work. Study the techniques for the excitation of a variety of samples: solutions, large solids, etc.

15–23. QUANTITATIVE ANALYSIS BY EMISSION SPECTROSCOPY

Equipment. The same equipment as in experiment 15–21, except that only iron and graphite electrodes are needed; microdensitometer.

A spark source is not needed for this experiment if a d-c arc is used.[66]

Reagents. Samples of known composition are prepared as indicated in Section 15–22. The unknown element may be, for instance, iron at a concentration between 0.1 to 1 per cent (expressed as Fe_2O_3). The element being sought can be changed to vary the experiments.

a. Calibration of Emulsion. The emulsion is calibrated by the two-line method[67] discussed in Section 8–6d. The following pairs of lines in the iron spectrum are recommended by Churchill: 3047.6 and 3037.4 A; 2966.9 and 3037.4 A; 2755.7 and 2739.6 A. If these lines are not in the range of wave lengths to be covered in the analysis, other homologous lines of iron may be selected (see tables of wave lengths).

The instructor will indicate the conditions for the recording of the iron spectrum to obtain the proper line intensities. The intensity of the lines can be altered with grating instruments by varying the distance between slit and source. No condensing lens should then be used to focus the arc on the slit. The grating aperture is changed, or a mesh screen or a neutral filter is interposed between source and slit with grating spectrographs.

b. Preparation of the Working Curve. Record a series of spectra with perhaps five samples of increasing concentration of the element being

[65]*Ibid.*, pp. 619–654.
[66]See L. H. Ahrens, *Spectrochemical Analysis*, Addison-Wesley Press, Cambridge, Mass., 1950.
[67]J. R. Churchill, *Ind. Eng. Chem., Anal. Ed.*, **16**, 653 (1944).

determined. If the latter is iron, the homologous pair at 2973 A (Fe) and 2987 A (Si) is selected for photometric analysis.[68]

Measure the line densities (see Section 8-6b), and convert them to exposures by means of the calibration curve. Plot the logarithm of exposure against the logarithm of the concentration of iron. The working curve may be used for the analysis of a sample of unknown composition.

Measure also the line density for Fe (3020 A) for each sample, and prepare a working curve for this line and Si (2987 A). Note the pronounced effect of self-absorption above 0.5 per cent iron.[68] Compare this curve with the one for (Fe) 2973 A and (Si) 2987 A, and explain the difference.

c. Influence of Sample Composition. Repeat the experiment 15-23b but with samples containing, in addition to the same amounts of iron as before, potassium sulfate at a concentration corresponding to approximately 1 per cent. Measure the line densities for Fe (3020 A) and Si (2987 A), and prepare a calibration curve. Note that the density ratio is larger than for the working curve without potassium. Explain this result.

d. Suggestion for Further Work. The quantitative analysis of an alloy with self-electrode is an alternative to experiment 15-23b.[69]

15-24. FLAME PHOTOMETRY

Equipment. Flame photometer or spectrophotometer with flame attachment; oxygen and hydrogen tanks with regulators; 10-ml burette; five 50-ml volumetric flasks.

Reagent. Standard solution containing 100 ppm of lithium as lithium chloride, solid sodium chloride, and sucrose.

a. Procedure for Lithium Analysis by the Direct-Reading Method
Prepare in 50-ml volumetric flasks solutions containing 2, 4, 6, 8, and 10 ppm of lithium by dilution of a standard solution of lithium chloride.[70]

Ask the instructor to light the burner of the instrument and to adjust the fuel (hydrogen) and oxygen pressures. Adjust the wave length of the monochromator to the strong lithium line at 6708 A.[71] Fill the cup of the instrument with the solution containing 10 ppm of lithium, and adjust the sensitivity of the instrument (slit width in the case of a spectrophotometer) to obtain full-scale deflection. Repeat the measurements for the other solutions and a blank with the same sensitivity. Plot instrument readings,

[68]See p. 96 of reference in footnote 66.

[69]See, for instance, *ASTM Methods for Chemical Analysis of Metals*, Am. Soc. Testing Materials, Philadelphia, 1950.

[70]Note that propyl or isopropyl alcohol must be added to aqueous solutions in the ratio 1:5 (why?) when the old attachment for the Beckman DU spectrophotometer is utilized.

[71]Wave lengths for other elements are listed by P. T. Gilbert, Jr., R. C. Hawes, and A. O. Beckman, *Anal. Chem.*, **22**, 772 (1950).

as corrected for the blank (flame background), against the lithium concentration.

If the flame photometer has a relatively low sensitivity, increase the lithium concentration (perhaps 10 times).

b. Influence of Oxygen and Fuel Pressure and the Rate at which the Sample is Atomized. Repeat the above experiment for a single lithium concentration (6 ppm lithium, for instance), but by decreasing the fuel pressure by 10, 20, and 40 per cent, the oxygen pressure being kept constant. Investigate in the same fashion the effect of a decrease in oxygen pressure for a given fuel pressure.

Study the influence of the rate at which the sample is atomized by increasing the viscosity of the lithium solution by the addition of 10, 20, or 40 per cent sucrose.[72] Be very careful not to plug the atomizer. The latter must be cleaned with distilled water after the experiment.

c. Interferences. Determine whether a large excess of sodium affects the lithium analysis by repeating experiment 15–24a with the solution containing 6 ppm lithium and also a varying amount of sodium ($10^{-3} M$, $10^{-2} M$, $10^{-1} M$ in sodium chloride).

15–25. SUGGESTIONS FOR MISCELLANEOUS EXPERIMENTS

The following experiments are suggested for small groups of advanced students or for demonstrations: recording of an infrared spectrum for a liquid and a solid (potassium bromide pellet technique); recording of a Raman spectrum for a liquid (carbon tetrachloride, benzene, etc.); recording of an X-ray diffraction pattern; example of X-ray fluorescence analysis of an alloy; X-ray absorption determination (bromobenzene, for instance); use of a radioactivity counter and the study of statistical errors;[73] use of a tracer in the study of a separation.

---

[72]For details, see J. W. Berry, D. G. Chappell, and R. B. Barnes, *Ind. Eng. Chem., Anal. Ed.*, **18**, 19 (1946).

[73]A proportional counter of the gas-flow type is recommended; very weak samples of a carbon–14 derivative can then be measured, and radiation hazards are minimized.

Author Index

Subject Index

Cathode-ray oscilloscope
    infrared spectrum recording, 223
    mass spectrum recording, 288
    spectrogram recording, 220
Cathodic layer, 172
Cell
    amperometric titrations, 345
    barrier layer, 213
    concentration, 17
    conductance, 148
    coulometric titrations, 135
    coulometry, 351
    electrochemical, 9
    electrolytic separations, 128
    H-cell, 94
    high-frequency, 151
    photometric titrations, 359
    polarographic, 93
    potentiometric titrations, 56
Cell constant, 149
Chromophore groups, 200
Classification
    electrochemical methods, 2
    instrumental methods, 2
    optical methods, 4
Color and wave length, 212
Colorimeters, 211
Comparator, 177
Concentration polarization, 65
Condensed spark, 174
Conductance
    applications, 156
    bridge, 150
    cell, 148
    equivalent, 144
    high-frequency, 152
    ionic equivalent, 145
    potassium chloride specific, 353
    specific, 144
    titrations, 146
Conductometric titration
    applications, 157
    definition, 3
    experiments in, 252
    historical, 143
    titration curves, 146
Conductometry
    definition, 3
    experiments in, 352
    historical, 143
Constant current electrolysis, 119, 349
Constant potential electrolysis, 124
Continuous balance, 35
Continuous variations, method of
    experiments, 360
    fundamentals, 229
Convection, 65

Conventions of signs, 13
Coolidge X-ray tube, 268
Cornu mounting, 166
Coulometer
    titration, 131
    water, 131, 140, 352
Coulometric titration
    applications, 136
    experimental, 135
    experiments in, 350
    external generation, 134
    historical, 132
    internal generation, 133
    principle, 133
Coulometry
    applications, 131
    constant potential, 130
    definition, 2
    determination of n by, 132
    experiments in, 351
    historical, 130
    micromethods in, 132
Counter
    absolute measurements, 306
    avalanche process, 300
    background correction, 307
    counting-rate meter, 305
    decatron, 304
    detector classification, 299
    discriminator for, 305
    errors, 306
    flow-type, 301
    four-pi method, 324
    Geiger-Müller, 301
    ionization chambers, 299
    ion multiplication in, 300
    paired sources, 308
    proportional, 300
    quenching agent, 302
    resolution time of, 307
    sample mounting for, 306
    scaling unit for, 304
    scintillation, 303
    self-absorption error, 310
    standard for, 306
    statistical error, 308
Counting equipment, see Counter
Counting-rate meter, 305
Cracking pattern, 287
Cross section of atoms, 316
Crystal detector, 270
Curie, 296
Current
    capacity, 86
    catalytic, 84, 340
    dark, 185, 254
    diffusion, 69